一九八四年十二月二十六日

震宇 購于欧亚

Development of Design and Operational Criteria for Wastewater Treatment

Development of Design and Operational Criteria for Wastewater Treatment

Carl E. Adams, Jr.

Davis L. Ford

W. Wesley Eckenfelder, Jr.

Enviro Press, Inc.
Box 40284
Nashville, TN 37204

CBI

CBI Publishing Co., Inc.
51 Sleeper Street
Boston, MA 02210

Printed in the United States of America

International Standard Book Number 0-937976-00-8
Library of Congress Catalog Card Number 80-69077

Enviro Press, Inc.
Box 40284
Nashville, TN 37204

CONTENTS

1   Characterization of Wastewaters   1

2   Sampling Techniques   21

3   Screening and Toxicity Methodology   39

4   Neutralization   57

5   Coagulation and Precipitation   71

6   Sedimentation   91

7   Dissolved Air Flotation   107

8   Hydraulics and Mixing Characteristics   131

9   Oxygen Transfer and Aeration Equipment Selection   143

10   Activated Sludge   169

11   Aerated Lagoon   209

12 Trickling Filter 223

13 Waste Stabilization Ponds 241

14 Anaerobic Treatment of Organic Wastes 255

15 Granular Media Filtration 279

16 Activated Carbon Adsorption 291

17 Ion Exchange 313

18 Chemical Oxidation 337

19 Gravity Thickening of Sludges 359

20 Aerobic Digestion of Biological Sludges 371

21 Vacuum Filtration 383

22 Centrifugation 401

23 Pressure Filtration 419

24 Air Drying of Sludges 435

25 Thermal Content of Sludges 445

26 Recovery of Physical-Chemical Sludges 465

Index 487

PREFACE

In designing and operating wastewater treatment facilities, it has become increasingly evident that comprehensive bench- and pilot-scale methodology is required to optimize the design and operation of these plants. Oversight in applying proper procedures has resulted in many over-designed treatment facilities or, worse, failed or inoperable treatment plants.

This book presents the experimental and systematic test procedures required to formulate and optimize a wastewater facility design and to optimize the operation of an existing treatment plant. The text is practically oriented and is written for use by design engineers, wastewater treatment operators, laboratory personnel, and students. The transition from small-scale to full-scale is discussed along with general limitations and considerations in applying experimental data to full-scale design and operation.

This text also defines an orderly approach to correlate experimental data for predicting effluent quality for conventional and advanced wastewater treatment technology.

The reader will obtain a greater understanding and appreciation for the background work and considerations that lead to more effective and efficient treatment design.

1

CHARACTERIZATION OF WASTEWATERS

SIGNIFICANT ORGANIC PARAMETERS

It is essential that the nature and characteristics of the wastewater be evaluated with respect to the unit processes considered. When one speaks of pollution, organic and oxygen demanding substances are of immediate concern. However, the single or conjunctive use of many parameters, both organic and inorganic, may be necessary to provide the proper analysis of a wastewater.

Biochemical Oxygen Demand

The biochemical oxygen demand (BOD) is an estimate of the amount of oxygen required to stabilize biodegradable organic materials in a sample of wastewater by heterogeneous microbial population. The procedures for performing the BOD test are described in *Standard Methods for the Examination of Water and Wastewater* [1]. The BOD test, however, is subject to many variables and constraints, particularly when considering complex industrial wastes. These are discussed as follows:

Time of Incubation. The importance of the time variable is indicated in the basic BOD equation. The standard BOD test is performed using a five-day period of incubation and results are usually reported on this basis as the five-day BOD (BOD_5). The complete stabilization of the organic matter in a wastewater, or the ultimate demand to be satisfied (BOD_u) depends on the nature of the waste. The attainment of the BOD_u may take many months. However, the degradation achieved in twenty days is often used an approximation of BOD_u.

Nitrification. The BOD test is normally considered to measure the carbonaceous fraction of the sample, although the oxidation of nitrogenous material will contribute to the oxygen demand depending on the time of incubation. This oxidation may be shown as:

$$NH_3 \xrightarrow[\text{Nitrosomonas}]{O_2} NO_2^- \xrightarrow[\text{Nitrobacter}]{O_2} NO_3^-$$

The nitrification rate constants are much lower than those for carbonaceous destruction, and although the two reactions may occur simultaneously, the nitrification state normally does not begin until the carbonaceous demand has been partially satisfied. A graphical presentation of these reactions is shown in Figure 1-1 and can be described mathematically by the equation:

$$y = S(1-10^{-k_1 t}) + S_n (1-10^{-k_2 t}) \tag{1-1}$$

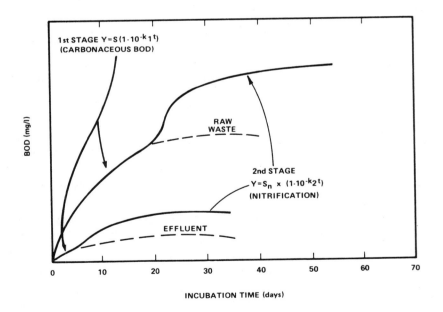

FIG. 1-1. BIOCHEMICAL OXYGEN DEMAND

2

where:

    y = BOD at time t, mg/l
    S = ultimate carbonaceous BOD, mg/l
    S_n = ultimate nitrogenous BOD, mg/l
    t = time of incubation, days
    k_1 = rate constant for carbonaceous demand, day^{-1}
    k_2 = rate constant for nitrogenous demand, day^{-1}

It should be noted, however, that BOD measurements on treated wastewater effluents from treatment processes where nitrification is occurring can include nitrification from the start of the measurement. This is because the waste is already seeded with nitrifying bacteria and no time is required for the development of these populations as in the BOD test on raw wastewater.

The measurement of oxygen demand exerted by the carbonaceous fraction of the waste can be accomplished in two ways; namely by inhibiting nitrification in the test bottle by the addition of nitrification inhibitor reagents, or by allowing nitrification to take place and subtracting its demand from the overall results. The former method is the most satisfactory. It should be recognized, however, that nitrification occurs in most effluents which have undergone partial oxidation of the waste components and this in effect represents a demand on the oxygen resources of the receiving body of water. It therefore should be recognized as a part of the total biochemical oxygen demand of the waste when considering the effect on streams and water courses.

Environmental Factors. The environmental factors of pH and temperature affect the BOD test. Although the standard test calls for an incubation temperature of 20°C, field conditions often necessitate incubation at other temperatures. The following equation can be used to estimate the effect of temperature on the rate constant for carbonaceous demand:

$$\frac{k_1(\text{temperature "T"})}{k_1\,(20°c)} = \theta^{(T-20)} \tag{1-2}$$

where:

$$\theta^{(4°\,-\,20°C)} = 1.135$$
$$\theta^{(20°\,-\,30°C)} = 1.056$$

Adjustment of the test sample pH to 7.2 is necessary before reliable BOD values can be obtained for wastes which are outside the range of pH 6-9.

3

Acclimation of Seed. The use of non-acclimated biological seed in the BOD test is probably the factor most commonly responsible for erroneous BOD results. This is particularly true when considering complex industrial wastes. It is best to acclimatize a biological culture to the wastewater in question in a continuous reactor although fill and draw batch units are frequently used. Detailed acclimation procedures are outlined in Chapter 3 entitled "Screening and Toxicity Methodology."

Toxicity. The presence of toxic materials in the wastewater sample may have a bio-toxic or bio-static effect on the seed microorganisms. This effect is usually evidenced by "sliding" BOD values, where the BOD magnitudes increase with increasing sample dilutions. This is indicative of the presence of toxic materials, and it is therefore necessary to predetermine the dilution value above which the BOD yields are consistent.

Chemical Oxygen Demand

The chemical oxygen demand (COD) is a measure of the oxygen equivalent of the organic fraction in the sample which is susceptible to permanganate or dichromate oxidation in an acid solution. This parameter has been used for over a quarter of a century in estimating the organic content of waters and wastewaters. However, correct interpretation of COD values is still a problem and one must understand those variables which affect the COD value of the sample in question.

Generally, one would expect the ultimate BOD of a wastewater to approach the COD. There are many factors which would negate this statement, however, especially when determining the BOD and COD for complex industrial wastes. These factors include:

1. Many organic compounds which are dichromate oxidizable are not biochemically oxidizable.
2. Certain inorganic substances, such as sulfides, sulfites, thiosulfates, nitrites, and ferrous iron are oxidized by dichromate, creating an inorganic COD, which is misleading when estimating the organic content of a wastewater.
3. The BOD results may be affected by lack of seed acclimation, giving erroneously low readings. The COD results are independent of this variable.
4. Certain organic compounds (e.g. straight chain, saturated aliphatic acids and alcohols) are not efficiently oxidized by $Cr_2O_7^{2-}$. A silver sulfate catalyst is added to ensure efficient oxidation of these compounds.
5. Chlorides interfere with the COD analysis and provisions must be made to eliminate this interference. Erroneously high readings will occur by the

oxidation of chlorides by dichromate:

$$6Cl^- + Cr_2O_7^{2-} + 14H^+ \longrightarrow 3Cl_2 + 2Cr^{3+} + 7H_2O \quad (1\text{-}3)$$

This interference can be eliminated by the addition of $HgSO_4$ to the mixture. Hg^{2+} combines with Cl^- to form the poorly dissociated complex, $HgCl_2$, which is not oxidized by $Cr_2O_7^2$.

$$Hg^{2+} + 2Cl^- \longrightarrow HgCl_2 \; (aq) \quad (1\text{-}4)$$

For Cl^- concentrations of greater than 1,000 mg/l, it is recommended that the standard and blank determinations be performed with identical Cl^- concentrations to the sample. A stock solution of NaCl can be used to spike the standard and blank sample. If insufficient amounts of $HgSO_4$ are added (a 10:1 weight ratio of $HgSO_4$:Cl^- is recommended in *Standard Methods* [1]), the excess Cl^- will precipitate with the silver catalyst as follows:

$$Ag^+ + Cl^- \longrightarrow AgCl_{(s)} \quad (1\text{-}5)$$

and incomplete and unpredictable oxidation of $AgCl_{(s)}$ by $Cr_2O_7^{2-}$ takes place. There are two methods commonly used for COD analysis. These are:

1. A two-hour reflux time Dichromate Oxidation [2]; and
2. A rapid COD test [3].

Two-hour reflux time Dichromate Oxidation. This method uses potassium dichromate as the oxidant. An Ag_2SO_4 catalyst is used and $HgSO_4$ is added to complex chloride. The sample and oxidant are digested under reflux in a 50 percent $^V/v$ sulfuric acid solution for two hours. The excess dichromate is titrated with ferrous ammonium sulfate. The extent of oxidation of organics in this test is affected by the reflux time. This effect is shown in Figure 1-2. The exact effect of reflux time on dichromate oxidation depends on the nature of the wastewater.

The significance of Figure 1-2 simply emphasizes that the final precision of the COD value depends on reflux time for particular wastewaters. Consequently, with unfamiliar or complex wastes, it is recommended that the reflux time be checked to determine its influence on final results.

Rapid COD Test. A COD test using a shortened digestion time has already been proposed [4]. An aliquot of wastewater sample is added to a dichromate-acid-silver solution and mixed. The contents are heated to 165°C and digested for 15 minutes. The sample is then diluted with distilled water and titrated with ferrous ammonium sulfate. Using this method the organics in domestic sewage are oxidized to about 66 percent of the value obtained using the two-hour reflux test. This yield may be higher or lower for other wastes, depending on the nature of the organic constituents.

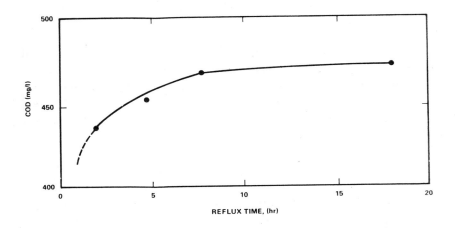

FIG. 1-2. EFFECT OF REFLUX TIME ON COD YIELD

Total Organic Carbon

Total organic carbon (TOC) has been used as a method for characterization of wastewater streams for many years. Various time-consuming methods have been utilized to determine the organic carbon concentration of an aqueous sample, including the Van Slyke-Folch wet carbon combustion method [5] and the Mohlman and Edwards test [6]. These tests involve the oxidation of organic materials to carbon dioxide and water and the titrimetic measurement of the CO_2 after trapping it in a standard caustic solution.

The recently developed carbon analyzer has provided a rapid and simple means of determining organic carbon levels in aqueous samples, enhancing the popularity of TOC as a fundamental method of analysis. The organic carbon determination is free of the many variables which plague the COD and BOD analyses, with more reliable and reproducible data being the net result.

The carbon analyzer basically involves the complete oxidation of a sample through the use of a catalytic combustion tube. A carrier gas conveys the resulting carbon dioxide and steam from the combustion tube, through a condenser where the steam is removed, into an infrared analyzer sensitized for carbon dioxide detection. As the amount of carbon dioxide is proportional to the initial sample carbon concentration, the response can be compared to a calibration curve and the total carbon determined. The organic carbon is evaluated either by acidifying and purging the sample of all inorganic carbon prior to analysis or by providing a dual combustion tube for total carbon analysis and a low temperature combustion tube for inorganic carbon analysis, the difference taken as total organic carbon [7]. This system is illustrated in Figure 1-3.

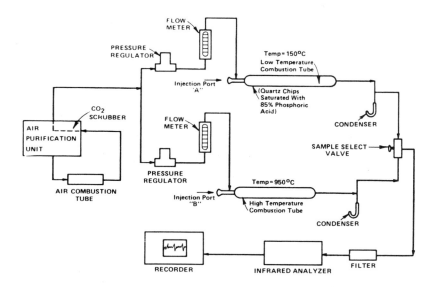

FIG. 1-3. SCHEMATIC ILLUSTRATION OF MODIFIED CARBON ANALYZER

The total organic carbon concentration in a wastewater is a measure of organic content. While TOC measurements give no indication of the oxidation state of the carbon, correlations can often be made between TOC and occasionally BOD values for individual wastes. Because the analysis time using the carbon analyzer is only several minutes, the efficacy of using this parameter is apparent, particularly when a TOC-BOD or TOC-COD correlation can be established.

Total Oxygen Demand

Another recently developed analyzer has provided a means for rapidly determining the oxygen demand of a sample rather than its carbon content [8]. The measurement is obtained by continuously monitoring the oxygen content of a mixed N_2/O_2 gas stream. This gas mixture flows through a platinum catalyzed combustion chamber, where the oxidizable constituents of the sample are converted to stable oxides by the O_2. The depletion of O_2 is measured in an electrolytic detector cell and is directly related to the oxygen demand of the sample.

The total oxygen demand (TOD) of a substance as measured by this analyzer includes organic and inorganic substances, but at varying reaction efficiencies. The chemical reactions that apparently take place in the apparatus are as follows:

1. Carbon is converted to carbon dioxide;
2. Hydrogen is converted to water;
3. Nitrogen in a -3 valence state is converted to nitric oxide;
4. The sulfite ion is partially converted to sulfate; and,
5. The sulfide ion is partially converted to sulfate.

The reaction efficiencies for each of the oxidations are reported in Table 1-1. It should be recognized that nitrates cause significant interference in the TOD analysis by providing oxygen to the carrier gas.

TABLE 1-1. TOTAL OXYGEN DEMAND REACTIONS

Reaction	Highest Stable Oxidation State	Reaction Efficiency (%)
C $+ O_2$	CO_2	95-100
$2H_2$ $+ O_2$	$2H_2O$	95-100
$2N^{3-}$ $+ O_2$	$2NO$	$\cong 95$
S^{2-} $+ 2O_2$	SO_4^{2-}	$\cong 78$
SO_3^{2-} $+ \frac{1}{2}O_2$	SO_4^{2-}	$\cong 72$

Comparative Analysis of the Organic Parameters

When considering the analysis of industrial wastes, it is imperative to evaluate the BOD and COD values for various classes of compounds. The BOD values for many pure organic compounds common to industrial discharges have been reported [9]. The COD and BOD values and the fractions of the theoretical oxygen demand (ThOD) represented by these values for alphatics, aromatics, nitrogenous organics and refractories are presented in Table 1-2 [10]. The

8

degree to which the COD and BOD tests reflect the theoretical oxygen demand can be evaluated from this table.

TABLE 1-2. COD, BOD AND THEORETICAL OXYGEN DEMAND FOR TEST ORGANIC CHEMICALS

Chemical Group	Th.OD (mg/mg)	Measured COD (mg/mg)	COD Th.OD (%)	Measured BOD$_5$ (mg/mg)	BOD$_5$ Th.OD (%)
ALIPHATICS					
Methanol	1.50	1.05	70	1.12	75
Ethanol	2.08	2.11	100	1.58	76
Ethylene glycol	1.26	1.21	96	0.36	29
Isopropanol	2.39	2.12	89	0.16	7
Maleic acid	0.83	0.80	96	0.64	77
Acetone	2.20	2.07	94	0.81	37
Methyl ethyl ketone	2.44	2.20	90	1.81	74
Ethyl acetate	1.82	1.54	85	1.24	68
Oxalic acid	0.18	0.18	100	0.16	89
Group Average			91		56
AROMATICS					
Toluene	3.13	1.41	45	0.86	28
Benzaldehyde	2.42	1.98	80	1.61	67
Benzoic acid	1.96	1.95	100	1.45	74
Hydroquinone	1.89	1.83	100	1.00	53
o - Cresol	2.52	2.38	95	1.75	70
Group Average			84		58
NITROGENOUS ORGANICS					
Monoethanolamine	2.49	1.27	51	0.83	34
Acrylonitrile	3.17	1.39	44	nil	0
Aniline	3.18	2.34	74	1.42	44
Group Average			58		26
REFRACTORY					
Tertiary — butanol	2.59	2.18	84	0	0
Diethylene glycol	1.51	1.06	70	0.15	10
Pyridine	3.13	0.05	2	0.06	2
Group Average			52		4

In attempting to correlate BOD and COD of an industrial waste with TOC, one should recognize those factors which might constrain or negate the correlation. These factors include:

1. A portion of the COD of many industrial wastes is attributed to the di-chromate oxidation of ferrous iron, nitrogen, sulfites, sulfides, and other

oxygen consuming inorganics. The TOC analysis does not include oxidation of these compounds;

2. The BOD and COD tests do not include many organic compounds which are partially or totally resistant to biochemical or dichromate oxidation. However, all of the organic carbon in these compounds is recovered in the TOC analysis; and,

3. The BOD test is susceptible to variables which include seed acclimation, dilution, temperature, pH, and toxic substances.

One would expect the stoichiometric COD/TOC ratio of a wastewater to approximate the molecular ratio of oxygen to carbon (32/12 = 2.66). Theoretically, the ratio limits would range from zero, when the organic material is resistant to dichromate oxidation, to 5.33 for methane or slightly higher when inorganic reducing agents are present. The BOD/TOC ratio of an industrial waste would be subject to many of the aforementioned variables and could not be expected to follow any particular pattern. This is underscored by the variability between the calculated and measured COD/TOC values for various compounds in Table 1-3.

TABLE 1-3. COD–TOC RELATIONSHIPS

Substance	COD/TOC (Calculated)	COD/TOC (Measured)
Acetone	3.56	2.44
Ethanol	4.00	3.35
Phenol	3.12	2.96
Benzene	3.34	0.84
Pyridine	3.33	nil
Salicylic Acid	2.86	2.83
Methanol	4.00	3.89
Benzoic Acid	2.86	2.90
Sucrose	2.67	2.44

This variability is attributed to the COD yield of the compounds, and wastestreams containing a portion of these substances would be subjected to a fluctuating COD/TOC ratio in the event of component concentration changes. The greater the variability in the character of an industrial wastestream, the more pronounced will be the change in its COD/TOC ratio. This in itself is a good indicator of the degree of consistency of wastewater constituents and can be a valuable aid in predicting the design organic load applied to a biological treatment facility.

Reported BOD, COD, and TOC values for several industrial wastewaters are listed in Table 1-4, the COD/TOC ratio varying from 1.75 to 6.65 [4, 11, 12, 13].

TABLE 1-4. OXYGEN DEMAND AND ORGANIC CARBON OF SELECTED INDUSTRIAL WASTEWATER

Type of Waste	BOD$_5$ (mg/l)	COD (mg/l)	TOC (mg/l)	BOD/TOC	COD/TOC
Chemical*	--	4,260	640	--	6.65
Chemical*	--	2,440	370	--	6.60
Chemical*	--	2,690	420	--	6.40
Chemical	--	576	122	--	4.72
Chemical	24,000	41,300	9,500	2.53	4.35
Chemical-Refinery	--	580	160	--	3.62
Petrochemical	--	3,310	900	--	3.32
Chemical	850	1,900	580	1.47	3.28
Chemical	700	1,400	450	1.55	3.12
Chemical	8,000	17,500	5,800	1.38	3.02
Chemical	60,700	78,000	26,020	2.34	3.00
Chemical	62,000	143,000	48,140	1.28	2.96
Chemical	--	165,000	58,000	--	2.84
Chemical	9,700	15,000	5,500	1.76	2.72
Nylon Polymer	--	23,400	8,800	--	2.70
Petrochemical	--	--	--	--	2.70
Nylon Polymer	--	112,600	44,000	--	2.50
Olefin Processing	--	321	133	--	2.40
Butadiene Processing	--	359	156	--	2.30
Chemical	--	350,000	160,000	--	2.19
Synthetic Rubber	--	192	110	--	1.75

*high concentration of sulfides & thiosulfates.

Although it has been difficult to correlate BOD with TOC for industrial wastes, relatively good correlation has been obtained for domestic wastewaters. This is reasonable when one considers the type and diversity of the waste constituents. The reported BOD yields for industrial wastewaters are often erratic and highly dependent on the previously mentioned variables. A BOD$_5$/TOC correlation for sewage has been reported by several investigators. A ratio of 1.87 has been reported by Wuhrmann [14]. Mohlman and Edwards have reported a range of 1.35 to 2.62 for raw domestic waste [6].

The calculated relationship between BOD$_5$ and TOC is:

$$\frac{BOD_5}{TOC} = \frac{O_2}{C} = (\frac{32}{12})\,(0.90)\,(0.77) = 1.85 \qquad (1\text{-}6)$$

where:

1. The ultimate BOD will exert approximately 90 percent of the theoretical oxygen demand; and,

2. The five-day BOD is 77 percent of the ultimate BOD for domestic wastes.

The fluctuation of the sewage COD/TOC and BOD/TOC ratios is not as pronounced as that shown in industrial wastewater analyses, and a valid correlation can be more generally applied.

In summary, it can be stated that TOC and TOD are both valid measures of the organic character and both can be correlated to COD values in many applications. These are extremely good control parameters for most wastewaters because of the abbreviated analysis time associated with the respective analyzers. It is less probable that TOD, TOC, or COD can be correlated to BOD unless the constituents in the wastewater remain relatively constant. The conjunctive use of these parameters in terms of BOD, COD, TOC, and TOC ratios can be helpful in properly evaluating the organic nature of an unknown waste. The relationship between the aforementioned parameters in terms of accuracy (percent of theoretical oxygen demand or carbon concentration) is illustrated in Figure 1-5.

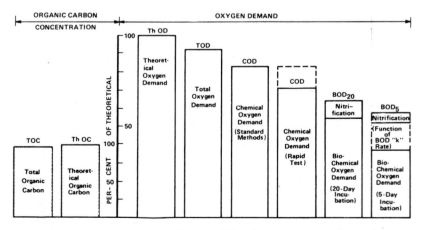

FIG. 1-4. RELATIONSHIP BETWEEN OXYGEN AND CARBON PARAMETERS

Miscellaneous Organic Parameters

As attention has been focused on the TOD, TOC, COD, and BOD parameters, it is necessary to recognize the importance of specific organic analyses such as oil or grease content, phenols, and organics containing toxic functional groups. Oil and phenol analyses are particularly significant when evaluating unit processes for the treatment of chemical, petrochemical, and refinery wastewaters.

SIGNIFICANT INORGANIC PARAMETERS

There are many inorganic parameters which are pertinent when assaying potential toxicity, general characterization, or process evaluation. Although special situations require the evaluation of any number of inorganic analyses, it is the intent here to discuss only the more relevant ones.

Acidity

The acidity of a water is defined as its quantitative capacity to neutralize a strong base to a designated pH. The acidity of a wastewater, or its capacity to donate protons, is important because a neutral or near-neutral water is required before biological treatment can be deemed effective, and many regulatory authorities have criteria which establish strict pH limits to final discharges. Acidity is attributable to the unionized portions of weakly ionizing acids, hydrolyzing salts, and free mineral acids. The latter is probably the most significant, as it is difficult to predict neutralization requirements when diverse forms of mineral acidity are prevalent. Microbial systems may reduce acidity in some instances through biological degradation of organic acids and salts.

Alkalinity

The alkalinity of a water is defined as its quantitative capacity to neutralize a strong acid to a designated pH. Alkalinity, or the ability of a wastewater to accept protons, is significant in the same general sense as acidity, although the biological degradation process does offer some buffer capacity by furnishing carbon dioxide as a degradation end-product of the system. It has been estimated that approximately 0.5 lb of alkalinity (as $CaCO_3$) are neutralized per lb of BOD removed [15].

Dissolved Solids

The dissolved solids can have a pronounced deleterious effect on many unit processes included in the waste treatment system. The limiting dissolved salts concentration for effective biological treatment, for example, is approximately 16,000 mg/l. Chloride concentrations of 8,000 to 15,000 mg/l (as Cl⁻) have also been reported to adversely affect biological systems, not only in reducing removal rates but also by decreasing sludge settling rates and increasing effluent turbidity.

Ammonia-Nitrogen and Sulfides

Ammonia nitrogen is present in many natural waters in relatively low concentrations ($<100\mu g/l$), although industrial streams often contain exceedingly high concentrations. The presence of ammonia nitrogen has proved to be inhibitory to many microorganisms present in a biological aeration basin at pH of 7.5. Sulphur is present in many wastewaters either as one of the forms of H_2S ($H_2S_{(aq)}$, HS^-, S^{2-}), depending on pH, sulfate (S_4^{2-}), sulfonated organic compounds, or metallic sulfides. Although odors can be caused by the presence of sulfides in concentrations of less than a few hundredths of a mg/l, no inhibitory or biotoxic effects on bacteria are noticed up to concentrations of 100 mg/l (as S^-). It should be noted, however, that some algal species are adversely affected by sulfide concentrations of 7 to 10 mg/l [16].

Heavy Metals

The influence of heavy metals on biological unit processes has been the subject of many investigations. For example, even under acclimated conditions Cu has been found to be toxic at 5 mg/l. Toxic thresholds for Cu and Cd are dependent on many factors such as the presence of complexing agents, although higher concentrations have been noted to have no effect on process efficiency. For example, zinc concentrations exceeding 10 mg/l had no adverse effect on a biological system treating a petro-chemical waste [12]. It should be noted that the biomass will complex heavy metals.

Instrumental (atomic absorption spectroscopy) and wet chemical colorimetric methods for heavy metals analyses are given in *Standard Methods* [1], although atomic absorption flame photometry is an effective and rapid method for determining small quantities of metals. This method is based on the measurement of a light absorbed at a given wave length by the unexcited atoms of the element being analyzed.

GENERAL SLUDGE CHARACTERISTICS

Although considerable research has been directed toward improving, and to some extent, standardizing, the parameters which define the soluble organic and inorganic constituents of wastewaters as previously discussed, there has been comparatively little effort toward establishing a similar definition of the associated solids fraction. A general sludge categorization is shown in Table 1-5.

TABLE 1-5. GENERAL CATEGORIZATION OF SLUDGES

Sludge Source	Unit Process Function	Significant Characteristics
Influent Suspended Solids (Primary Sludge)	Collection and Concentration of Suspended Material	1. Concentration of SS 2. Inorganic Constituents 3. Organic Constituents 4. Specific Gravity, Settleability 5. Dewaterability
Chemical Treatment Sludge	Coagulation, Precipitation and Concentration of Particulates	1. All of those mentioned above 2. Effects of pH changes 3. Effect of treatment chemicals on subsequent processes or water use
Excess Biological Sludge	Concentration, Digestion, Dewatering, Heat Drying, and Combustion	1. Fraction of inert materials 2. Amenability of organic fraction to digestion 3. Heat value/unit wt of sludge 4. Settleability 5. Dewaterability
Effluent Suspended Solids		1. Concentration of SS 2. Biological activity in terms of oxygen demand 3. Composition of effluent sludge in terms of nutrients, both organic and inorganic 4. Microbial analysis

The parameters, or set of parameters, selected for defining a sludge (raw, digested, or industrial) should be consistent with respect to their use and meaning as applied to effects of the solids or sludge fraction on receiving bodies of water, process selection, and process operation.

Sludge Settling Characteristics

The settleability of a sludge, although a valid parameter, must be defined within the context of the conditions at which the settling rate is determined. The flocculent settling rate of influent suspended solids, for example, is dictated by the solids concentration, the liquid viscosity, the size and configuration of the settling basin, and the physical, chemical, and electrostatic nature of the suspended material. The zone settling rates of more concentrated sludges are subject to even more variables, especially when a major portion of the sludge is biological in nature.

The settling rate of biological solids such as those in an activated sludge aeration basin depends upon the predominant type of microorganisms present which in turn responds to the organic loading, nature of the substrate, and miscellaneous environmental stresses [17].

Bound water, the water in the activated sludge floc which is bound by colloid micelles with properties different from those existing in a free liquid state, also affects the settling rate by virtue of its effect on the floc specific gravity [18].

Although it is ascertained from the foregoing discussion that sludge settling rates are a poor representation of its characteristics, it is nonetheless indicative of which might be expected in a primary or secondary settling tank if most of the variables affecting its settleability are understood and defined.

Chemical Composition of Sludges

Many chemical analyses of sludges have been reported and these values are useful for many reasons. As there is a wide variation in the fertilizer value of sewage and industrial sludges, a chemical analysis establishes a level of utilization in this respect. The concentration of sludge nitrogen, phosphoric acid, and potash content as well as the organic fraction is indicative of the fertilizer value. Additionally, the degree of digestion to which the sludge has been subjected is important, as digestion reduces sludge nitrogen and digestible organic matter, and thus its value as a fertilizer. The organic fractions for sewage sludges are itemized in Table 1-6 [19]. Knowledge of the specific organic components of a sludge is important in predicting which conditions will prevail during dewatering as well as determining what specific effects the sludge will have on soil characteristics.

TABLE 1-6. ORGANIC FRACTIONS FOR VARIOUS SLUDGES (% OF DRY WEIGHT)

Constituents	Plain Settled	Digested	Activated	Raw Activated	15%* Oxidized	80%* Oxidized
Organic Matter	60-80	45-60	62-75	67	64	23.4
Total Ash	20-40	40-55	25-38	33	36	----
Pentosams	1.0	1.6	2.1	7.2	2.4	0
Grease & Fat**	7-35	3.17	5-12	21.0	19.2	1.8
Hemicellulose	3.2	1.6	----	----	----	----
Cellulose	3.8	0.6	7.0	----	----	----
Lignin	5.8	8.4	----	----	----	----
Protein	22-28	16-21	32-41	12.4	8.4	0.5

*Solids Fraction Only
**Ether Extract

TABLE 1-7. CONTENTS OF SEWAGE FRACTIONS

Sewage Fraction	Total Solids (mg/l)	Volatile Solids (mg/l)	Organic Nitrogen (mg/l)	COD (mg/l)
Settleable	70.9 (18%)	52.4 (28%)	2.6 (23%)	76.5 (34%)
Supracolloidal	51.2 (13%)	39.4 (22%)	3.2 (27%)	58.8 (27%)
Colloidal	27.6 (7%)	20.9 (11%)	1.1 (8%)	32.2 (14%)
Soluble	244.1 (62%)	73.2 (37%)	5.1 (42%)	56.1 (25%)
Totals	393.8	185.9	12.0	223.6

A more comprehensive investigation of the composition of various sewage fractions was reported. As noted from Table 1-7, the particulate fraction of domestic wastewater contained more COD and organic nitrogen than did the soluble fraction, underscoring the pollution potential associated with this portion [20]. A more specific categorization of the particulate fraction is described in Table 1-8, the organic material recovered, using the prescribed analytical techniques, being approximately 80 percent of the volatile solids concentration for domestic wastewater [21].

17

TABLE 1-8. ORGANIC CONSTITUENTS OF PARTICULATE MATTER IN SEWAGE

Component	Settleable Fraction (mg/l)	Supracolloidal Fraction (mg/l)	Colloidal Fraction (mg/l)
Total Grease	11.70	9.57	5.55
Alcohol Soluble Matter	4.62	2.01	1.40
Amino Acids			
Alcohol — Soluble	1.05	0.28	0.66
Alcohol — Insoluble	7.54	12.56	4.71
Carbohydrates and Lignin	18.05	10.60	6.09
Total Organic Matter	42.96	35.02	18.41

Biological Characteristics of Sludges

The parametric expression of the biological nature of the sludge is particularly important when considering its treatability or pollutional characteristics. Investigators have proposed several approaches in the evaluation of the biological sludge fraction, namely, the BOD concentration, Deoxyribonucleic Acid (DNA) concentration, plate count, or specific oxygen uptake rate (mg O_2 per mg VSS per day). The first three approaches are somewhat constrained because of the complexity and nonspecificity of the tests. The specific oxygen uptake rate (mg/l O_2 utilized/unit time/mg/l VSS) is a better indication, although the low rates of oxygen utilization displayed by most sludges affect the precision of the test. Perhaps a more practical approach would be to measure the sludge enzymatic activity per unit weight of volatile solids. Sludge viability, as measured by the microbial dehydrogenase enzyme activity using a tetrazolium salt (triphenyltetrazolium chloride, or TTC), has been used by several investigators [22, 23, 24]. The application of these tests is explained in Chapters 3 and 10 on "Screening and Toxicity Methodology" and "Activated Sludge," respectively.

REFERENCES

1. *Standard Methods for the Examination of Water and Wastewater,* 15th Edition, American Public Health Association Inc. (1979).
2. *Standard Methods for the Examination of Water and Wastewater,* 14th Edition, American Public Health Association, Inc. (1976).
3. Jeris, J. S., "A Rapid COD Test," *Water and Wastes Engineering,* 5:4, 89-91 (1967).
4. Foulds, J. M. and Lunsford, J. V., "An Analysis of the COD Method," *Water and Sewage Works,* 115, 112-115 (1968).
5. Van Slyke, D. D., Plazin, J. and Weisiger, J. R., "Reagents for the Van Slyke-Folch Wet Carbon Combustion," *Jour. Biol. Chem.,* 191, 299-304 (1951).
6. Mohlman, F. W. and Edwards, G. P., "Determination of Carbon in Sewage and Industrial Wastes," *Ind. Eng. Chem.,* Anal. Ed., 3, 119-123 (1931).
7. Ford, D. L., "Application of the Total Carbon Analyzer for Industrial Waste-Water Evaluation," Proceedings, 23rd Industrial Waste Conference, Purdue University, Lafayette, Ind. (1968).
8. Clifford, D., "Total Oxygen Demand: A New Instrumental Method," American Chemical Society, Midland, Michigan (November, 1967).
9. Heukelekian, H. and Rand, M. C., "Biochemical Oxygen Demand of Pure Organic Compounds," *Sewage and Industrial Wastes,* 27, 1040-1053 (1955).
10. Buzzell, J. C., Young, R. H. F. and Ryckman, D. W., Behavior of Organic Chemicals in Aquatic Environment, *Part II, Report to the Manufacturing Chemicals Association* (April, 1962).
11. Gloyna, E. F. and Ford, D. L., Unpublished Report (1967).
12. Gloyna, E. F., Eckenfelder, W. W. and Ford, D. L., Unpublished Report (1968).
13. Eckenfelder, W. W., Ford, D. L. and Burleson, N., Unpublished Report (1968).
14. Wuhrmann, K., "Hauptwirkungen und Wechselwirkungen einiger Betriebsparameter im Belebtschlaminsystem. Ergebnisse mehrjahriger Grossversuche," Schweiz. Z. Hydrol., 26, 218-270 (1964).
15. Eckenfelder, W. W., "Protection of River Waters Against Pollution," Supplement Manual Prepared for the World Health Organization (July 1968).
16. Gloyna, E.F. and Espino, E., "Sulfide Production in Waste Stabilization Ponds," *J. San. Eng. Div.,* ASCE, 95, 607-627 (1969).

17. Ford, D. L. and Eckenfelder, W. W., "The Effect of Process Variables on Sludge Floc Formation and Settling Characteristics," Center for Research in Water Resources Report 13, The University of Texas, Austin, Texas (1966).

18. Heukelekian, H. and Weisberg, E., "Bound Water and Activated Sludge Bulking" *Sewage and Industrial Wastes,* 28, 558-574 (1956).

19. Teletzke, G., "Wet Air Oxidation of Sewage Sludges," *Process Biochemistry,* London, (1966).

20. Hunter, J. V. and Heukelekian, H., "The Composition of Domestic Sewage Fractions," Water Pollution Control Federation, 37, 1142-1163 (1956).

21. Burd, R., "A Study of Sludge Handling and Disposal," *Publication WP-20-4,* Water Pollution Control Administration, U.S. Department of Interior (May, 1962).

22. Farkas, P., Formal Discussion, Paper 11-5, "Determination of Sludge Activity — A Possibility of Controlling Activated Sludge Plants," Proceedings 3rd International Conference on Water Pollution Research, Munich, Germany (1966).

23. Bucksteeg, W. and Theile, E. W., *Gas and Wasserfach,* 100, 916 (1959).

24. Ford, D. L., Eckenfelder, W. W., and Yang, J., "Dehydrogenase Enzyme as a Parameter of Activated Sludge Activity," Proceedings, 21st Industrial Waste Conference, Purdue University, West Lafayette, Ind. (1966).

SAMPLING TECHNIQUES

GENERAL CONSIDERATIONS FOR
SAMPLING WASTEWATER

A comprehensive sampling and characterization program of an industrial waste is desirable for several reasons. In order to properly conduct the pilot investigations described in this book, it is essential that representative samples be obtained and characterized so that the design criteria developed during the pilot program are generated on representative samples. Other reasons for implementing a waste monitoring program include:

1. To assure the regulatory agencies that the industry is in compliance with the effluent quality requirements in the discharge permit;
2. To ensure cognizance of product and material losses to the sewer;
3. To maintain sufficient control of plant operations so that violation of permit specifications are minimized; and
4. To develop the necessary data needed to ensure proper operation of the wastewater treatment facilities.

Much of this section of this chapter has been derived from a manual entitled, "Monitoring Industrial Wastewaters," prepared for the Environmental Protection Agency by Associated Water and Air Resources Engineers, Inc. [1]. This manual can be obtained through the Technology Transfer Division of the U.S.E.P.A.

Organizing the Sampling Program

The basic steps involved in planning and implementing an effluent sampling and monitoring program are illustrated in Figure 2-1. It is invariably found that the organization of a monitoring program is most economically approached by providing a capable staff to plan and initiate the program. Proper attention to planning is necessary for the establishment of an inexpensive, convenient and

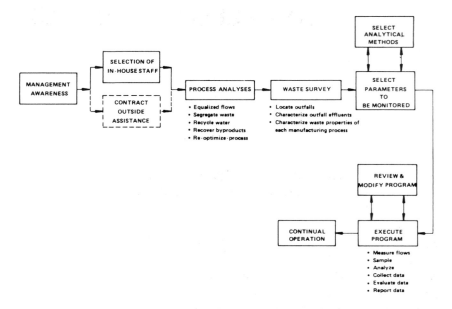

FIG. 2-1. STEPS INVOLVED IN ESTABLISHING AN EFFLUENT MONITORING PROGRAM

effective program which will not interfere with production operations. Since the program will be an integral part of the manufacturing process, the same attention should be given to its efficiency as is given to profitability and product quality control.

The basic objective of the monitoring program should be to provide a characterization and understanding of the water-borne waste materials being produced by the manufacturing process. Although regulatory agencies will only require monitoring of those wastestreams which are discharging from the plant site, it is well established that a comprehensive monitoring program will locate inefficient and wasteful operations and most probably lead to reduced manufacturing costs. Moreover, in-plant monitoring is essential in detecting changes in process waste load in sufficient time to allow correction before violations occur.

In establishing a monitoring program, one of the first objectives should be an examination of the water usage and waste generation characteristics of the manufacturing process itself. Very often, a simple water conservation survey can eliminate unneeded water discharges within the plant even before a formal sampling and monitoring program is initiated.

Waste Survey

In conducting a monitoring program, existing knowledge of the waste flow is usually insufficient to provide the basis for establishing a comprehensive study. The waste survey will provide material balance of the flow of pollutants through a system.

The difficulty in locating sewer lines and establishing the manufacturing source responsible for waste discharged to each outfall becomes a time consuming and complex problem in older facilities. Piping diagrams are seldom updated as changes are made over the years, and these drawings must be accepted with this understanding, and caution exercised in their use. The first consideration in the development of an industrial wastewater survey is a review of the entire production process. The complete picture may be acquired by constructing a material flow sheet of the entire plant, drawn in sufficient detail to include all raw materials, additives, end products, by-products, and liquid and solid wastes for each operation. The requirements of a useful flow diagram are summarized below:

1. Detailed information concerning each production process.
2. The type of operations should be identified as continuous, batch, or intermittent, with frequency of waste releases given for the latter two.
3. Raw materials, products and wastes should be listed on the flow diagram.
4. The waste characteristics, such as flow, temperature and pH, should also be included.

Following the construction of such a flow sheet, the next step is to construct a mass balance around each operation and, subsequently, to develop an up-to-date sewer map showing water, wastewater, sanitary storm and drain lines.

In order to determine the sources of wastewater in sewers, it is frequently convenient to add a tracer to the wastewater in the outlet of a production unit. By plotting the flow of a tracer, it is possible to establish a sewer map. Commonly used tracers are dyes, floats, and smoke. Many different dyes are available as tracers, including methyl orange, nigrosine, fluorescene, or rhodamine B. The usual procedure is to add about ten grams of powdered dye to a bucket of water, mix, then pour the fluid into the sewer at the source of the waste. Methyl orange is red in acid solutions and yellow in alkaline solutions. Nigrosine imparts a black color to acid and alkaline waste. Fluorescene sodium salt gives a brilliant green in alkaline solutions, but gives no color in acid solutions. Rhodamine B in high concentrations imparts a red color to the water, but in low concentrations does not yield a visible color. Rhodamine B has the advantage, however, of being detected in extremely low concentrations by fluorometric techniques.

After establishing a material flow sheet in a sewer map, location of the sampling station should be determined. Important factors to be considered in selecting the sampling stations are:

1. The flow of the wastestream should be known or easily estimated or measured;
2. The sampling station should be easily accessible with adequate safeguards; and
3. The wastewater should be well mixed.

When it is not possible to collect samples from a sewer line of a production unit, a mass balance around a point of discharge may give an indication of waste production of the particular process. Sampling stations may be located in a sewer upstream and downstream from an inaccessible discharge connection. Subsequently, a mass balance around the inaccessible discharge will allow an accurate estimation of the significant parameters of the production unit under investigation.

A wastewater survey may be considered a nuisance to some production staff members. Some manpower has to be allocated to this survey to install apparatus, and to report process changes such as batch dumps or spills. Personnel responsible for the wastewater survey should be relieved of all other assignments during the sampling program. The time intervals and other circumstances peculiar to the sampling procedure require constant attention of the individuals performing this task. When the plant operates on a continuous basis, the sample collection period should continue for 24 hours; otherwise the sample collection should last as long as the plant is in operation, including plant clean up. Major spills should be reported and noted in order to enable a proper evaluation of the results from the wastewater survey.

SAMPLING TECHNIQUES

The basis for any plant pollution abatement program or anticipated design criteria depends on information obtained by sampling. Thus, all subsequent decisions may be based on incorrect information if this step is not accurately implemented. If a few basic principles are observed, and if those persons responsible for sampling are forewarned, reliable results can be obtained without expensive and costly resampling. A good sampling program should:

1. Ensure that the sample taken is truly representative of the wastestream;
2. Use proper sampling techniques; and
3. Protect the samples until they are analyzed.

The usual method for accounting for flow variations and changes in waste constituents and for minimizing the analytical effort is to composite the samples. Greater accuracy is obtained if the amount of sample in the composite is taken in proportion to the flow. In general, the greater the frequency of samples taken for the composite, the more accurate and representative the result. If batch processes which "slug" the system are present, compositing can lead to erroneous results unless the sampling is done at a very high frequency (possibly continuously) or unless the flow is dampened by flow equalization techniques.

Grab Samples

Grab samples may be taken manually or automatically from the wastestream. Each sample indicates the waste characteristics at the time the sample is collected. Automatic sampling is essentially identical to taking a series of grab samples at regular intervals. The volume of the grab samples depends on the total number of separate analyses that must be performed. A grab sample may be more desirable than a composite sample when:

1. The water to be sampled does not flow on a continuous basis such as might occur with an intermittently dry discharge outlet or when contaminated process tanks are periodically dumped. A grab sample from such a discharge is sufficient to obtain the waste characteristics of a batch dump.
2. The waste characteristics are relatively constant. For such wastes, a complex sampling program is not justified since an occasional grab sample may be entirely adequate to establish waste characteristics.
3. It is desired to determine whether or not a composite sample camouflages extreme conditions of the waste. For example, a composite sample may infer a neutral pH while individual grab samples may exhibit a wide pH range.

Grab samples are mandatory when analyzing wastestreams for parameters, such as dissolved gases, residual chlorine, soluble sulfides, temperature, pH, and other constituents that degrade or change significantly over a compositing period.

Composite Samples

Composite sampling should be valid as long as the ratio of flow to individual sample volume remains the same. Depending on the time and variability of plant operations, 2, 4, 8, 16, or 24-hour composites may be collected. Samples may be composited on the basis of either time or flow.

1. *Flow:* The amount of samples collected or added to the mixture during the sampling period is proportional to the waste flow at the time of sampling. Samplers are available that automatically composite on the basis of flow.

2. *Time:* Another approach for compositing samples is to collect a fixed volume of sample after a certain quantity of waste flow passes the sampling station.

MANUAL AND AUTOMATIC SAMPLING

Manual sampling is recommended during the preliminary survey. This preliminary survey should determine when and where automatic samplers are needed and the portion of the wastewater samples that should be pumped, for example. Manual sampling has the advantage that the sample collector can observe unusual conditions.

When several points are to be examined at frequent intervals, or when a continuous record is required, it may be more convenient to install automatic samplers. The installation cost of automatic samplers is often offset by the savings on labor required for manual collection. Continuous samplers are marketed commercially and must be examined carefully to see that they are suitable for the waste characteristics in question. Automatic samplers are available which will obtain composite samples either as a function of time or flow.

Frequency of Sampling and Duration of Sampling Program

The frequency of sampling depends on the flow rate and the wastewater characteristics. The expected range in flow rate and waste concentration should be determined during the preliminary survey. The frequency of grab samples is often performed once per hour. When the results of the survey indicate low variability, the grab samples may be taken at longer intervals of 2, 4, 8, 16, or even 24 hours. The time over which samples should be composited also depends on the variability of the wastestream. For high variability, individual samples for compositing should be taken as frequently as every 3 minutes up to one sample per hour. The maximum time over which a sample can be composited is controlled by the ability to store the individual samples adequately, but should never be longer than 24 hours. Compositing samples over a period of time less than 2 hours is not usually necessary because a sewer system and treatment facilities may have already provided such an equalization effect. A generalized sampling schedule for certain significant wastewater parameters is shown in Table 2-1. It is recognized that special conditions justify a significant deviation from this format, and that regulatory agencies may impose a specific schedule as stipulated on permits, such as those issued by EPA under the National Pollution Discharge Elimination System (NPDES).

TABLE 2-1. SUGGESTED SAMPLING OR COMPOSITING SCHEDULE

Characteristic	High Variability	Low Variability
BOD[a]	4 hr	12 hr
COD or TOC[a]	2 hr	8 hr
Suspended Solids	8 hr	24 hr
Alkalinity or Acidity	1 hr grab	8 hr grab
pH	Continuous	4 hr grab
Nitrogen and Phosphorous[b]	24 hr	24 hr
Heavy Metals	4 hr	24 hr

[a]The compositing schedule where continuous samplers are not used depends on variability, i.e., 15 min for high variability to 1 hr for low variability.

[b]Does not apply to nitrogen or phosphorous wastes (e.g., fertilizer).

An intensive plant survey will generally last between 5 and 10 days of normal plant operations. However, in many instances due to variability in plant operations and seasonal products, the program may continue on a limited schedule over a period of several months.

Sample Handling and Preservation

In order to obtain a representative sample, many precautions are necessary. Some of these precautions and general sampling rules are as follows:

1. The sample should be taken at a place where the wastewater is well mixed, such as near a Parshall flume or a location in a sewer with hydraulic turbulence. Weirs tend to enhance the settling of solids immediately upstream and the accumulation of floating oil or grease immediately downstream.

Such locations should be avoided as a sample source.

2. The sample should be taken in the center of the channel of flow where the velocity is highest and the possibility that solids have settled is a minimum. In order to avoid an excess of floating materials, the mouth of the collecting container should be placed a few inches below the water surface.

3. A low level of turbulence can be induced by blowing air through the wastestream. This practice of inducing turbulence by introducing air is not advisable if the wastestream is to be analyzed for dissolved gases or volatile matter. Mechanical stirring may be used to induce turbulence with much less influence on the results.

4. The sampling of wastestreams with immiscible fluids, such as a mixture of oil and water, requires special attention. At places in the wastestream where oil floats, it is simple to obtain a sample of the oil to analyze, but difficult to determine the quantity of oil flowing per day. A method commonly used to estimate total volume is to divert the wastestream into a container. After separating the two fluids, it is possible to measure the thickness of the oil layer and thus ascertain the volume of oil present. Another problem with oil is adherence to the sampling device, requiring frequent cleaning.

5. The required volume of a grab sample should be between 1 and 2 liters in order to provide sufficient quantities for all required analyses including repeating doubtful analyses. Individual samples constituting a composite sampling should be at least 50 ml. Depending on the frequency of sampling and the individual sample volume, the total composited sample should be ideally between 2 and 4 liters in volume.

6. In some cases, it may be desirable to accumulate a number of individual samples for compositing at one time, such as the end of a work shift or the end of a work day. It would be possible to use only a portion of each aliquot in compositing the total; however, it is more desirable to mix the entire volume of all individual samples and then use a portion of the total mixture for analytical purposes. In either choice, it is a prerequisite that the individual samples are representative of the flow at the time collected so that the integrity of the total composited sample is maintained.

7. The samples should be stored in a manner that prevents alteration of the characteristics to be analyzed. Refrigeration in some instances will be necessary. When the storage of a sample interferes with a particular analysis, it is preferred to take separate samples for such analyses which may require special preservation techniques.

8. The sample container and sampling device should be clean and uncontaminated. Before the sample is taken, the container should be rinsed several times with the wastewater.
9. Each sample should be labeled with an identification card containing, as a minimum, the following information:
   a. Designation or location of sample collection;
   b. Date and time of collection;
   c. Indication of grab or composited sample with appropriate time and volume information; and
   d. Notation of information that may be changed before laboratory analyses are made. This includes temperature, pH, and appearance.

Samples should be analyzed as soon as possible after collection; however, in practice, it is seldom feasible to perform the analyses immediately. Cognizance should therefore be taken of certain time-dependent chemical changes which can occur in samples, such as:

1. Metal cations may precipitate as hydroxides and carbonates and may form complexes.
2. Some species may be oxidized (e.g. S^{2-} to SO_4^{2-}) or reduced [e.g. Fe (III) to Fe (II)].
3. Some species (e.g. metal cations, phosphate) may be absorbed onto the surface of glass or plastic containers.

Microbial activity may also change the characteristics of the sample as follows:

1. Cell lysis may increase the soluble BOD and soluble COD and decrease the suspended solids;
2. Cell productivity may change the total BOD and total COD;
3. The nitrogen and phosphorus forms and content may be altered.

Preservatives that do not interfere with the analyses should be added immediately after the sample is collected. Sample preservation methods for specific parameters are given in Table 2-2. Some authors have proposed alternative methods of preservation for certain constituents, such as:

1. For nitrogen and phosphorus, add 1 ml concentrated H_2SO_4 per liter;
2. For cyanides, raise the pH to at least 11 (maximum storage time is 24 hours); and
3. Samples for heavy metal analysis should be filtered at the site of collection and acidified to a pH of approximately 3.5 with 1:1 nitric acid.

Sampling Equipment

Many types of sampling equipment are presently available for manual, automatic, nonproportional,.and proportional sampling. The reader is referred to the partial list of manufacturers in Table 2-3 for reference. Some types of samplers, both improvised and commercially available, are illustrated in Figures 2-2 through 2-6.

TABLE 2-2. RECOMMENDED SAMPLE PRESERVATION TECHNIQUES

Parameter	Preservative	Maximum Holding Period
Total Acidity-Total Alkalinity	None required	Indefinite*
Biochemical Oxygen Demand	Refrigeration at 4°C	6 hours
Bacteria	Refrigeration at 4°C	24 hours
Calcium	None required	Indefinite*
Chemical Oxygen Demand	2 ml conc H_2SO_4 per liter	7 days
Chloride	None Required	Indefinite
Chlorine	Determine on site	None
Color	Referigeration at 4°C	24 hours
Cyanide	NaOH to pH 10	24 hours
Dissolved Oxygen	Determine on site	None
Flouride	None required	Indefinite
Hardness	None required	Indefinite*
Metals, Total	5 ml HNO_3 per liter	Indefinite*
Metals, Dissolved	Filtrate: 3 ml 1:1 HNO_3 per liter	Indefinite*
Nitrogen, Ammonia	40 mg $HgCl_2$ per liter -4°C	1 day
Nitrogen, Kjedahl	40 mg $HgCl_2$ per liter -4°C	1 day
Nitrogen, Nitrate-Nitrite	40 mg $HgCl_2$ per liter -4°C	6 hours
Oil and Grease	2 ml conc H_2SO_4 per liter -4°C	24 hours
Total Organic Carbon	2 ml conc H_2SO_4 per liter (pH2)	7 days
pH	Determine on site	None
Phenolics	1.0 g $CuSO_4$/l + H_3PO_4 to pH 4.0 -4°C	24 hours
Total Phosphorus	40 mg $HgCl_2$ per liter -4°C	24 hours
Total Solids	None available	1 day
Specific Conductance	None required	Indefinite*
Sulfate	Refrigeration at 4°C	7 days
Total Sulfide	2 ml Zn acetate per liter in a filled, N_2- flushed container	7 days
Threshold Odor	Refrigeration at 4°C	1 day
Turbidity	None available	1 day

* as long as no precipitates form

The sampling system, illustrated in Figure 2-2, is a nonproportional sampler and may be used when the flow is nearly constant. As the water drains from the upper carboy, the vacuum created siphons waste into the lower bottle. The rate of flow is regulated by the screw clamp. This sampler, although appearing primitive, can be very useful when there is no power available at the sample location and a less sophisticated approach is acceptable.

A sampler based on flow, or a proportional sampler, may be similar to the scoop-type device shown in Figure 2-3. The scoop rotates at a constant velocity and, after a pre-determined period of time, the scoop submerges in the water and takes a sample. The volume of sample depends on the water level in the channel. The scoop-type sampler is limited to wastewater without high suspended or floating solids and must be installed at locations where the flow has a known relationship with the depth.

TABLE 2-3. LIST OF SOME MANUFACTURERS OF WASTEWATER SAMPLING EQUIPMENT

1. BIF Sanitrol, P. O. Box 41, Largo, Florida 33540

2. Brandywine Valley Sales Co., P. O. Box 243, Honeybrook, Pa. 19344

3. Instrumentation Specialties Co. (ISCO), P. O. Box 5347, Lincoln, Nebraska 68505

4. Markland Specialty Engineering Ltd., Box 145; Exoicoke, Ontario, Canada.

5. N-Con Systems Company, Inc., 308 Main Street, New Rochelle, New York 10801.

6. Quality Control Equipment Company, P. O. Box 2706, Des Moines, Iowa 50215

7. Sigmamotor, Inc., 14 Elizabeth Street, Middleport, New York 14105.

8. Sirco Controls, 402 Second Ave. West, Seattle, Washington 90119.

9. Tri-Aid Sciences, Inc., 161 Norris Drive, Rochester, New York 14601.

The flow-proportional sampler may be connected to a flow measurement device equipped with an integrator as schematically illustrated in Figure 2-4. Note that the flow measuring device may be an electric proble, a bubbler system, or a float. Another type of flow-proportional sampler, equipped with a solenoid valve is shown in Figure 2-5. A constant sampling flow is pumped through a pipe or hose tap. After a predetermined volume has passed the flow meter, the solenoid operating valve is opened and a sample is taken. The advantages of constantly pumping the wastestream through the sampling hose include minimizing

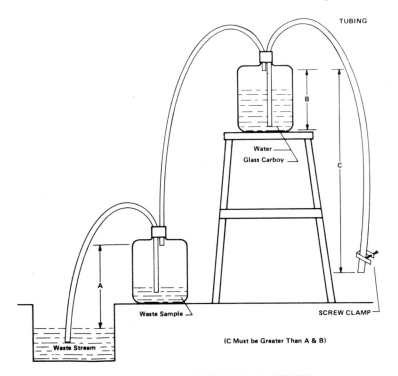

FIG. 2-2. CONTINUOUS SAMPLER

bacterial growth and prevention of sample deterioration while standing in the sampling hose. This sampler can collect volumes of waste from inaccessible sewers.

For water with high suspended solids content, or in which it is not desired to pass the stream through a pump, a vacuum can be used to obtain the samples. A vacuum-type, automatic sampler is shown in Figure 2-6. An interval timer activates the vacuum system which lifts liquid through a suction line into the sample chamber. When the sample is filled, the vacuum is automatically closed. The pump then shuts off and the sample is drawn into the sample container. A secondary float check prevents any liquid from reaching the pump, and the suction line drains by gravity back into the source line. The maximum lift attainable under normal conditions is limited to about 20 ft.

Many automatic instruments are available for continuous sampling and provision of a continuous sampling and monitoring record of certain wastestream characteristics. A few comments on the advantages and disadvantages of automatic monitoring are included here for reference. Automatic monitoring has the following advantages:

1. The parameters of interest are recorded on a continuous basis and a clear

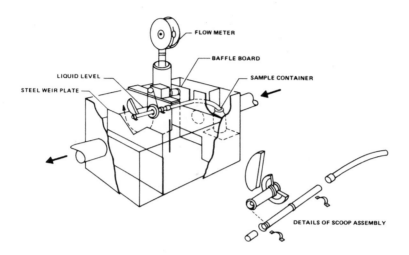

FIG. 2-3. THE "SCOOP" SAMPLER INSTALLATION AND DETAILS OF ASSEMBLY (Courtesy of Brandywine Valley Sales Company)

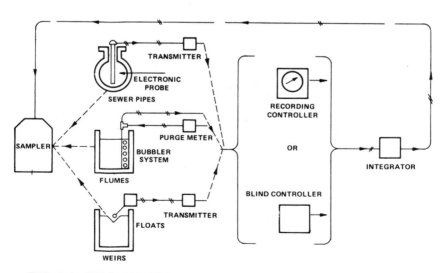

FIG. 2-4. "FLOW-PROPORTIONAL" SAMPLER CONTROL SYSTEMS (Courtesy of Quality Equipment Company)

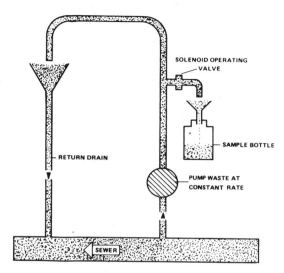

FIG. 2-5. CONSTANT FLOW SYSTEM

picture is obtained of the variation of the recorded parameters with time. It should be noted, however, that continuous-flow measurement data must also be available in order to calculate the total amount of pollutants flowing on a daily basis.

2. There is a shorter time lag between sampling and analysis than in manual sampling. In addition, problems resulting from storage of samples are eliminated.

3. Automatic monitoring systems can be combined with an alarm system that will give advance warning when a high concentration of an undesirable parameter occurs. For example, an automatic conductivity measurement instrument could be set to detect high values. When this occurs, a by-pass valve could be opened and the wastestream directed to a storage basin from which it could be gradually added into the waste treatment system.

Disadvantages of automatic monitoring are:

1. The sensor of the system may not be capable of registering unusual circumstances that may occur at the place of sampling;

2. The initial cost of automatic monitoring is high;

3. The wastewater characteristics need to be known before installing automatic monitoring equipment; and

4. At present only relatively simple continuous measurements are dependable, such as pH, temperature, conductivity, and dissolved oxygen.

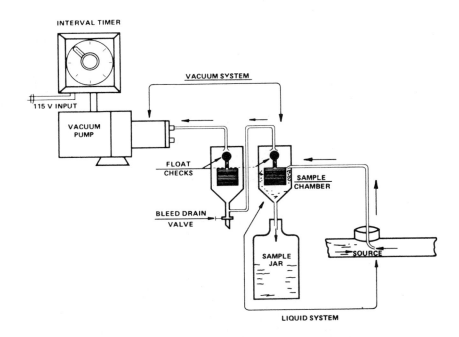

FIG. 2-6. "CVE" SAMPLER SYSTEM SCHEMATIC
(Courtesy of Quality Control Company)

Automatic monitoring can be of great value when it is combined with the operation of treatment facilities. The sensor could be a simple electrode, such as used to monitor pH, or it may be a much more sophisticated piece of equipment. Normally, data are collected on a strip chart recorder, however other appurtenances such as pumps or valves, may also be activated by the sensor. Problems to be anticipated when using automatic monitoring equipment include:

1. Loss of calibration. Regular maintenance is necessary to prevent errors. The flow system and sensor may fail to operate correctly when suspended bacteria are permitted to grow. Therefore, regular cleaning of the system is necessary. Self-cleaning sensors are available and have a definite advantage when used in situations requiring frequent cleaning.
2. Mechanical damage may occur if the intake system or the sensor is not protected by a screen.
3. Miscellaneous problems can be expected to result from power failure, mishandling, pump difficulties, and vandalism.

4. Interferences cause many problems and should be known before installing the monitoring system.

CORRELATION OF RESULTS

The variability of the parameters measured in the monitoring system may result from various phenomena, some of which are listed below:

1. In-plant spills or poor housekeeping;
2. Temporary modifications of in-plant processes;
3. Chemical reactions resulting from various combinations of waste discharges;

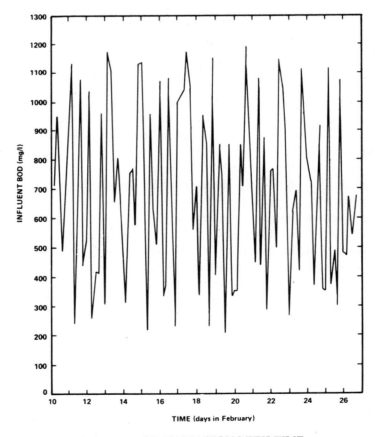

FIG. 2-7. BOD VARIATION WITH TIME

4. Improper maintenance and/or operation of monitoring equipment; and

5. Errors in calculation or analysis of measured parameters.

Those deviations which are not representative of the individual waste treatment processes employed must be identified prior to the evaluation of the sampling results. They may indicate the need for improvement in the maintenance and operation of the industrial processes, waste treatment processes, or the monitoring system itself. The variability of the parameters may be random, resulting from the random effects on the process and its measurement, or cyclic, resulting from periodic phenomena affecting the process (daily periods, weekly, etc.).

Statistics aid in the development of general predictions resulting from numerous individual determinations which by themselves may be meaningless. The resulting relationships are part of the fundamental function of statistics, which express the data obtained from the investigative process in a condensed and meaningful form. Thus, the average or mean is often used as a single value to represent a group of data. The variability of the group of observations is expressed by the value of the standard deviation, and trends in concentration measured during the monitoring process are expressed in the form of regression coefficients.

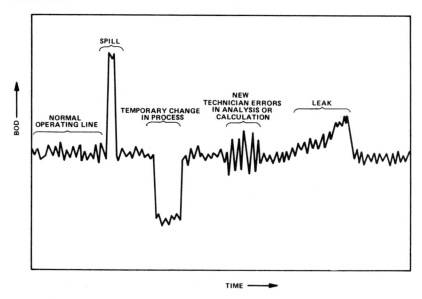

FIG. 2-8. BOD VARIATION WITH TIME

Statistics and data analyses are very broad topics and the scope of this book does not permit thorough discussion of any of the techniques available. Several good references can be cited for use in which a statistical approach is desired. References 2 and 3 provide basic definitions of statistical terms and offer methods for determining accuracy and precision. References 4 and 5 are useful in suggesting ways in which data obtained with a wastewater survey may be presented. The use of a probability paper and flow diagrams are discussed. Detailed information about statistics, including several tests for significance, can be found in References 6 and 7.

The main point of significance which is emphasized herein is that the investigator must understand the influence of randomness and certain plant operations on the variability observed in the data collected. For example, the chronological plot in Figure 2-7 indicates that the collected BOD values were random with no distinct pattern. Had the plot appeared as shown in Figure 2-8, it would have indicated several events, such as in-plant spills, changes in normal plant processes, and differences in samples. In this case, physical understanding of the methods of data generation is obviously more important than statistical treatment of the data.

REFERENCES

1. *Handbook for Monitoring Industrial Wastewater*, EPA Technology Transfer, U.S. Environmental Protection Agency, Washington, D.C. (1973).

2. *Handbook for Analytical Quality Control in Water and Wastewater Laboratories*, EPA Technology Transfer, U.S. Environmental Protection Agency, Washington, D.C. (1972).

3. *Standard Methods for the Examination of Water and Wastewater*. 14th Edition, American Public Health Association, Inc., New York (1976).

4. Eckenfelder, W.W., *Industrial Water Pollution Control*, McGraw-Hill Book Co., New York (1966).

5. Eckenfelder, W.W., *Water Quality Engineering for Practicing Engineers*, Barnes and Noble, Inc., New York (1970).

6. Kennedy, J.B. and Neville, A.M., *Basic Statistical Methods for Engineers and Scientists*, 2nd Edition, Harper and Row, Publishers, New York, (1976).

7. Velz, C.J., "Graphical Approach to Statistics," *Water and Sewage Works*, 97, 195-200, 309-314 and 393-400 (1950); 98, 66-73, 262-265 and 289-293 (1951).

3

SCREENING AND TOXICITY METHODOLOGY

DISCUSSION OF PRINCIPLES

It is frequently necessary with industrial wastes to analyze individual waste-streams or increasing concentrations of a single wastestream in order to predict potential deleterious effects on biological treatment systems. These inhibitory effects on biological systems may be evidenced by reduced organic removal efficiencies, poor settling characteristics of activated sludge organisms, a higher susceptibility to shock loads, or complete inhibition of the system with negligible biological activity. With the regulatory agencies placing greater emphasis not only on average but also maximum levels of effluent quality, biological systems can no longer afford the frequent mild upsets which cause temporary deterioration in effluent quality. Consequently, the importance of toxicity or inhibition cannot be overemphasized.

The effects of toxicity may be evidenced as acute or chronic responses of the organisms. Acute toxicity may occur from sudden pH shocks, specific toxic organisms, or the effects of compounds, such as the organic acids, which become toxic at lower pH values (less than 6.5) due to a lower degree of dissociation and greater penetration into the biological cell. Chronic toxicity may occur from a longer term exposure to heavy metals or inorganic salts both of which can inhibit the organic removal efficiencies or simply cause settling problems with little effect on organic removals.

In conducting toxicity investigations, it is essential that an acclimated biological seed be employed. Otherwise, the results may indicate inhibition when actually a non-acclimated seed was utilized. Often, the presence of inhibitory constituents makes acclimation extremely difficult and the acclimation procedures become a major part of the investigation.

Toxicity and inhibition responses of microorganisms are generally monitored by some measure of the activity of the organisms. This may be observed by decreased organic removal efficiency, changes in specific oxygen uptake rate or chemical tests which measure the concentration of certain bio-chemical agents. Examples of these specific tests include the triphenyl tetrazolium chloride test (TTC) which measures the dehydrogenase activity or another specific test which measures adenosine triphosphate (ATP) [1].

Respirometer techniques are very effective for measuring acute toxicity responses and are useful for evaluating the relative strength of a specific waste and the need for dilution. These techniques are also beneficial for screening different wastestreams. Two respirometer devices which have been successfully used for toxicity screening are the Warburg and Hach devices. These devices employ manometric techniques to evaluate the oxygen utilization by biological systems. It is also possible to screen toxicity effects and acute inhibition with the use of batch activated sludge reactors in which a biological seed and various wastestreams or different concentrations of a specific waste are mixed. Periodic measurement of oxygen uptake, organic removal efficiencies, or enzymatic activity, indicate biological responses to the various conditions.

In order to effectively observe the effects of chronic toxicity, it is necessary to set up continuous-flow systems and measure the responses as discussed in

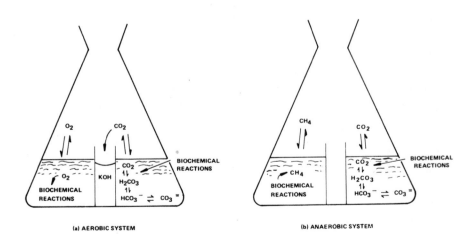

(a) AEROBIC SYSTEM   (b) ANAEROBIC SYSTEM

FIG. 3-1. WARBURG REACTION FLASKS

Chapter 10 on "Activated Sludge." It is impossible to accurately predict the effects of toxic constituents on parameters, such as settling properties of activated sludge, using the shorter-term batch reactors. Sometimes operation of these continuous-flow studies for as long as three months may be necessary in order to properly evaluate the effects of certain potential toxic compounds.

Warburg Apparatus

The Warburg apparatus consists of a manometer and a reaction flask and is frequently used to evaluate toxicity in aerobic biological systems. However, the apparatus has also been employed to evaluate photosynthetic reactions of algae and anaerobic digestion and methane fermentation. The Warburg device can be used to measure toxicity in either aerobic or anaerobic systems with the

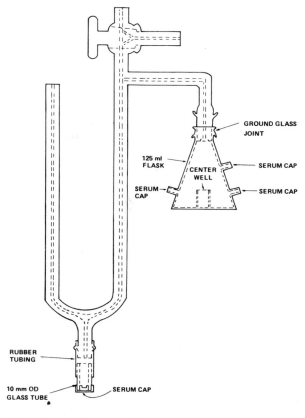

FIG. 3-2. SCHEMATIC DIAGRAM OF THE WARBURG FLASK

reactions as shown in Figure 3-1. The reaction flasks are connected to a manometer as shown in Figure 3-2 and either a production or uptake of gases, such
as methane or oxygen, will be recorded by changes in the liquid level in the
manometer tube. The flask is suspended in a water bath which is maintained at
a constant temperature as shown in Figure 3-3.

For toxicity screening investigation, an acclimated biological seed is mixed
in the desired proportion with the wastewater and added to the manometric
flasks. As the microorganisms utilize the organic constituents of the wastewater,
oxygen is removed from the gas above the liquid and the corresponding pressure

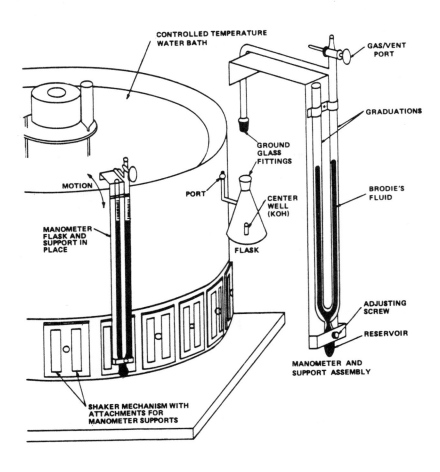

FIG. 3-3. COMPLETE WARBURG APPARATUS

differential in the closed system is recorded. The cumulative oxygen utilization values can be plotted versus time, and toxic or inhibitory thresholds are indicated by significant drops in the relative oxygen uptake rates.

Hach Apparatus

The Hach apparatus is shown in Figure 3-4 and utilizes essentially the same principles as the Warburg device. A desired mixture of waste and biological seed is added to the reaction bottle and as the organisms utilize the oxygen in the air above the liquid, the mercury is drawn up into the manometer arm proportionately. Since the manometer arm is calibrated to read in oxygen units, direct readings can be taken periodically and the results correlated identically as the Warburg results.

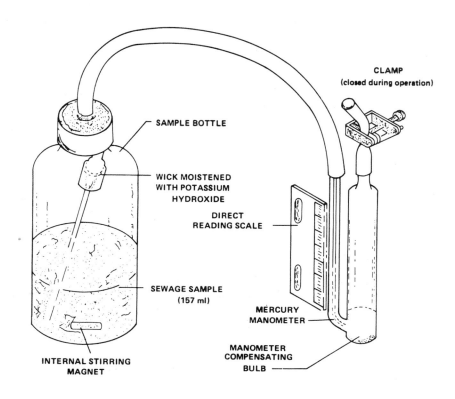

CLAMP
(closed during operation)

SAMPLE BOTTLE

WICK MOISTENED
WITH POTASSIUM
HYDROXIDE

DIRECT
READING SCALE

SEWAGE SAMPLE
(157 ml)

MERCURY
MANOMETER

MANOMETER
COMPENSATING
BULB

INTERNAL STIRRING
MAGNET

FIG. 3-4. DIAGRAM OF HACH MANOMETRIC BOD APPARATUS, SHOWING ONE CELL (Courtesy of Hach Co.)

EQUIPMENT REQUIRED

Warburg Apparatus (See Figure 3-3)

1. Warburg shaker tank with constant temperature water bath;
2. 125-ml flasks with side arms and serum caps as shown in Figure 3-2;
3. A 20 percent KOH solution;
4. Lanolin or vaseline petroleum jelly;
5. Manometer support and assembly for holding the 125-ml flask;
6. Brodie's or Krebs' solution (See Experimental Procedures);
7. Associated glassware and pipettes for making up various waste dilutions.

Hach Apparatus (See Figure 3-4)

1. Hach stirring mechanism for mixing 5 bottles. This mechanism, obtained from the manufacturer, incorporates the manometer tubes in the side.
2. Special 500-ml bottles with manometer and connecting tube. The manometer is actually attached to the side of the Hach stirring mechanisms.
3. Cotton wick for each bottle which will be saturated with potassium hydroxide solution (KOH).
4. A 20 percent KOH solution.
5. Metallic mercury, if required, for filling the manometers.
6. Associated glassware for making the waste dilutions.

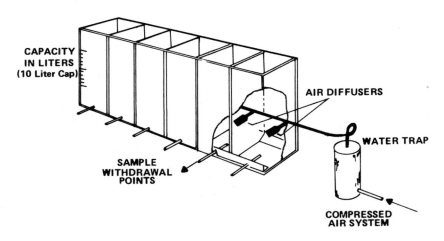

CAPACITY IN LITERS (10 Liter Cap)

AIR DIFFUSERS

WATER TRAP

SAMPLE WITHDRAWAL POINTS

COMPRESSED AIR SYSTEM

FIG. 3-5. BATCH REACTOR FOR TOXICITY SCREENING

Batch Reactors (See Figure 3-5)

1. Batch reactors or polyethylene containers of at least 10 liters capacity.
2. Diffused air stone for each reactor for aeration.
3. A dissolved oxygen probe for measuring oxygen uptake rate.
4. Associated glassware.

EXPERIMENTAL PROCEDURES

Basically, the experimental procedures consist of first developing an acclimated seed to the various waste constituents and then conducting toxicity tests using one of the above methods. Unfortunately, it is often difficult to develop an acclimated seed or to know exactly when the seed is ready to begin the toxicity investigations. It is generally best to develop a seed under continuous-flow conditions as described in Chapter 10 on "Activated Sludge." Occasionally, with exceptionally difficult wastes which may contain toxic compounds or may be toxic above certain dilutions, it is necessary to acclimate with a modified batch procedure which will be explained herein. This procedure will give an approximate maximum concentration to which the organisms can be adapted.

Batch Acclimation with Potentially Toxic Waste

1. Initially set up 7 batch reactors of 10 liter capacity with approximately 2,500 mg/l volatile suspended solids (VSS) (See Figure 3-6).
2. Aerate 1 to 2 hours and then cut off air and allow the organisms to settle.
3. Dilute the raw waste with tap water to obtain a solution of 10 percent waste and 90 percent tap water. Neutralize within the pH range of 7 to 8 and add nitrogen and phosphorus as required.
4. Add a sufficient volume of this diluted mixture so that the food-to-microorganism (F/M) ratio in the batch containers is 0.3 mg BOD/mg VSS. This is accomplished by withdrawing the settled supernatant from Step 2 so that total volume remains constant at 10 liters (See Figure 3-6-a).
5. Turn the air on and allow 1 to 2 minutes for mixing. Immediately take a sample for VSS, BOD, COD, or TOC determinations. Run an oxygen uptake test and compute the specific oxygen uptake (mg O_2/mg VSS-day).
6. Aerate for 1 to 2 days and repeat the analyses in Step 5 at the end of this period.
7. Dilute the raw waste as in Step 3 so that the final mixture is now 30 percent raw waste and 70 percent tap water. Again, adjust the pH and add

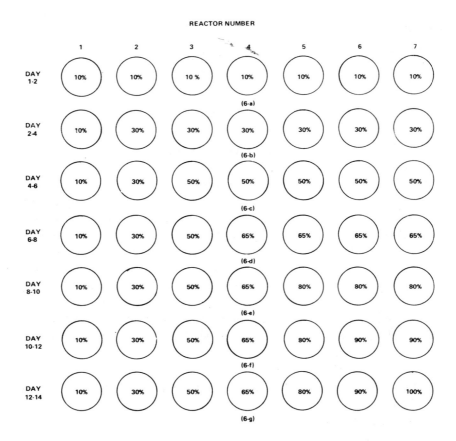

REACTOR NUMBER

**FIG. 3-6. SERIAL BATCH ACCLIMATED PROCEDURE FOR
POTENTIALLY TOXIC WASTES**

sufficient nutrients, if necessary.

8. Calculate the volume of waste required at a 30 percent dilution to produce an F/M of 0.3 in the system.

9. Add this amount of waste to Reactors 2, 3, 4, 5, 6, and 7 as shown in Figure 3-6-b. To Reactor 1, continue to add the 10 percent dilution as in Steps 3 and 4.

10. Repeat Steps 5 and 6.

11. Repeat Steps 8 and 9 with Reactors 3, 4, 5, 6, and 7 except use a waste dilution of 50 percent raw waste and 50 percent tap water. Continue to

operate. Reactor 1 at a 10 percent waste dilution and Reactor 2 at a 30 percent dilution (See Figure 3-6-c).

12. This serial procedure is continued as shown in Figure 3-6 until the concentration of waste becomes so great that either the systems at that concentration fail, or until 100 percent of the waste strength is reached.

13. If a reactor fails as indicated by a severe drop in specific oxygen uptake or organic removal efficiency, go back to the last successful dilution and increase the concentration in smaller increments.

This batch acclimation method has been successfully used to delineate approximate threshold concentrations for toxicity and to develop a biological seed on exceedingly difficult wastes. However, the procedure is tedious and requires considerable time to correctly implement. Moreover, because of the large reactor volumes needed with low strength wastes, this method is considered cumbersome at raw waste BOD concentrations less than 3,000 mg/l. For mixtures of several wastestreams, low concentrations may cause toxicity effects due to the presence of a very toxic stream. Generally, the mixture is acclimated to as high a concentration as possible, then one of the following methods is used to delineate which wastestream is causing the toxic problems and the possible threshold concentration.

Warburg Procedures (See Figure 3-3)

The Warburg procedure consists of adding a specified quantity of waste and acclimated seed to the reaction flask and mixing under constant temperature conditions. The oxygen uptake is periodically monitored by observing the change in liquid level in the manometer tubes. A special liquid, referred to as Brodie's or Krebs' solution, is used for the manometer measurement. The center well of the reaction flask is filled with the potassium hydroxide solution in order to absorb any CO_2 given off by the respiring organisms so that interference with the decrease in oxygen content will not be observed. The procedure is as follows:

1. Prepare the Brodie's or Krebs' solution as outlined below.
   a. *Brodie's manometer fluid*
      23 grams sodium chloride (NaCl)
      5 grams sodium choleate (Merck)
      0.1 gram Evans Blue (or Acid Fuchsin) for color in 500 ml water
      Density = 1.033 g/cm^3 at 20°C
      Standard pressure = 10,000 mm Brodie's solution
                      = 760 mm Hg

47

b. *Krebs' manometer fluid*

44 grams anhydrous NaBr

0.1 gram of syrupy commercially-available solution of Lissapol N (Imperial Chemical Industries, Ltd.) or Stergene (Domestos, Ltd.), or 0.3 gram of Triton X 100 (Rohm & Haas Co.), or comparable non-ionic detergent may be used.

0.3 gram Evans Blue (or Acid Fuchsin)

1,000 ml water

Density = 1.033 g/cm^3 at 20°C

Standard pressure = 10,000 mm Krebs' solution

= 760 mm Hg

2. Add the solution prepared above to the manometer by using a hypodermic syringe and injecting into the rubber tubing. Gently tap the tubing and the manometer to clear all air bubbles.

3. Carefully wash all Warburg flasks with soap and water and dry in a 103°C oven. After drying and cooling, it might be necessary to clean the flasks with chloroform to remove the grease from the center well and manometer joint. The flasks are again dried at 103°C, cooled and cleaned with dichromate cleaning solution. The flasks should then be rinsed several times with water, dried at 103°C and placed in an inverted position to cool.

4. Fill the water bath to the proper level and adjust water to the desired temperature.

5. Lubricate all stopcocks and ports with vaseline. Also coat the rim of the center well to prevent migration of the potassium hydroxide solution into the main flask chamber.

6. Add the 20 percent KOH solution to the center well and fill approximately ¼ full. The absorption of CO_2 may be enhanced by inserting an accordion-folded piece of paper into the center well to increase the surface area.

7. Add the calculated volume of wastewater to the main flask compartment and add the required volume of acclimated seed through the side arm. Generally, the total volume of seed and wastewater ranges from 20 to 50 ml. All flasks should contain exactly the same volume of liquid including the potassium hydroxide. These calculations are outlined in Step 9.

8. Make up the various dilutions, adjust the pH to 7.0, and add sufficient nitrogen and phosphorus.

9. To a 125-ml flask, add the proper mixture and waste so that the total

volume is 20 ml and the VSS concentration is 1,000 mg/l. The VSS concentration of the stock seed is 3,000 mg/l.

a. The amount of seed in the sample flask will be:

$$\text{Seed} = 1,000 \text{ mg/l} \times 20 \text{ ml} \times \frac{1 \text{ liter}}{1,000 \text{ ml}} = 20 \text{ mg}$$

b. The amount of stock seed to add is therefore:

$$\frac{20 \text{ mg}}{3,000 \text{ mg/l}} \times 1,000 \text{ ml/l} = 6.7 \text{ ml}$$

c. The amount of waste to add is:

Total volume of seed + waste = 20 ml
Waste = 20 – 6.7 = 13.3 ml of diluted waste

d. The actual concentration of waste to add, so that the concentration in the sample flask is the desired level, is calculated as follows for a 10 percent dilution:

In 20 ml, 10 percent of waste by volume would be 2 ml. Therefore, add 2 ml of raw waste in the 13.3 ml of the diluted mixture (See Step c). Thus, the dilution of the raw waste would be:

$$\frac{2}{13.3} = 15 \text{ percent}$$

Therefore, add 13.3 ml of the 15 percent waste dilution to the sample flask in order to obtain a 10 percent waste mixture within the flask.

10. Set up two thermobarometers by adding distilled water only. The volume of the distilled water should be identical to the total volume in the other sample flasks. The thermobarometers are set up to monitor any changes in atmospheric conditions which would cause a rise or fall in the manometer liquid. The readings from these flasks are used to correct the sample flasks accordingly.

11. Set up seedblanks which contain only biological seed in order to establish an oxygen uptake due to the endogenous activities of the organisms. An identical quantity of organisms (20 mg, see Step 9) should be in an equal volume of tapwater plus nutrients (20 ml) as that which the sample flask contains.

12. Attach the flask to the support assembly with rubber bands or springs. Recheck the water level of the bath. The water should just approach the bottom of the ground glass fitting which joins the manometer to the flask.

13. Turn on the shaking mechanism with the gas/vent port open to the atmosphere. Allow the flask and solution to equilibrate for 5 to 10 minutes.

During this time, tap the manometer again to ensure that all air bubbles are removed and check all fittings to ensure a proper seal.

14. Turn the shaker off and adjust the manometer reading to the reference point (150 mm) on the closed side of the manometer (right side) with the stopcock open.

15. Close the stopcock, turn on the shaking assembly, and begin readings at

TABLE 3-1. EXPERIMENTAL DATA FROM WARBURG RUN

	Thermobarometers				Seed Blanks					Waste Samples				
Time (hrs)	Flask* Reading (mm)		Avg	Diff.	Flask* Reading (mm)	Diff.	Corr.	Sum x K**	Sum x K**	Flask* Reading (mm)	Diff.	Corr.	Sum x K**	Sum x K**
	1	2		3	4	5	6			7	8	9		
0.00	150	150	150	0	149	0	0	0	0	150	0	0	0	0
0.25	152	152	152	+2	144	5	7	7	6	147	3	5	5	4
0.50	158	158	158	+6	138	6	12	19	15	140	7	13	18	14
0.75	162	159	160	+2	134	4	6	25	20	133	7	9	27	23
1.00	165	163	164	+4	126	8	12	37	30	130	3	7	34	27
1.25	159	156	158	-6	126	0	-6	31	25	130	0	-6	28	22
1.50	158	157	158	0	124	2	2	33	26	119	11	11	39	31
1.75	161	157	159	+1	121	3	4	37	30	114	5	6	45	36
2.00	160	157	158	-1	121	0	-1	36	29	100	14	13	58	46
2.25	158	154	156	-2	121	0	-2	34	27	96	4	2	60	48
2.75	158	156	157	+1	120	1	2	36	29	82	14	15	75	60
3.25	160	158	159	+2	116	4	6	42	34	72/152≠	10	12	87	70
3.75	162	157	160	+1	110	6	7	49	39	147	5	6	93	74
4.25	167	162	164	+4	102	8	12	61	49	142	5	9	102	82
4.75	173	157	170	+6	95	6	12	73	58	136	6	12	114	91
5.25	174	169	172	+2	90	6	8	81	65	133	3	5	119	95
5.75	180	174	177	+5	85	5	10	91	73	126	7	12	131	105
6.25	179	172	176	-1	83	2	1	92	73	122	4	3	134	107
6.75	175	167	171	-5	83	0	-5	87	69	112	10	5	139	111
7.25	174	167	171	0	80	3	3	90	72	105	7	7	146	117
7.75	173	167	170	-1	77	3	2	92	73	99	6	5	151	121
8.25	173	166	170	0	74	3	3	95	76	92/151≠	7	7	158	126
8.75	174	167	171	+1	74	0	1	96	77	145	6	7	165	132
9.25	169	162	166	-5	66	8	3	99	79	135	10	5	172	138
9.75	167	161	164	-2	62	4	2	101	81	130	5	3	175	140

*Raw data, direct manometric readings.

**Mg/1 O$_2$

K = constant (0.8)

≠ Manometric pressure readjustment.

selected time intervals. Prior to taking each reading, turn the shaker off, adjust the closed arm to the reference point and read the left or open arm. Make a note each time the gas/vent stopcock must be opened to the atmosphere in order to readjust the manometer fluid so that it will not be pulled over into the reaction flask.

16. Read the manometer arm on a regularly scheduled time basis. Check the temperature after each series of readings. On long or extended runs (greater than 3 or 4 days) barometric weather changes should be checked in order to avoid the calamity which occurs when the solution is forced back into the flask.

17. Record the data on a form similar to that shown in Table 3-1 and correlate the cumulative oxygen uptake as shown in Figure 3-7. When the substrate has been sufficiently utilized and the summation of oxygen uptake remains relatively constant, the run can be terminated.

18. At the end of the run, check the TOC, pH, and other parameters as required, remaining in solution.

Hach Procedures (See Figure 3-4)

1. Clean the sample bottles as described in Step 3 under the Warburg procedures.

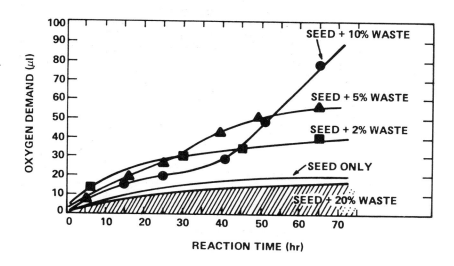

FIG. 3-7. DILUTION EFFECT ON RESPIRATION RATES

2. Prepare the approximate waste dilutions and add to the respective flask bottles.
3. Add the calculated quantity of seed to each bottle so that the VSS concentration is the same in all bottles.
4. Saturate the wick with KOH and place the wick carefully in each bottle. Take care not to spill the KOH on the side of the wick when saturating so that there is no possibility for the KOH to diffuse into the waste-seed solution.
5. Check the mercury level in the reservoir and, if necessary, replenish. Fasten the cap to the top of the bottle but do not force a snug fit yet.
6. Turn on the magnetic stirrers and allow approximately 5 minutes for the solutions to equilibrate. After 5 minutes, adjust the manometer scale to read zero at time "zero" and securely tighten the caps to the bottle so that there is no air leak.
7. Read the manometer scale on a periodic basis and record the cumulative oxygen uptake. These results can be plotted directly as oxygen uptake and generate a similar plot to the Warburg data in Figure 3-7.

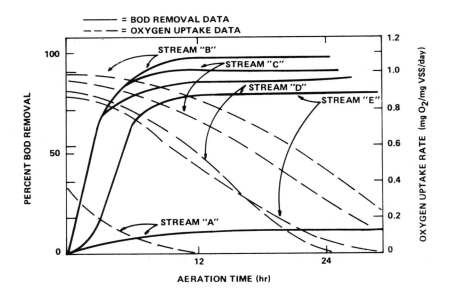

FIG. 3-8. BATCH RESULTS FOR TOXICITY OF DIFFERENT WASTES

Batch Experimental Procedures (See Figure 3-5)

1. An acclimated biological seed should be added to each of the test reactors so that the final VSS concentration will be in the range of 1,000 to 1,500 mg/l when the waste is added. Measure the TOC, COD, or BOD of the seed liquid filtrate.

2. Add the different test streams or varying concentrations of one stream to each of the batch reactors. Mix the reactors with air for approximately 1 to 2 minutes and immediately run an oxygen uptake test and sample for an organic parameter, such as TOC, COD, or BOD. The organic analysis should be performed only on filtered samples.

3. Aerate the contents of each reactor and withdraw samples at the end of 1, 2, 4, 8, 12, and 24 hours aeration and measure the filtered TOC, COD, or BOD. Additionally, perform oxygen uptake measurements at each of these times.

4. Correlate the organic removal and oxygen uptake results as shown in Figures 3-8 and 3-9.

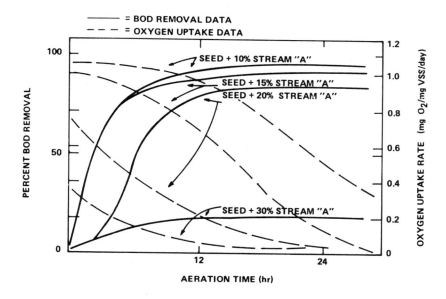

FIG. 3-9. BATCH SCREENING RESULTS FOR TOXICITY AT VARIOUS WASTE CONCENTRATIONS

CORRELATION OF RESULTS

Warburg Experimental Results

It is desired to determine the concentration at which a waste becomes toxic to activated sludge organisms. Dilutions have been made up to 2, 5, 10, and 20 percent wastes for analysis on the Warburg.

1. Record the data as shown in Table 3-1. Calculations are also presented in Table 3-1. Changes in fluid level due to barometric pressure are recorded in Columns 1 and 2. The seed blank and actual sample readings are shown in Columns 4 and 7, respectively. The sample and seed readings are

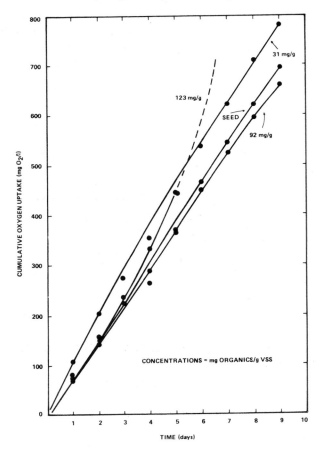

FIG. 3-10. WARBURG DATA: NON-DEGRADABLE NON-TOXIC WASTE

corrected by adding the thermobarometer difference (Column 3) to the net seed and sample readings (Columns 5 and 8, respectively) to obtain the corrected readings (Column 6 and 9). Finally, the corrected readings are converted to oxygen utilization by the flask constant. The final reading is expressed in mg/l. The flask constant is generally given for each flask or can be determined by a tedious method described in most Warburg references [2].

2. The individual results for the different dilutions are plotted in Figure 3-7 and show that the waste was not toxic until the seed was exposed to greater than a 10 percent concentration of waste. It might be desirable to now go back and repeat the tests at concentrations between 10 and 20 percent in order to better delineate the toxic threshold concentration.

Other types of Warburg results are shown in Figures 3-10 and 3-11. Figure 3-10 indicates a non-degradable but also non-toxic waste while Figure 3-11 indicates an extremely toxic waste.

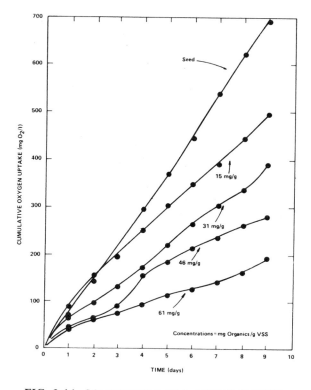

FIG. 3-11. WARBURG DATA: TOXIC WASTE

Batch Experimental Results

The results of the batch tests are shown in Figures 3-8 and 3-9 and simply are plots of the organic removal and specific O_2 uptake versus the time of batch aeration. As can be seen in Figure 3-8, a 20 percent dilution of Stream A was the minimum dilution at which no toxicity occurred. This is substantiated by the oxygen uptake data in Figure 3-8. Figure 3-9 shows that Stream E was a toxic stream while the other streams were highly degradable. It would not be desirable to go back and examine various dilutions of Stream E to see if there was a certain concentration which could be degraded biologically.

LIMITATIONS AND SCALE-UP

Probably, the most important criteria in performing toxicity investigations is to ensure that an acclimated biological seed is utilized. Frequently, it is very difficult to generate an acclimated seed due to the presence of an unknown toxic constituent in the wastestream. It is impossible, using the manometric and batch techniques described herein, to evaluate long-term inhibitory effects to biological organisms. Subsequently, after techniques described in this chapter have been used to delineate toxic threshold concentrations and certain waste-streams which should not be included for biological treatment, it is then necessary to conduct longer term continuous-flow studies which would define the chronic responses of the organism to the specific waste in question. Such studies might be oriented towards examining the settleability of activated sludge organisms which is essential for proper performance of the system. It must also be emphasized that the oxygen uptake and organic removal efficiencies observed during the screening operations should not be used for design since considerably different conditions will result in the prototype system. For design purposes, the next step is to follow the procedures outlined in Chapters 10 and 11.

REFERENCES

1. Ford, D.L. and Eckenfelder, W.W., "Effect of Process Variables on Sludge Floc Formation and Settling Characteristics," *Journal Water Pollution Control Federation*, 39, 1850-1859 (1967).
2. Umbreit, W.W., Burris, R.H., and Stauffer, J.F., *Manometric Techniques*, 4th Ed., Burgess Publishing Co., Minneapolis, Minn. (1964).

4

NEUTRALIZATION

DISCUSSION OF PRINCIPLES

Many wastewaters contain acidic or alkaline substances which must be neutralized prior to being discharged into receiving bodies of water or conveyed to subsequent unit treatment processes. Neutralization, or adjustment of pH, may be used in the latter case not only to protect downstream unit processes, but also to optimize their effectiveness.

Neutralization entails the reaction of solutions having active hydrogen or hydroxyl ions to form water and neutral salts. An example is the neutralization of caustic soda (NaOH) with sulfuric acid (H_2SO_4):

$$H_2SO_4 + 2NaOH \longrightarrow Na_2SO_4 + 2H_2O \qquad (4\text{-}1)$$

The first parameter to consider is pH which, by definition, is the logarithm of the reciprocal of the active hydrogen ion concentration in an aqueous solution. This means that a change of one pH unit indicates a change of hydrogen ion concentration by a factor of 10.

An acid may be strong or weak, depending on the amount of free hydrogen ions in solution at a specified concentration. The pH of an acid is not to be confused with its acidity, which is the volume of a base required to obtain a specified pH. Nitric acid, for example, is a strong acid as most nitric acid molecules dissociate into active hydrogen and nitrate ions. Conversely, acetic acid is weak as most of the acetic acid molecules do not dissociate into hydrogen and acetate ions. Equal molar concentrations of either acids, however, have the same total acidity and thus require the same amount of neutralizing base. The same applies to bases. Sodium hydroxide is a strong base while ammonia and soda ash are weak bases, but equal molar concentrations of these bases have the same capacity to neutralize a given quantity of acid.

There are several process modes for accomplishing neutralization or pH adjustment. These include slaked lime neutralization of acid wastes in a properly designed rapid mix basin, limestone bed neutralization using upflow or down-flow configurations, and acid or caustic neutralization (using various acids or carbon dioxide) in a rapid mix, fluidized basin. This may be on a continuous-flow or batch basis. The main factors to be considered in each of these process approaches are:

1. Dampening influent flow and pH variations to the maximum extent possible prior to maximizing the stability of the neutralization process;

2. Establishing a proper basis for the neutralization process design based on laboratory or pilot plant studies, developing titration curves over the spectrum of acidity/alkalinity of the flow to be neutralized (examples of such curves are shown in Figure 4-1 and 4-2);

3. Predicting the qualitative and quantitative characteristics of any sludge generated as a result of pH change;

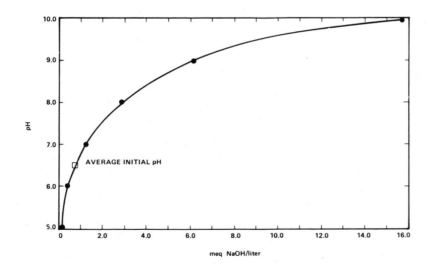

FIG. 4-1. REPRESENTATIVE NEUTRALIZATION CURVE

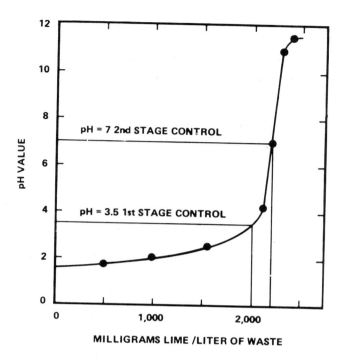

pH = 7 2nd STAGE CONTROL

pH = 3.5 1st STAGE CONTROL

MILLIGRAMS LIME /LITER OF WASTE

FIG. 4-2. LIME-WASTE TITRATION CURVE

4. Determining the effect, if applicable, of the chemical constituents added during the neutralization step on subsequent unit process effectiveness (such as influence on solids/liquid separation, biochemical removal rates, adsorption rates, etc.) and residual water quality (such as an increase in sulfate, total dissolved solids, etc.); and also to optimize their effectiveness; and

5. Developing an effective process control system.

Control Systems

Of the above, the pH control system most likely represents the critical path as this ultimately dictates the success or failure of the process. Control systems can generally be classified into four categories [1]. These are described as follows:

Two-position (on-off). This sytem is designed so that the element controlling reagent addition is completely on or closed. This control approach is usually limited to systems where the flow rate is low and residence time is high. The control element is usually a solenoid or air-actuated, solenoid-controlled valve. The liquid in the neutralization tank is sensed by the electrodes and the solenoid valves actuated by the "feedback" amplified signal from the electrodes.

Multimode or Proportional Control Systems. In these systems, the neutralizing reagent is added continuously, the rate depending on the proportionality set up by the system and the controller. These systems are generally applicable when the basin has a relatively short residence time (less than three minutes), although this must be sufficient time for the reaction to go to completion.

Cascade Control Systems. This system is generally applied when extremely large neutralization basins are used. It is two-staged with the first stage providing a high mixing intensity, this being less critical in the second stage. The control elements and sensing systems are similar to those in the multimode control systems.

Feedforward Control Systems. Feedforward control is commonly applied when variables such as pH and flow change significantly and frequently. Where flow is the main variable, it is possible to use it as a "feedforward" signal to make an immediate correction to the reagent feed rate rather than waiting for the feedback system to sense the change. A tighter control can be effected by this approach.

In situations where waste strength and flow are highly variable, the control system should be two-staged. The first stage dampens this fluctuation with rough pH control, where the second stage can "fine tune" the process effectiveness through good pH control. A schematic of a two-stage control system for neutralization of a waste acid is shown in Figure 4-3.

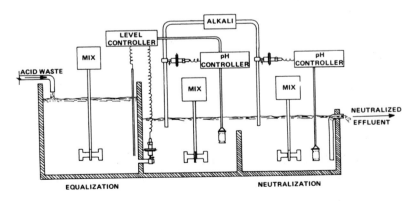

**FIG. 4-3. FLOW DIAGRAM OF TREATMENT PLANT FOR
NEUTRALIZATION OF WASTE ACID**
(Courtesy of Parsons Corp., Pasadena, CA)

Adequate mixing is necessary for proper pH control using fluidized systems. Gradients within the basins will cause erroneous feedback information to the control system and poor overall control will be the result. Thus, the proper power level and mixer design is very important. A typical power level-detention time relationship for proper mixing is shown in Figure 4-4.

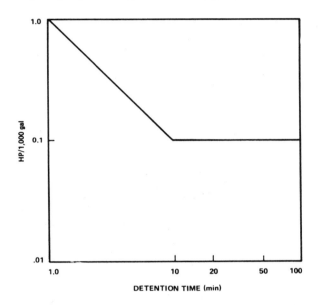

FIG. 4-4. TYPICAL POWER LEVEL-DETENTION TIME RELATIONSHIP FOR COMPLETE MIXING

Control of pH as Pretreatment

It should be recognized that certain aspects not previously mentioned should be considered when pH adjustment of wastewater is required before conveyance to subsequent unit processes such as activated sludge or other forms of biological treatment. Biological systems have the ability to effect pH changes in an aeration basin through various mechanisms. These include:

Reduction of pH in Biological Systems

1. Destruction of hydroxide alkalinity by biochemical production of CO_2;

$$CO_2 + OH^- \longrightarrow HCO_3^- \qquad (4-2)$$

61

2. Biochemical oxidation of reduced forms of sulfur to sulfuric acid;

$$H_2S + O_2 \xrightarrow[\text{oxidation}]{\text{biochemical}} H_2SO_4 \qquad (4\text{-}3)$$

$$\text{Sulfonates} \xrightarrow[\text{oxidation}]{\text{biochemical}} H_2SO_4 \qquad (4\text{-}4)$$

3. Oxidation of ammonia (nitrification);

$$NH_4^+ + 2O_2 \longrightarrow NO_3^- + 2H^+ + H_2O \qquad (4\text{-}5)$$

4. Production of organic acids as a biological reaction intermediate.

Increase of pH in Biological Systems

1. Biochemical oxidation of organic acids.
2. Biochemical destruction of salts of organic acids.

The addition of chemicals prior to biological treatment to maintain pH control may have other ramifications which should be considered in any overall design. For example, the addition of lime to a water of low carbonate alkalinity, combined with active biological production of carbon dioxide, will result in an

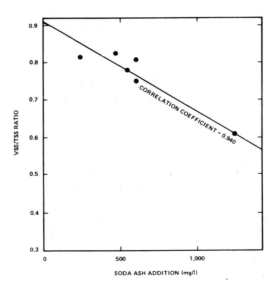

FIG. 4-5. EFFECT OF PRIMARY SODA ASH ADDITION ON
MIXED LIQUOR VSS/TSS RATIO

increase of available calcium ions in the effluent which will precipitate out as calcium carbonate when combined with more alkaline waters. If the waste is sufficiently buffered and the pH remains in the 8 to 10 range, then calcium carbonate will be formed in the aeration basin, and the buildup of inert solids could occur. An example of this is reflected in the decrease of the VSS/TSS ratio in an activated sludge aeration basin, shown in Figure 4-5, where soda ash was added following lime neutralization to buffer the system, thereby providing carbonate ions and generating calcium carbonate precipitation [2]. Such a phenomenon can be both advantageous and disadvantageous. A decrease in the VSS/TSS ratio can result in a decrease in the biological treatment efficiency because of the reduction of active biomass-substrate contact in the system. However, the calcium carbonate may, in fact, act as a weighting agent in the final clarifier, enhancing solids/liquid separation and improving the overall attributable efficiency to a higher removal of suspended solids and those organics and other constituents associated with the non-soluble fraction. Pilot studies can be used to assess this effect and to develop pH control systems specifically designed to maximize the effectiveness of the biological process.

EQUIPMENT REQUIRED

Basic neutralization data are usually developed in the laboratory using standard titration procedures on representative wastewater samples. If the project size merits a more comprehensive study, however, bench or pilot scale neutralization studies are justified. The equipment required is tabulated subsequently.

Bench-Scale — Liquid Alkaline or Acid Neutralization

1. Beakers, 1,000 ml
2. Pipettes
3. pH meter
4. Mixer

Bench-Scale — Limestone Neutralization

1. Neutralization columns (See Figure 4-6)
2. Screened and washed crushed limestone
3. Beakers, 1,000 ml or larger
4. Bench-scale pumps, capacity — 2 to 25 liters/hr

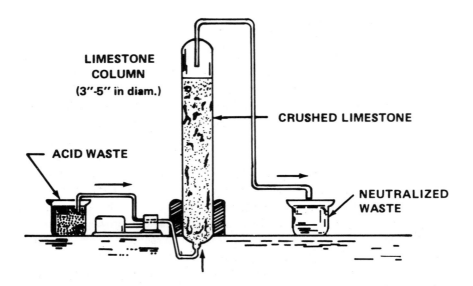

**LIMESTONE
COLUMN
(3"-5" in diam.)**

CRUSHED LIMESTONE

ACID WASTE

**NEUTRALIZED
WASTE**

FIG. 4-6. BENCH-SCALE LIMESTONE NEUTRALIZATION
COLUMNS

Pilot Scale

1. Chemical feed metering pumps (with recycle and blowdown provisions if required)
2. Slurry pumps
3. Chemical storage tanks/bins — agitators if required
4. Reaction tanks and mixers
5. Clarification tanks (if required)
6. pH control system — complete with recorder-controllers, pH probes, and amplifiers

EXPERIMENTAL PROCEDURES

Bench-Scale Liquid Alkaline or Acid Neutralization

1. Add 500 ml of wastewater to 1,000 ml beaker.
2. Add the lime slurry in increments, checking the pH after it reaches equilibrium following each incremental addition of lime slurry. The waste mixture should be continuously stirred and the pH observed until equilibrium

is reached. Caution should be observed in pipetting the lime slurry to avoid deposition of the lime in the pipette.

3. Continue lime addition until a terminal pH of 10.0 is reached.
4. Plot the neutralization curve, pH vs mg lime/liter of wastewater, as shown in Figure 4-2.
5. For the desired terminal pH, a separate test can be devised to check the mixing time required to attain equilibrium or to complete the reaction.

The basic design procedure for alkaline wastes is similar to acidic wastes. A mineral acid such as H_2SO_4 or, in some cases, CO_2 or scrubbed flue gas can be used.

Bench-Scale Limestone Neutralization

1. Fill the neutralization columns (as shown in Figure 4-6) with limestone, after washing and screening, to depths of 1 ft, 2 ft, and 3 ft.
2. Adjust the upward flow rate of the acid wastewater to each column. Flow rates varying from 50 gph/sq ft to 1,000 gph/sq ft should be used.
3. Check the effluent pH from each column until it is stabilized.
4. After each run, replace the quantity of limestone used to the column

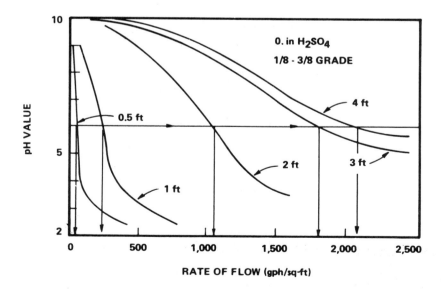

FIG. 4-7. NEUTRALIZATION THROUGH CALCINED MAGNESITE

(recorded by weight) and record the volume of wastewater neutralized.
5. Plot .terminal pH as a function of flow rate for each depth of limestone (as shown in Figure 4-7).

Pilot Scale

There are many different configurations of a pilot-scale neutralization system which can be used. A typical one used for acid wastewater neutralization is shown in Figure 4-8.

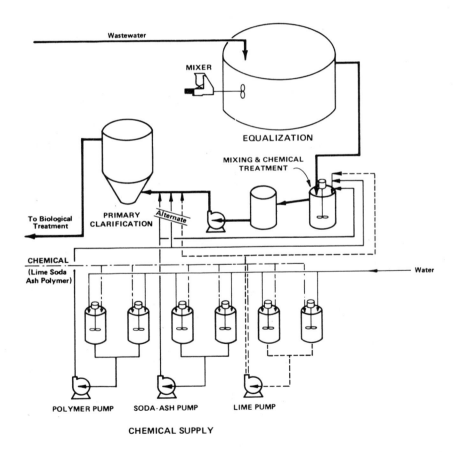

FIG. 4-8. PILOT PLANT NEUTRALIZATION FACILITY FOR TREATMENT OF ACID WASTES

1. Bring the acid stream(s) into a mixed equalization basin or tank to dampen fluctuations to the maximum extent possible.
2. The acid waste is then fed to a mixing tank or drum where the chemicals are added by highly controlled metering pumps. Dual feed tanks with agitators allow for makeup of fresh solutions while maintaining chemical feed. A loop lime slurry feed system is often required to prevent lime plugging and provide flexibility.
3. The pH adjusted wastewater is then conveyed to a clarifier if precipitation occurs. If this is not the case, then the clarification step can be eliminated.
4. The system should be monitored for chemical characteristic changes which might occur when the pH is altered. The effectiveness of the pH control system under varying degrees of influent acidity (or basicity) also can be evaluated.

CORRELATION OF RESULTS

The formulation and evaluation of pilot plant results can be developed according to the specific objectives of the program, although the emphasis of pilot work is generally in control system evaluation of strict process performance.

The following example will serve to illustrate the calculations involved for correlation of the results of a limestone neutralization experiment:

It is desired to neutralize a waste acid stream containing 0.1 N H_2SO_4 to pH 6.0 through a limestone bed. The waste flow rate is 3,000 gph. Assume the neutralization curves shown in Figure 4-7. The calculations will be tabulated in Table 4-1.

TABLE 4-1. LIMESTONE BED NEUTRALIZATION RESULTS

Parameter	Experiment Number				
	I	II	III	IV	V
Bed Depth, ft	0.5	1	2	3	4
Flow Rate, gph/sq ft	65	250	1,040	1,800	2,100
Area, sq ft	46	12	2.9	1.67	1.42
Volume of Limestone, cu ft	23	12	5.8	5.0	5.7
Flow Rate, gph/cu ft	130	250	520	600	525

1. The design flow rates (gph/sq ft) are determined for each bed depth for pH 6 from Figure 4-7. These values are presented in Table 4-1.
2. Calculate the bed area for each bed depth by dividing the waste flow rate (3,000 gph) by the design flow rates from Step 1 (See Table 4-1).
3. Compute the volume of the limestone bed (area computed in Step 2 times bed depth).
4. Compute the flow rate in gph/cu ft. (Waste flow rate, 3,000 gph, divided by bed volume from Step 3.)
5. Plot the flow rate (gph/cu ft) versus bed depth as shown in Figure 4-9.

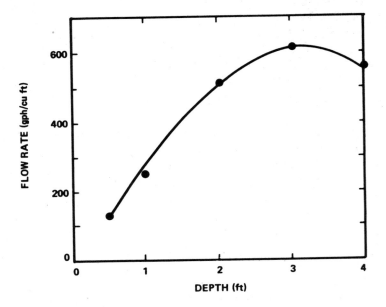

FIG. 4-9. DETERMINATION OF OPTIMUM BED DEPTH

From Figure 4-9, it is seen that a 3-ft deep limestone bed will be most economical.

6. For each terminal pH using the 3-ft bed depth, compute the limestone requirement (volume or lb) per 1,000 gal based upon the limestone replacement from Step 4 in the Experimental Procedures. Plot the volume of limestone per 1,000 gal versus terminal pH as shown in Figure 4-10.

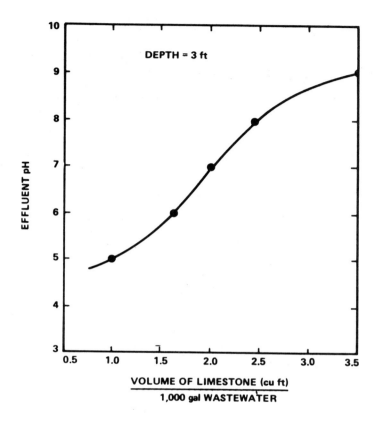

FIG. 4-10. LIMESTONE BED REQUIREMENTS

LIMITATIONS AND SCALE-UP

The obvious limitations in bench-scale evaluation of neutralization systems is the inability to evaluate control of and fluctuations in wastewater acidity and/or alkalinity. The difficulty of obtaining representative samples often translates to bad predictions for chemical feed requirements based on bench-scale studies. A bench-scale evaluation of limestone neutralization has the danger of short-circuiting in the columns which may provide more accurate information as they "ride the line," thereby indicating the degree of control which can be effected under field conditions. Precipitation effects, control systems, and material evaluations also can be more accurately assessed in pilot scale studies.

REFERENCES

1. Hoffmann, F., "How to Select a pH Control System for Neutralizing Waste Acids," *Chemical Engineering*, 79:24, 105-110 (1972).

2. Engineering-Science, Inc., Confidential Report, Houston, Texas (June 1973).

5

COAGULATION
AND PRECIPITATION

DISCUSSION OF PRINCIPLES

Coagulation has been defined as the addition of a chemical to a colloidal dispersion which results in particle destabilization by the reduction in forces which tend to keep particles apart. Coagulation involves the reduction of surface charges and the formation of complex hydrous oxides. The process involves forming either flocculant suspensions of compounds which entrap desired pollutants and carry them out of solution or the formation of insoluble precipitates of the pollutants themselves. Examples of the former include organic suspended materials and examples of the latter include precipitates of phosphorus and heavy metals.

Initially, the coagulation phase of treatment is practically instantaneous and the particles are usually sub-microscopic in size. These colloidal particles then agglomerate to form settleable solids by the process of flocculation. Where coagulation utilizes forces of electrostatic or interionic nature, flocculation occurs by chemical bridging or physical enmeshing mechanisms. After coagulation to destabilize the particles and flocculation to generate large particles, the materials can subsequently be separated from the wastewater by sedimentation, flotation, or filtration.

Most microscopic and colloidal particles are stabilized by the formation of layers of ions which collect around the particle and form a protective barrier for stabilization. These ionic layers tend to act as part of the particle and travel with it through solution, inhibiting the close approach of respective particles to each other. Both the thickness of the ionic layers and the surface charge density are sensitive to the concentration and valence of ions in solution. Therefore, the stability of a suspension may be markedly affected or altered by adding suitable ions to the solution.

Zeta Potential

The zeta potential is a measure of the stability of a particle and indicates the potential which would be required to penetrate the layer of ions surrounding the particle for destabilization. Therefore, the higher the zeta potential, the more stable the particle. The purpose of coagulation is to reduce the zeta potential by adding specific ions and then to induce motion for the destabilized particles to agglomerate.

The measurement of the zeta potential can be accomplished by the determination of the electrophoretic mobility of the charged particles under an applied voltage [1]:

$$\zeta = \frac{4\,\pi\,\mu\,(EM)}{X(D)} \qquad (5\text{-}1)$$

where:

ζ	=	zeta potential
D	=	dielectric constant of the medium
X	=	applied potential
EM	=	electrophoretic mobility
μ	=	viscosity

which reduces to:

$$\zeta = \left[\frac{113,000}{D}\right] \mu\ EM \qquad (5\text{-}2)$$

Electrophoretic mobility is associated with Brownian movement. When the medium is placed under an impressed voltage, electrophoresis occurs causing a migration of particles in the direction of electron travel or positive to negative depending on the colloidal charge. The rate of migration divided by the voltage gradient is defined as the electrophoretic mobility. Electrophoretic mobility can be calculated by the following equation:

$$EM = \frac{(G)\,(L)}{(V)\,(T)} \qquad (5\text{-}3)$$

where:

G	=	length of grid division (μ^m)
L	=	length of electrophoresis cell (cm)
V	=	voltage (volts)
T	=	time (seconds)

Zeta potential measurement involves tracing the path of colloidal particles under an applied voltage over a measured distance. A test cell containing the liquid and equipped with a platinum or molybdenum electrode is viewed by the use of a stereoscopic microscope and the velocity of the colloidal particles is calculated. The electrophoretic mobility is calculated from Equation 5-3.

Significant Considerations for Coagulation

There are several pertinent factors which must be considered when evaluating coagulation as a feasible treatment process:

1. What are the relative proportions of particulate colloidal, soluble, and non-absorbable fraction of materials in the raw wastewater?
2. What is the best and most economical coagulant for the particular wastewater?
3. What effluent quality can be expected using the selected coagulants under the appropriate operating conditions?
4. How much sludge will be produced and how well will it dewater?
5. Is coagulant recovery feasible?
6. What incidental removal of other compounds may occur under the operating conditions required to remove a specific pollutant?
7. What is the nature of the coagulated materials and should gravity sedimentation or dissolved air flotation be employed for removal of these materials?

The three major types of chemicals used in coagulation of wastewaters include lime, alum and iron salts. Various polymers are often used as coagulant acids.

Coagulation with Lime

Lime reacts with bicarbonate alkalinity or orthophosphorus compounds to form the insoluble precipitates of calcium carbonate or hydroxy apatite as shown in the following equations:

$$Ca(OH)_2 + Ca(HCO_3)_2 \longrightarrow 2CaCO_3\downarrow + 2H_2O \qquad (5\text{-}4)$$

$$5Ca^{2+} + 4OH^- + 3HPO_4^{2-} \longrightarrow Ca_5\ OH(PO_4)_3\downarrow + 3H_2O \qquad (5\text{-}5)$$

The calcium phosphate or hydroxy apatite is a crystalline precipitate of varying composition and the calcium:phosphorus ratio varies from 1:3 to 2:0. This variation results from the substitution of calcium and hydrogen ions at the surface and within the crystaline structure. Polyphosphate compounds are not removed unless orthophosphate compounds are present, and it is generally believed that the polyphosphate materials are absorbed onto the orthophosphate–calcium flocs. Phosphorus may also be absorbed onto the surface of calcium carbonate particles. The solubility of calcium phosphate decreases rapidly with an increase in pH and, therefore, phosphorus removal increases with increased pH levels. Consequently, the lime dosage to achieve a given phosphate or turbidity removal is more a function of wastewater alkalinity than concentration.

At a pH of 9.5, most of the phosphorus is precipitated as hydroxy apatite; however, this is generally accompanied by high turbidity. This turbidity is common with calcium precipitates and results from colloidal-dispersed particles of calcium compounds. As the pH is increased above 9.5, magnesium compounds begin to precipitate until the reaction is complete at 11.0. These magnesium compounds tend to produce a highly clarified effluent; however, the magnesium hydroxide which is formed is gelatinous in nature and difficult to dewater. Thus, the presence of magnesium will not only affect the effluent quality with respect to clarity, but may also influence the specific sludge handling procedures.

Coagulation with Aluminum Compounds

When alum is added to water, it is believed that the aluminum ions enter into a series of hydrolytic reactions with water to form a series of multivalent-charged hydrous oxide species. These species may range from positive compounds at low pH to negative at high pH values as shown below:

$$[Al(H_2O)_6]^{3+} + H_2O \leftrightharpoons [Al(H_2O)_5OH]^{2+} + H_3O^+ \qquad (5\text{-}6)$$

$$[Al(H_2O)_5(OH)]^{2+} + H_2O \leftrightharpoons [Al(H_2O)_4(OH)_2]^+ + H_3O^+ \qquad (5\text{-}7)$$

These reactions continue until negative species are formed: $[Al(H_2O)_2(OH)_4]^-$. A series of polymerization reactions has been credited with formation of "olation" products which contain several aluminum ions bridged by two hydroxyl ions:

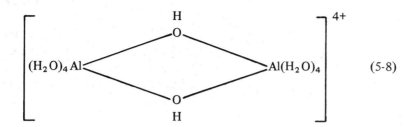

$$(5\text{-}8)$$

The most important point is that both hydrogen (H^+) and hydroxyl ions (OH^-) are involved; therefore, the pH is important.

Another equation in which aluminum combines to form the insoluble precipitate, aluminum phosphate, is shown below:

$$Al_2(SO_4)_3 + 2PO_4^{3-} \longrightarrow 2AlPO_4 \downarrow + 3SO_4^{2-} \qquad (5\text{-}9)$$

All of the above equations compete for aluminum ions. Phosphate compounds are removed both by complexing with aluminum or by absorption onto aluminum hydroxide flocs. If the hydrolyzing reactions did not compete, there would be a requirement of approximately 0.87 lb of aluminum per lb of phosphorus removed. Actually, in practice the ratio is 2 to 3 lb of aluminum required per lb of phosphorus removed. Alum (aluminum sulfate) is the most common aluminum salt used for wastewater coagulation.

Coagulation with Iron

Iron salts, particularly ferric chloride, react similarly to the aluminum reactions described above. Approximately 1.8 lb of iron is required per lb of phosphorus removed, plus, approximately 10 mg/l of iron for hydroxide formation. Generally, 0.3 to 0.5 mg/l of an anionic polyelectrolyte is added to enhance supernatant clarity.

Role of Polyelectrolytes in Coagulation

Polymeric flocculants or polyelectrolytes can be either synthetic or natural in nature. Many natural compounds are cellulose materials, polysaccharide gums and proteinaceous materials. Synthetic polyelectrolytes have the advantage that they can be tailored to meet specific requirements. They are classified by the type of charge: a negative charge is called an anionic polymer; a positively charged polymer is referred to as cationic; and, a nonionic polymer has no charge. The major advantage of the polymer compounds is to increase the floc size of the coagulated particulates.

The performance of anionic polymers is a function of pH, the alkalinity of the water, hardness of the water, and turbidity. The optimum polymer dose increases linearly with the coagulant, such as alum, dosage. Some cationic polymers will actually perform the coagulation process themselves and are not dependent on the presence of metal coagulants. These compounds can often reduce the alum or iron requirement. They can minimize interferences by tripolyphosphates and lignin compounds and can also flocculate live organisms, such as algae and bacteria.

In summary, the coagulation process principles can be stated as follows:
1. The specific coagulating salts are added to water.
2. Reactions occur with water and other salts to form multi-positive hydroxyl and polymeric compounds.
3. There is an electrostatic attraction between negative turbidity particles and positive hydrolysis products. The hydrolysis products are rapidly absorbed onto the surface of the negatively charged turbidity and colloidal particles. Consequently, the electrical charge of the particles is reduced. The zeta potential now measures in the range of slightly negative to neutral to slightly positive depending on the pH and the coagulant dosage. The suspension is now considered stabilized.
4. The particles agglomerate and are ready to be separated from solution by gravity sedimentation, flotation, or filtration.

EQUIPMENT REQUIRED

1. Jar test apparatus (Figure 5-1) and/or zeta meter and electrophoresis cell (Figure 5-2).
2. Various commercially available coagulants and coagulant aids such as lime, alum, ferric chloride, and polyelectrolytes.
3. Stopwatch
4. Zone settling apparatus.
5. Graduated cylinders and beakers.
6. Equipment for measuring suspended and volatile suspended solids and other parameters of interest, such as color, TOC and BOD_5.

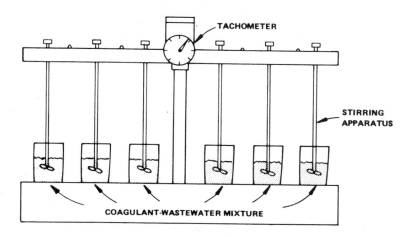

**FIG. 5-1. LABORATORY SCALE JAR TEST ASSEMBLY
FOR COAGULATION STUDIES**

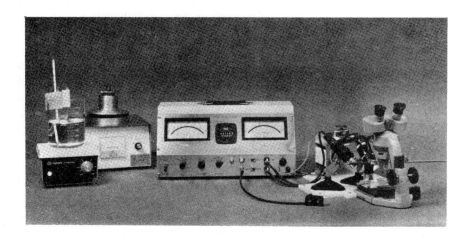

**FIG. 5-2. ELECTROPHORESIS CELL AND
ZETA POTENTIAL METER**

EXPERIMENTAL PROCEDURES

Initially, it is desired to determine the optimum condition, namely, coagulant dosage and operating conditions, for maximum removal or coagulation of the desired wastewater constituents. Generally, the selected coagulant is added to the wastewater under specified conditions, such as dosage, pH, or temperature, and then the mixture is rapidly mixed followed by the addition of a coagulant aid and gentle flocculation. After determining the best coagulant and the optimum conditions of applications, other design parameters, such as settling properties and sludge production should be determined. The optimum conditions can be delineated by either the jar test apparatus or the zeta potential meter as explained in the following procedure.

Defining the Optimum Operating Conditions for Coagulation: Jar Test

1. Thoroughly characterize the wastewater with respect to the parameters of concern, such as color, BOD, TOC, suspended solids, and TDS.
2. Select a coagulant and determine the approximate minimum dosage for which a floc will be formed. This may be accomplished by adding the coagulant in 1 ml increments to 200 ml of the raw wastewater and slowly stirring until the first evidence of a floc is observed.
3. Prepare a neutralization curve for the wastewater and quantify the acidity or alkalinity of the selected coagulant. It should be recognized that coagulants such as lime and ferric chloride exhibit respectively significant amounts of alkalinity or acidity. The neutralization curve will facilitate subsequent pH adjustment.
4. At the approximate coagulant dosage determined in Step 2, prepare 1-liter samples of the wastewater to be treated in the jar test beakers shown in Figure 5-1. Mix the sample and coagulant and then adjust the pH in 6 increments of 1 pH unit ranging from pH 4 to pH 9. Certain coagulants, such as ferric chloride, may be examined over a narrow range, such as pH 4 to 7 at increments of 0.5 pH units.
5. Rapid mix (maximum RPM) the samples for 2 minutes and then flocculate (10-20 RPM) slowly for 15 minutes. The rate of flocculation should be slow enough that floc shear does not occur. Record the time for a visible floc to form in each sample and after flocculation, shut off the jar test device and allow all samples to settle.
6. Determine the residual parameters of interest, such as TOC, and color in the supernatant. Also measure the pH after the material has settled and use

this as the pH level for subsequent correlation. Correlate pH versus the parameter of interest such as TOC shown in Figure 5-3. While the flocs are settling, visually note the relative settling at the different pH levels and make pertinent comments, as to the settleability being rapid, slow or poor.

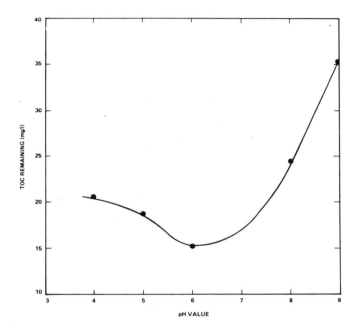

FIG. 5-3. OPTIMUM pH VALUE DETERMINATION

7. Again, prepare 1-liter samples of the wastewater in the jar test beakers. Add to each beaker a varying amount of coagulant in order to examine the effect of coagulant dosage. A good rule of thumb is to vary the coagulant dosage from 25 percent to 200 percent of the concentration determined in Step 2.

8. Mix the sample and coagulant and adjust the pH to the approximate optimum pH found in Step 6 above after coagulant addition.

9. Repeat Step 5 by rapidly mixing for 2 minutes then slow flocculation for 15 minutes. Again record the time of formation of the visual floc. If polyelectrolytes are to be added, a cationic polymer should be added toward the end of the rapid mix. Anionic polymers should be added about the middle of the flocculation step.

10. Cut off the jar test stirrers and allow the samples to settle for 20 minutes. After settling, measure the desired parameters in the supernatant liquid. Also, measure the supernatant suspended solids in each sample.
11. Determine the optimum dosage of coagulant by correlating the coagulant dosage versus the parameter of interest as shown in Figure 5-4.

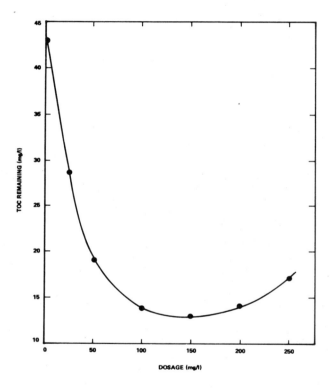

FIG. 5-4.   OPTIMUM DOSAGE DETERMINATION

12. Record the settled sludge level and sludge concentration.
13. Repeat Steps 3 through 12 with other pertinent coagulants and decide on the relative economics of each coagulant in order to obtain corresponding supernatant quality. For example, one coagulant may require a higher dosage, but would not necessitate pH adjustment so that the overall cost, including sludge handling, may be cheaper. After selecting a coagulant and establishing the optimum dosage and operating conditions, an accurate determination of sludge quantities and settling properties may be established.

14. To 1,500 ml of wastewater, add the proper dosage of coagulant and aids and adjust the pH to the proper level.

15. Rapid mix the solution and add 1,000 ml to a 1-liter cylinder for gentle flocculation for 20 minutes. If it is not possible to flocculate in the cylinder, then slow mix in the beaker and add the mixture very slowly to the cylinder in order not to shear the flocs.

16. As the suspended sludge settles, measure the height of the interface with time and plot the height of the interface in ml versus time. The slope of the straight line portion of the curve is the zone settling velocity (ZSV).

17. Allow the sample to settle for 20 minutes and record the settled sludge and sludge concentration as in Step 12 above. The supernatant should be siphoned off taking care not to disturb the settled sludge and then a sample of the sludge can be taken for measuring the suspended solids and moisture content.

If lime is used as a coagulant and magnesium is present, then magnesium hydroxide will be formed above a pH of 10 which will significantly aid in clarifying the solution but may adversely affect the settling properties of the sludge. It may be desired to recarbonate the sludge by the addition of CO_2 gas to redissolve the magnesium hydroxide prior to dewatering operations. This step is accomplished by lowering the pH of the sludge from 10.5 to 11.5 down to 9.5. The beneficial effects on dewatering may be found by performing the tests as described in Chapter 21.

Defining the Optimum Operating Conditions for Coagulation: Zeta Potential

1. Place 400 ml of wastewater in a beaker.
2. Add a given dosage of coagulant and rapid mix.
3. Place a sample of the mixture in the electrophoretic cell.
4. Measure the velocity of the particles in the cell at the described voltage which is stated in the manual provided with the meter. At least 6 separate particles should be measured.
5. Repeat the velocity measurement for increments of coagulants up to and past the directional change of the colloidal particles. In other words, at low coagulant dosages, the particles will migrate in one direction in the electrophoretic cell. At increasing dosages of coagulant, the rate of migration will gradually slow down and eventually reverse direction.
6. Calculate the velocity of the colloidal flow and the electrophoretic mobility from Equation 5-3.

7. Calculate the zeta potential from Equation 5-2. Correlate the zeta potential and pH versus the coagulant dosage as shown in Figure 5-5. The optimum coagulant dosage is that dosage which results in the zeta potential being 0. The optimum pH is that pH which corresponds to the optimum coagulant dosage. Steps 14 through 17 for the jar test can now be followed to delineate the sludge properties.

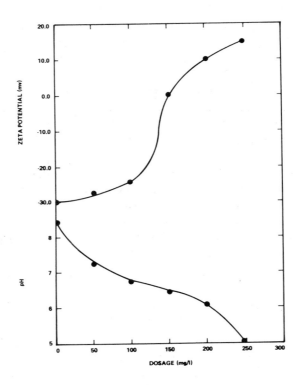

FIG. 5-5. CORRELATION OF ZETA POTENTIAL AND pH TO COAGULANT DOSAGE

Beneficial Effects of Solids Recirculation

With lime and a few other coagulants the time required to form a settleable floc is a function of the time necessary for calcium carbonate or other calcium precipitates to form a nuclei on which other calcium materials can deposit and grow until large enough to settle. This flocculation time can be substantial and can necessitate long coagulation and flocculation periods. It is possible to both reduce the coagulant dosage and the time of floc formation by seeding the influent raw waste with previously formed nuclei or by recirculating a portion of the precipitated sludge. The procedure for delineating the feasibility of solids recirculation is simple and is outlined below.

1. Follow Steps 1 through 13 above for the jar test apparatus or Steps 1 through 7 with the zeta meter with lime in order to define the optimum coagulant dosage and operating conditions.

2. Treat 5 gallons of the wastewater at the optimum conditions in order to generate sufficient sludge for the study.

3. Add 10 percent of the sludge by volume to the wastewater sample and vary the coagulant dosage around the optimum dosage determined in Step 1 of this procedure to see if the recycled sludge will reduce the coagulant requirement. Measure the time for floc formation and the resultant supernatant quality.

4. Repeat Step 3 at various sludge percentages on the order of 20, 30, 40 and 50 percent sludge by volume of the raw waste samples. At each percentage of sludge in the raw waste sample, correlate the various coagulant dosages with the effluent quality observed as shown in Figure 5-6. From this figure, the optimum dosage of each sample may be determined.

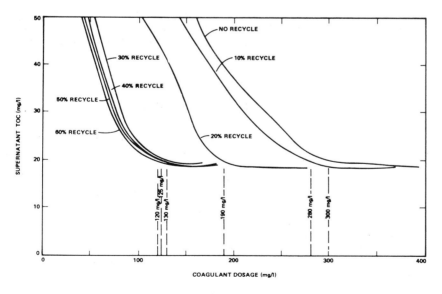

FIG. 5-6. DETERMINATION OF OPTIMUM COAGULANT DOSAGE WITH SOLIDS RECYCLE

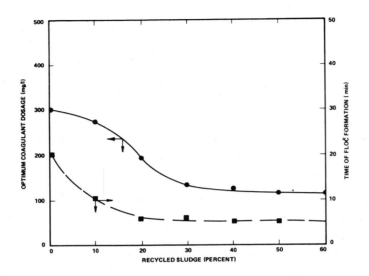

**FIG. 5-7. DETERMINATION OF OPTIMUM QUANTITY OF
RECYCLED SLUDGE**

5. Correlate the optimum coagulant dosage determined for each percent of
   recycled sludge in Step 4 with the percent of sludge recycle. Also correlate
   the minimum time of floc formation with percent sludge recycle as shown
   in Figure 5-7.

CORRELATION OF RESULTS

Assume that a wastewater is to be coagulated for organic and suspended
solids removal. A series of preliminary tests indicated that alum was the most
economical coagulant. It is desired to delineate the optimum dosage and conditions for alum use including an estimate of the sludge production.

Correlation of Jar Test Results

1. The wastewater had an initial pH of 6 and TOC was selected as a measure
   of the efficiency of coagulation. A 1 percent alum solution was employed
   for coagulation.
2. Using 200 ml of wastewater, it was observed that 2 ml of the 1 percent
   alum solution were required to produce a visual floc. This quantity is equal

to:

1 percent solution	=	10,000 mg/l
	=	10 mg/ml
2 ml	=	20 mg in 200 ml of waste solution
Alum concentration	=	20 mg/200 ml
	=	100 mg/l

3. Six beakers were then set up at 100 mg/l of alum and the pH adjusted to initial values of 4, 5, 6, 7, 8, and 9. After coagulation and settling, the final pH and TOC of the effluent were recorded as shown in Table 5-1. These values were plotted in Figure 5-3 and infer that the optimum pH is 6.3.

4. Using the optimum pH of 6.3, the alum dosage was varied to determine the optimum dosage at a constant pH. These results are shown in Table 5-2 and correlated in Figure 5-4. The optimum dosage is observed to 150 mg/l with the time of the floc formation equal to 1 minute.

TABLE 5-1. DETERMINATION OF OPTIMUM pH: JAR TEST

Time of Floc Formation (min)	pH	TOC Remaining (mg/l)
10:36	4.1	20
3:50	5.0	18
2:00	6.0	15
2:00	7.1	24
2:00	8.0	24
2:00	8.8	35

5. It was also desired to determine the effects of polymer on the supernatant clarity. At a pH of 6.3 and an alum dosage of 150 mg/l, 2 gallons of wastewater were treated and split into 6 beakers. Polyelectrolyte dosages of 0.5, 1.0, 1.5, 2.0, and 2.5 mg/l were added during the flocculation step.

6. These results were plotted in Figure 5-8 and indicate that the addition of polyelectrolyte can reduce the effluent suspended solids to less than 10 mg/l. The optimum dosage to achieve these results was observed to be 1.5 mg/l.

TABLE 5-2. DETERMINATION OF OPTIMUM COAGULANT DOSAGE: JAR TEST

Time of Floc Formation (min)	Coagulant Dosage (mg/l)	TOC Remaining (mg/l)
3:28	25	29
1:00	50	19
1:00	100	14
1:00	150	13
1:00	200	14
1:00	250	17

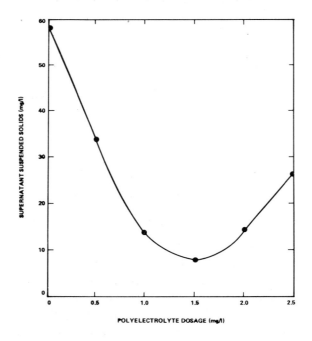

FIG. 5-8. DETERMINATION OF OPTIMUM POLYELECTROLYTE DOSAGE

7. On a larger sample, 2 gallons or more, the sludge volume and percent moisture can be calculated.

When removing constituents, such as phosphorus, it might be desirable to present the results as the ratio of coagulant to the constituents on a molar basis as shown in Figure 5-9. This figure indicates that the optimum aluminum to phosphorus ratio using alum was approximately 2.5:1 and the optimum pH for coagulation was 5.5. The effect of pH on residual phosphate concentration is presented in Figure 5-10.

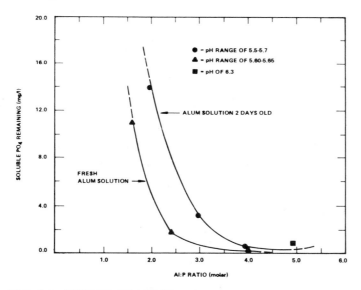

FIG. 5-9. EFFECT OF ALUMINUM DOSAGE ON PHOSPHATE REMOVAL: ALUMINUM SULFATE

Correlation of Zeta Potential Results

1. The data at various alum dosages are collected from the zeta meter and presented in Table 5-3 along with other test conditions.
2. Calculate the electrophoretic mobility (EM) from Equation 5-3. For

$$EM = \frac{(G)(L)}{(V)(T)}$$

$$= \frac{(160)(10)}{(50)(16.8)}$$

$$= 1.905 \ \mu m \text{ - cm/volt - sec}$$

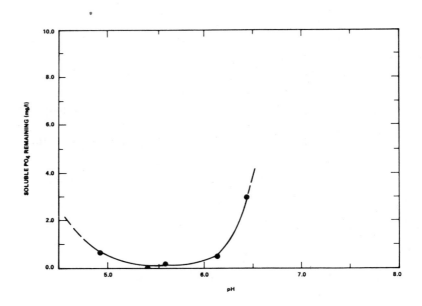

**FIG. 5-10. EFFECT OF pH ON RESIDUAL PHOSPHATE
CONCENTRATION: ALUMINUM SULFATE**

**TABLE 5-3. DETERMINATION OF OPTIMUM COAGULANT DOSAGE:
ZETA POTENTIAL**

Alum Dosage (mg/l)	pH	Time* (sec)	Voltage (volts)	EM	Zeta Potential (mv)
0	8.4	16.3	47	2.089	- 29.4
50	7.2	16.8	50	1.905	- 26.8
100	6.8	19.0	50	1.684	- 23.7
150	6.4	--	50	0	0
200	6.1	45.0	50	0.711	+10.0
250	5.0	33.0	50	1.970	+13.7

*This is the time of travel of the particles between 160 μm divisions.
Cell length = 10 cm
Test performed at 20°C.

3. Calculate the zeta potential using Equation 5-2 as shown below at an alum dosage of 50 mg/l:

$$\zeta \quad = \quad \left[\frac{113{,}000}{D}\right]\mu \ EM$$

$$= \quad \frac{(113000)\,(0.01)}{80.18}\ (1.905)$$

$$= \quad 26.8 \ mv$$

4. Correlate zeta potential and pH versus alum dosage as shown in Figure 5-5. Thus, the optimum dosage is 150 mg/l of alum and the optimum pH is 6.4.

Correlation of Solids Recirculation Results

1. Using lime, an optimum dosage of 300 mg/l at an optimum pH of 9.5 was determined from the preceding steps.
2. Five gallons of wastewater were treated under these conditions and generated 0.5 gallons of sludge which was approximately 10 percent by volume.
3. One hundred ml of this sludge was placed into five containers with 1000 ml of raw wastewater. To these wastewater and sludge samples, lime dosages of 100, 200, 300 and 400 mg/l were added, respectively. These samples were rapidly mixed, flocculated and settled. The residual TOC was monitored.
4. Step 3 was repeated using 200, 300 and 500 ml of sludge in 1000 ml of wastewater samples. The results are correlated as shown in Figure 5-6. As can be seen, the optimum dosage at each percent of sludge recycle can be determined as the break point in the curve.
5. From Figure 5-6 the optimum dosage for each percent solids recycle is determined along with the minimum time for floc formation and is correlated with the percent of solids recycle as shown in Figure 5-7.
6. Thus, it can be seen that the minimum required sludge recycle is 30 percent and this will result in a decreased lime dosage from 300 to 150 mg/l. There is also a decrease in time of floc formation from 20 minutes to 5 minutes.

LIMITATIONS AND SCALE-UP

Probably the most significant error in coagulation test procedures originates from inaccurate measurement of the coagulant dosages and improper application of the coagulant. When dealing with polyelectrolytes for reducing effluent suspended solids or to increase settling rates, the proper handling in the laboratory is difficult and requires special precautions. When preparing stock solution, care must be taken to ensure that all of the polymer is actually in solution and not suspended in minute globules. It is best to use liquid polymers where possible and, if the polymer is added volumetrically with the pipette, care must be taken to flush all the polymer from the pipette into the dispersing water. Whenever possible, it is advised to obtain a pre-mixed and diluted polyelectrolyte solution directly from the manufacturer. Also, all coagulants should be freshly prepared on the day of use. Alum will quickly deteriorate in quality after a few hours and should be prepared immediately before use. Solutions of alum more than 12 hours old should not be used.

It is essential that sufficient time be allowed for proper flocculation to occur in the laboratory or the results may indicate a higher required chemical dosage than is actually needed.

In scaling-up to field systems, proper seeding of recycled sludge should be practiced. Some solids recirculation clarifiers accomplish recirculation within the clarifier up into the center well. Other reactor-clarifiers actually pump the thickened sludge from the bottom of the clarifier to the influent pipe prior to entry into the center-feed well. The point of application of recycled sludge is very important as is the time of application, and the correct method of seeding should be practiced in the laboratory as will be expected to occur in the actual field clarifier.

REFERENCES

1. Eckenfelder, W. W. and Ford, D. L., *Water Pollution Control: Experimental Procedures for Process Design*, Jenkins Publishing Co., Austin and New York, (1970).

6

SEDIMENTATION

DISCUSSION OF PRINCIPLES

Sedimentation is a unit process employed in wastewater treatment to primarily remove suspended solids from suspension. However, if the majority of the solids are organic or degradable in nature, a substantial portion of the raw waste BOD might also be removed. These particles will settle when gravity overcomes the inertial and viscous forces acting on the suspended materials. The settling process can be classified according to the type of particle and the concentration as indicated below:

1. **Discrete Settling.** In discrete settling, the particle maintains its individuality and does not change in size, shape, or density during sedimentation. The particles do not interact and the settling velocity is constant as illustrated in Figure 6-1.

2. **Flocculant Settling.** In flocculant settling the particles interact and agglomerate during the settling. This agglomeration results in a change in specific gravity and settling rate and, although the floc density generally decreases with agglomeration, the overall settling velocity increases as depicted in Figure 6-1.

3. **Zone Settling.** In this case the particles are so concentrated that they are in intimate contact with other particles and maintain a special relationship, settling as a mass, and exhibiting a distinct interface during the settling process. The mass of particles tend to settle slower than individual, flocculated particles because the upward velocity of water, displaced by the settling mass, reduces the effective downward velocity of

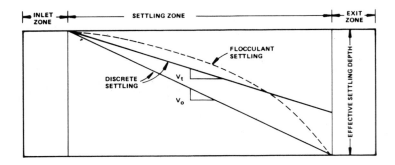

**FIG. 6-1. ILLUSTRATION OF DISCRETE AND FLOCCULANT
SETTLING PRINCIPLES**

the mass of particles. An illustration of water flow in a circular clarifier is
shown in Figure 6-2.

4. **Compression.** Sedimentation resulting from compression is caused when
   the concentration of particles is such that they rest upon each other and
   the bottom mass supports the above layers of particles. The mass is concentrated or compressed because the weight of upper particles slowly
   squeezes water from the bottom layers. Compression generally occurs
   in the bottom of a clarifier separating flocculant or zone settling materials and is not really considered a separate sedimentation process in itself. Consequently, this operation will not be discussed further herein.

Discrete Settling

Since discrete settling is characterized by individual particles which maintain
their individuality during settling, Stokes' Law can be used to describe the
settling velocity as follows:

$$V = \frac{d^2\ g(S_s - 1)}{18\eta} \qquad (6\text{-}1)$$

where:

d	=	diameter of particle
S_s	=	specific gravity of the particle
g	=	acceleration of gravity
η	=	kinematic viscosity

In an ideal quiescent settling basin, the percent removal of particles can be
described as:

$$\% \text{ Removal } = (V/V_o) \times 100 \qquad (6\text{-}2)$$

in which V_o is the velocity at the overflow rate, Q/A (flow rate divided by effective surface area) and V is the particle settling velocity.

The removal of discrete particles is related only to the overflow rate. The

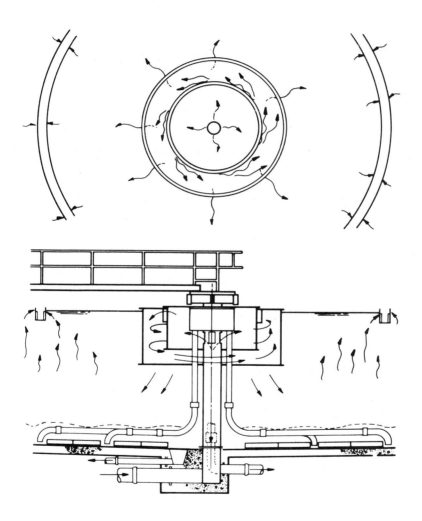

FIG. 6-2. SCHEMATIC OF CENTER-FEED, PERIPHERAL TAKEOFF, HYDRAULIC SLUDGE REMOVAL CLARIFIER

percent removal to be expected for a given overflow rate can be estimated if the size distribution of the particles is known [1]. The total removal is defined by Equation 6-3a.

$$\text{Total Removal} = R = (1 - C_o) + \int_{o}^{C_o} \frac{V}{V_o} \, dc \qquad (6\text{-}3a)$$

$$= 1 - C_o + \frac{1}{V_o} \int_{o}^{C_o} V \, dc \qquad (6\text{-}3b)$$

where:

C_o = the fraction of particles having a settling velocity equal to or less than V_o.

The integral portion of Equation 6-3b can be determined by plotting the settling velocity versus the percentage of particles remaining as shown in Figure

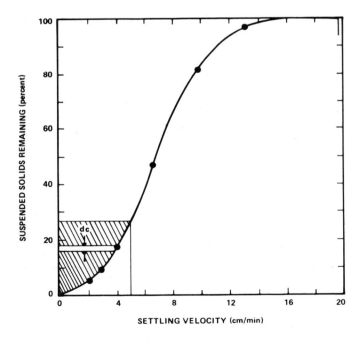

FIG. 6-3. RELATIONSHIP OF SETTLING VELOCITY AND PARTICLE REMOVAL FOR DISCRETE PARTICLES

6-3. The integral portion of the equation can be graphically integrated and the total percent removal correlated with overflow rates as shown in Figure 6-4.

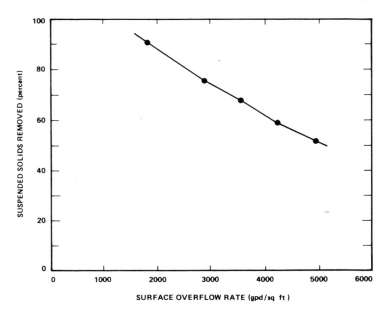

FIG. 6-4. RELATIONSHIP OF OVERFLOW RATE AND SOLIDS REMOVAL

Flocculant Settling

The flocculant settling of suspended particles cannot be described mathematically. Generally, flocculant settling is enhanced by:

1. A high concentration of particles;
2. A wide distribution of particle sizes;
3. Larger, denser particles; and
4. A low viscosity of the surrounding liquid.

Both the detention time and overflow rate affect the efficiency of removal with flocculated suspensions. At a particular overflow rate or settling velocity, V_o, all particles with a settling velocity greater than V_o will be completely removed. Particles at settling velocities less than V_o ($V < V_o$) will be removed in proportion to V/V_o. For a given settling depth and detention time, a certain percentage will be completely removed. Particles in each additional 10 percent removal range will be removed in proportion of V/V_o or in proportion to the average settled depth divided by the total settling depth (d/d_o). Consequently, total removal of solids can be approximated by:

$$\text{Total removal} (\%) = \% \text{ removed at } V_o + \frac{d_1}{d_o}(10\%) + \frac{d_2}{d_o}(10\%)$$

$$+ \frac{d_3}{d_o}(10\%) + ... \frac{d_n}{d_o}(10\%) \tag{6-4}$$

where:

d_o = total settling depth

$d_1, d_2, ...d_n$ = settling depths less than d_o

The various percent removals must be determined from multiple depth settling tests in which the percent removals with time are correlated at various settling depths as shown in Figure 6-5.

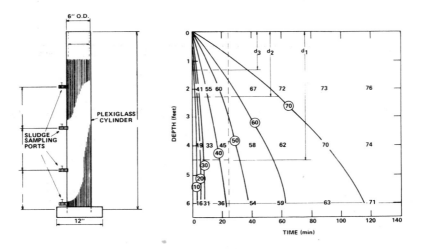

FIG. 6-5. SETTLING COLUMN AND SETTLING PROFILE OF SUSPENDED SOLIDS

Zone Settling

Zone settling is characterized by activated sludge and flocculated chemical

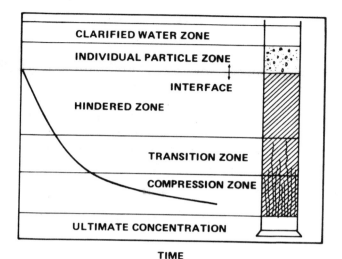

FIG. 6-6. SEDIMENTATION PHASES DURING ZONE SETTLING

suspensions when the concentration generally is greater than 500 mg/l. Assuming that all the sludge is at an initial uniform concentration in the test cylinder, the settling process is distinguished by three zones as shown in Figure 6-6.

1. **Uniform Settling Velocity.** Initially, the sludge settles at a uniform settling velocity depending on the initial suspended solids concentration.
2. **Zone of Transition.** As the settling velocity decreases due to the increasing concentration of solids, a zone of transition occurs.
3. **Compression Zone.** When the rising layer of settled solids reaches the interface of the settling suspension, compression occurs.

In designing a clarifier for zone settling, two principles are significant: clarification and thickening. For clarification, the overflow rate is important and requires that the average rise velocity of the liquid be less than the zone settling velocity of the suspension under the specified conditions of operation. On the other hand, the surface area required for thickening to a desired underflow concentration concentration is related to the solids loading to the clarifier and is expressed in terms of mass loading, such as, lb/sq ft-day. The design of a clarifier for thickening is identical to the design of a gravity thickener, the theory and details of which are explained in Chapter 19 entitled, "Gravity Thickening of Sludges." Consequently, the reader is referred to this Chapter for further theory and concepts of zone settling.

EQUIPMENT REQUIRED

The equipment required in developing design criteria for sedimentation is generally simple and only requires settling columns and stirring devices. Obviously, the necessary apparatus to measure the desired parameters such as suspended solids or BOD is needed.

For discrete settling tests, a 1000-ml cylinder can be used without stirring. However, for flocculant settling a larger diameter cylinder is desired, on the order of 3 to 6 inches in diameter, as shown in Figure 6-5. The column should have sampling ports at 2-ft intervals. With flocculant suspensions a stirrer should be used in the column which rotates at approximately 4 to 6 revolutions per hour. It is desirable to have a diffused air zone in the bottom of the larger column for mixing the solids prior to conducting the settling tests.

EXPERIMENTAL PROCEDURES

The development of design criteria for discrete and flocculant settling suspensions is unique for each suspension and requires entirely different procedures and data correlation. The design data can be collected for each type of settling by the following procedures.

Discrete Settling
1. Fill a 1000-ml cylinder with the suspension of varying sized discrete particles.
2. Thoroughly mix the contents of the cylinder and allow the suspension to settle without mixing.
3. Periodically collect samples at a pre-determined depth below the surface of the cylinder. With a 1000-ml cylinder, a 20-cm sampling depth is adequate.
4. Analyze the samples, which were collected at specific time intervals, for suspended solids and any other desired parameters such as BOD or COD. Tabulate the data as shown in Columns 1 and 2 of Table 6-1.
5. Repeat the above steps at different initial suspended solids concentrations in order to cover the range of concentrations anticipated under field conditions.

Flocculant Settling
1. Fill the settling column with wastewater. The column should be 6 inches

TABLE 6-1. SETTLING DATA FROM DISCRETE SUSPENSION

Time (min)	Suspended Solids (mg/l)	Settling Velocity (cm/min)	Percent Suspended Solids Remaining (%)
0.0	485	--	100.0
1.0	484	20.0	99.8
1.5	471	13.3	97.1
2.0	397	10.0	81.9
3.0	227	6.7	46.8
5.0	86	4.0	17.7
7.0	46	2.9	9.5
10.0	27	2.0	5.6

in diameter, have 6-ft liquid depth, and sampling ports at 2-ft intervals, as shown in Figure 6-5.

2. Thoroughly mix the column to obtain a uniform concentration of suspended solids and allow the flocculant suspension to settle quiescently. In a column of this size efficient mixing may be effectively performed by an air diffuser located on the bottom of the column.
3. Collect samples at each 2-ft sampling port at periodic time intervals and analyze for suspended solids and other pertinent parameters.
4. Calculate the percent suspended solids removal at each depth with time and tabulate as shown in Table 6-2.
5. Repeat the above steps at different suspended solids concentrations to cover the anticipated minimum and maximum levels expected.

CORRELATION OF RESULTS

Discrete Settling

In order to determine the total removal of suspended solids under discrete

TABLE 6-2. RESULT OF SETTLING COLUMN STUDY
OF FLOCCULANT WASTE

Time (min)	Depth from top of settling Column		
	2 ft	4 ft	6 ft
5	41	19	15
10	55	33	31
20	60	45	38
40	67	58	54
60	72	62	59
90	73	70	63
120	76	74	71

Initial Suspended Solids Concentration = 300 mg/l
(All values in terms of percent removed)

settling conditions, it is necessary to construct Figure 6-3. Therefore, it is necessary to calculate the settling velocity at each settling time and correlate this to the percent suspended solids remaining at the same time.

1. Calculate the settling velocity (V) at each respective time in Table 6-1. The settling velocity is equal to the distance settled, D (20 cm) divided by the settling time (Column 1): $V_t = D/t$. Subsequently, Column 3 is calculated by dividing 20 cm by the respective settling times given in Column 1.
2. Calculate the percent suspended solids remaining at each time as shown in Column 4.
3. Plot Column 3 versus Column 4 as shown in Figure 6-3.
4. Select a settling velocity and calculate the total suspended solids removal which would occur at this velocity in an ideal settling basin in accordance with Equation 6-3b:

$$R = (1 - C_o) + \frac{1}{V_o} \int_0^{C_o} V \, dc \qquad (6\text{-}3b)$$

5. For example, assume a settling velocity of 5 cm/min. From Figure 6-3 C_O = 26.8 percent. The shaded area shown in Figure 6-3 is equal to the integral in Equation 6-3b. This area can be graphically integrated to equal 0.848. (In computing the total removal percentage, removal should be expressed in decimal form.)

6. Therefore, calculate the total removal as:

$$R = (1 - 0.268) + \frac{1}{5.0}(0.848)$$
$$= (1 - 0.268) + (0.17)$$
$$= 0.902$$
$$= 90.2\%$$

7. Calculate the overflow rate which corresponds to the assumed settling velocity.

$$V_t = 5 \frac{cm}{min} \times \frac{in.}{2.54 \ cm} \times \frac{ft}{12 \ in.} \times 60 \frac{min}{hr}$$
$$= 9.84 \ ft/hr \times 180$$
$$= 1,770 \ gpd/sq \ ft$$

8. Repeat Steps 5-7 at various settling velocities and correlate the overflow rate to the total percent removal as shown in Figure 6-4.

9. Consequently, for any desired percent removal, a design overflow rate can be obtained from Figure 6-4.

Flocculant Settling

In order to calculate the total percent removal of suspended solids in accordance with Equation 6-4 for flocculant suspensions, it is necessary to perform graphical manipulations with Figure 6-5. The procedures for calculating the total percentage removal versus a design overflow rate are described in order below.

1. Plot the laboratory data, tabulated in Table 6-2 and shown in Figure 6-5. These data present the percent suspended solids removed with time for each sampling depth.

2. Considering the percentage solids removal as a function of cylinder depth and settling time, the settling rate-time relationship curves shown in Figure 6-5 can be developed for the conditions of the test .

3. Select a settling time and calculate the total percent removal in accordance with Equation 6-4.

101

4. At a specific time, the settling velocity, V_o, is the effective depth of the column divided by the time for a given solids percentage to settle through this depth. For example, at a settling time of 23 min (See Figure 6-5):

$$V_o = \frac{6 \text{ ft}}{23 \text{ min}} \times \frac{60 \text{ min}}{\text{hr}} = 15.6 \text{ ft/hr}$$

5. At 23 min (settling velocity of 15.6 feet per hour in the 6-ft column), 40 percent of the suspended solids is completely removed. In the percent interval from 40 to 50 percent (a 10 percent interval), the additional suspended solids removal is calculated as a ratio of the average depth settled to the total depth (6 ft). From Figure 6-5 it is seen that the average settled depth between 40 and 50 percent suspended solids removal at 23 min is estimated at the mid-point. This procedure is outlined as follows. The intersection of 23 minutes and 40 percent removal is 6 feet. The intersection of 23 minutes and 50 percent removal is 3 feet. The difference in depth between 40 and 50 percent removal is 3 feet. The mid-depth is then 4.5 feet (0.5 x 3 ft; 6 - 1.5 = 4.5). Consequently, the removal in this interval is:

$$\% \text{ Removal (40-50\% interval)} = \frac{4.5}{6.0} (10\%) = 7.5\%$$

TABLE 6-3.   CORRELATIONS OF SETTLING COLUMNS RESULTS

Time (min)	Settling Velocity (ft/hr)	Removal of SS (%)	Overflow Rate (gpd/sq ft)
5	72.0	33	12,950
7	51.5	34	9,300
9	40.0	39	7,200
23	15.6	55	2,810
38	9.5	52	1,710
63	5.7	69	1,025
116	3.1	72	560

6. Repeat Step 5 at additional 10 percent intervals and add the individual percentage removals as shown below:

$$
\begin{array}{rcl}
100\% \text{ Removal @ } 40\% & = & 40.0\% \\
40 - 50\% \text{ Interval} = (4.5/6)10 & = & 7.5 \\
50 - 60\% \text{ Interval} = (2.3/6)10 & = & 3.8 \\
60 - 70\% \text{ Interval} = (1.3/6)10 & = & 2.3 \\
70 - 100\% \text{ Interval} = (0.5/6)10 & = & 0.9 \\
\text{Total removed at 23 min} & = & 54.5\%
\end{array}
$$

7. Repeat Steps 4 to 6 at various settling times and determine the percent suspended solids removal as a function of overflow rate as shown in Table 6-3.

8. Plot Column 3 versus Column 4 in Table 6-3 as shown in Figure 6-7. For any desired percentage suspended solids removal, the design overflow rate can be obtained from Figure 6-7.

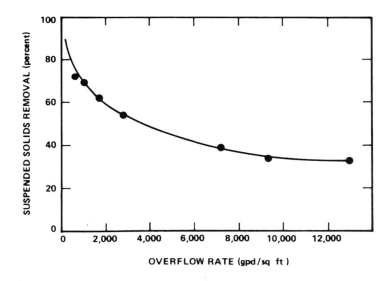

FIG. 6-7. RELATIONSHIP OF OVERFLOW RATE AND SUSPENDED SOLIDS REMOVAL: FLOCCULANT SETTLING

9. The percentage of suspended solids removed can also be correlated to detention time by plotting Column 1 versus Column 3 in Table 6-3 as shown in Figure 6-8.

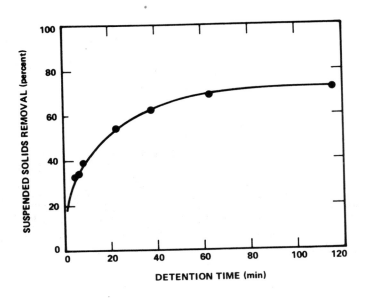

FIG. 6-8. RELATIONSHIP OF DETENTION TIME AND SUSPENDED SOLIDS REMOVAL: FLOCCULANT SETTLING

SCALE-UP AND LIMITATIONS

The development of design criteria described herein has been based on ideal settling conditions in the laboratory in small-diameter columns. With highly concentrated materials, especially those resulting in zone settling, the wall effects in smaller columns become significant. Figure 6-9 illustrates the effects of cylinder diameter on settling velocities at various suspended solids concentrations [2]. At a diameter of 36 inches, it was assumed that there were no significant wall effects. In order to minimize any wall effects which might occur in the small diameter columns frequently used in obtaining laboratory settling data, it is recommended that the suspension be continuously stirred at a speed of approximately 4 to 6 revolutions per hour.

In scale-up from laboratory data, it is necessary to add adequate volume to the settling basin to allow for entrance and exit turbulence effects. The entrance transition zone will be approximately 1 to 2 depths of the basin while the exit transition zone will comprise approximately 1 depth. Therefore, for a rectangular basin with a length-to-width ratio of 4, the design surface area should be

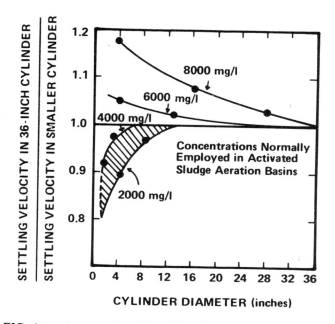

FIG. 6-9.   EFFECT OF TEST CYLINDER DIAMETER ON ZONE
SETTLING VELOCITY

increased by 20 to 40 percent to minimize turbulence effects in the entrance
and exit zones.

REFERENCES

1. Camp, T. R., "Sedimentation and the Design of Settling Tanks," *Transactions,*
   ASCE, 111,895 (1946).
2. Vesilind, P. A., "The Effects of Stirring in the Thickening of Biological
   Sludge," Ph.D. thesis, University of North Carolina, Chapel Hill, N.C. (1968).

7

DISSOLVED AIR FLOTATION

DISCUSSION OF PRINCIPLES

Dissolved air flotation (DAF) has been used for many years in the treatment of wastewaters for separation of suspended solids, oils, greases, fibers, and other low density solids from the carrier liquid as well as for the thickening of activated sludge and flocculated chemical sludges.

The flotation process is accomplished by introducing pressurized wastewater to atmospheric pressure and releasing the dissolved gas in excess of saturation. This reduces the specific gravity of suspended or oily material by the attachment of fine gas bubbles to the particulate matter, enhancing gravity separation.

There are three basic flotation design schemes; namely, pressurized full flow dissolved air flotation without recycle, pressurized dissolved air flotation with recycle, and induced air flotation. The pressurized full flow and recycle systems are shown in Figures 7-1 and 7-2, respectively. The full flow unit has the advantage of providing maximum bubble-particle contact, although the recycle operation requires a smaller pressurizing pump, utilizes similar controls, minimizes emulsion formation, and optimizes floc formation [1].

The design variables for these two systems (dissolved and induced) include pressure, recycle ratio, overflow rates, and retention period. The solids loading is considered when DAF is used for thickening. The pressurized tank is usually maintained at 40 to 60 psig (approximately 3 to 5 atmospheres). The hydraulic loading varies from one to four gpm/sq ft (including recycle), and retention period generally falls between 20 and 40 minutes. In order to obtain sufficiently

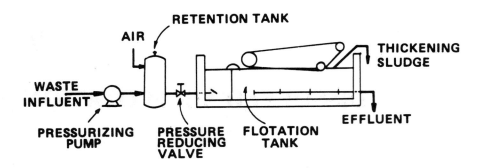

FIG. 7-1. PRESSURIZED FULL FLOW DAF UNIT (without recycle)

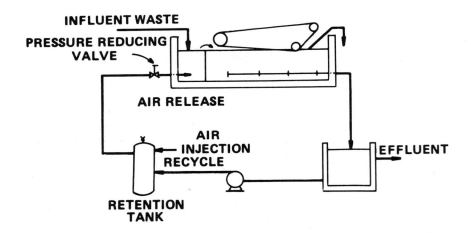

FIG. 7-2. PRESSURIZED RECYCLE DAF UNIT

high air/solids ratios, pressurized recycle of the treated effluent is usually recommended. For pretreatment purposes (lower air requirements), recycle ratios of 10 to 60 percent of the influent flow are representative. However, because of the higher solids levels, sludge thickening will necessitate recycle ratios on the order of 100 to 500 percent. A schematic of an operating dissolved air flotation system with recycle is shown in Figure 7-3.

The induced air flotation system shown in Figure 7-4 operates using the same principles as the pressurized air DAF units. The gas, however, is self-induced by a rotor-disperser mechanism. The rotor, the only moving part of the mechanism

108

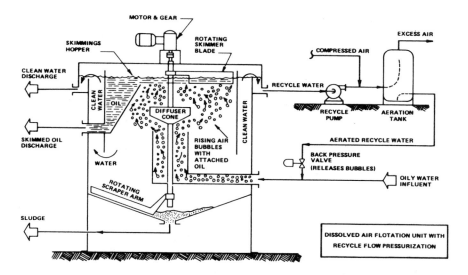

**FIG. 7-3. SCHEMATIC OF OPERATING DISSOLVED
AIR FLOTATION SYSTEM**

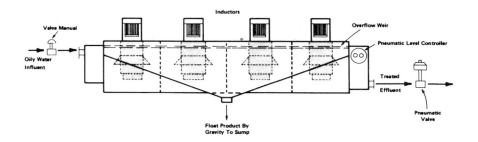

FIG. 7-4. WEMCO INDUCED AIR FLOTATION SYSTEM

which is submerged in the liquid, forces the liquid through the disperser open-
ings, thereby creating a negative pressure that pulls the gas downward into the
liquid causing an intimate gas-liquid contact. The liquid moves through a series of
four cells before leaving the tank, and the float skimmings pass over effluent
weirs on each side of the unit. This type of DAF system offers the advantages of

significantly lower capital cost and smaller space requirements than the pressurized systems, and current performance data indicate the systems have the capacity to effectively remove free oil and suspended materials. The disadvantages include higher connected power requirements than pressurized systems, performance dependence on strict hydraulic control, less chemical addition and flocculation flexibility, and relatively high volumes of float skimmings as a function of liquid throughput (3 to 7 percent of incoming flow for induced air systems as compared to less than 1 percent for pressurized air systems).

A brief review of the theory associated with DAF first alludes to Henry's law which states that the concentration of a dissolved gas is a function of its partial pressure in accordance with Equation 7-1:

$$C_s = K_s P \tag{7-1}$$

where:

C_s = saturation concentration of dissolved gas in water
K_s = Henry's Law Constant
P = partial pressure of the gas in the gas phase

The quantity of gas which will be theoretically released from solution when the pressure is reduced to atmospheric can be calculated from the following:

$$A = R(C_z - C_s) 8.34 \tag{7-2}$$

where:

A = quantity of air released, lb/day
R = pressurized flow, mgd
C_z = concentration of dissolved air under pressure, mg/l
C_s = air saturation at atmospheric conditions, mg/l

Henry's Law can be used to define C_z as below:

$$C_z = f P_a C_s \tag{7-3}$$

where:

f = air solubility in wastewater/air solubility in water
P_a = absolute pressure, atm

The absolute pressure, P_a, can be related to the gauge pressure, P, as below:

$$P_a = \frac{P}{14.7} + 1 \tag{7-4}$$

where:

$$P \quad = \quad \text{gauge pressure, psig}$$

Substitution of Equations 7-3 and 7-4 into Equation 7-2 results in the following equation which can be used to calculate the quantity of gas released.

$$A = RC_s \left[f\left(\frac{P}{14.7} + 1\right) - 1 \right] 8.34 \qquad (7\text{-}5)$$

TABLE 7-1. AIR CHARACTERISTICS AND SOLUBILITIES*

Temp.		Volume Solubility		Weight Solubility		Density	
°C	°F	ml/l	c.f./ 1,000 gal.	mg/l	lb/ 1,000 gal.	g/l	lb/c.f.
0	32	28.8	3.86	37.2	0.311	1.293	0.0808
10	50	23.5	3.15	29.3	0.245	1.249	0.0779
20	68	20.1	2.70	24.3	0.203	1.206	0.0752
30	86	17.9	2.40	20.9	0.175	1.166	0.0727
40	104	16.4	2.20	18.5	0.155	1.130	0.0704
50	122	15.6	2.09	17.0	0.142	1.093	0.0682
60	140	15.0	2.01	15.9	0.133	1.061	0.0662
70	158	14.9	2.00	15.3	0.128	1.030	0.0643
80	176	15.0	2.01	15.0	0.125	1.000	0.0625
90	194	15.2	2.05	14.9	0.124	0.974	0.0607
100	212	15.9	2.13	15.0	0.125	0.949	0.0591

*Values presented in absence of water vapor and at 14.7 psia pressure

The solubility of air in water as a function of temperature is shown in Table 7-1 [2].

An air to solids parameter, A/S, based on influent suspended solids has been used to relate process performance. These relationships for no recycle and recycle are:

$$A/S = \frac{C_s \left[f\left(\frac{P}{14.7} + 1\right) - 1 \right]}{S_i} \qquad \text{(No recycle)} \quad (7\text{-}6)$$

where:

A/S = air/solids ratio, lb air released/lb solids applied

S_i = influent suspended solids, mg/l

and:

$$A/S = \frac{RC_s \ [f(\frac{P}{14.7} + 1) - 1]}{QS_i} \qquad \text{(with recycle) (7-7)}$$

where:

R = pressurized recycle, mgd

Q = wastewater flow, mgd

The relationship between the A/S ratio and process performance can be determined experimentally as subsequently described in this chapter.

The chemical treatment aspects of DAF are extremely important, particularly when the soluble, colloidal, or emulsified components of the wastestream to be treated are affected. The effect of chemical addition (coagulants and/or poly-electrolytes) can be assessed using bench-scale jar test procedures subsequently described. If the efficacy of chemical addition is proven, then a rapid mix tank and flocculation basin is incorporated into the design of a pressurized full flow or recycle DAF system. In an induced air flotation unit, chemicals are normally added in the influent line to the unit, sometimes employing a static mixer to enhance contact, then allowing flocculation to occur in the first cell of the induced air system. Rapid mixing in either scheme must accomplish the complete contacting of the coagulant and/or coagulant aids with the incoming wastewater. Efficient flocculation is then mandatory for ensuring maximum DAF effectiveness when chemicals are added. As DAF design is based on the average particle rise rate, the importance of particle size and its dependence on flocculation time is underscored as reported by previously conducted experimental work shown in Figures 7-5 and 7-6 [4].

Chemical addition is particularly important when applying DAF for oil removal. In this regard, a brief discussion of what constitutes oil is merited. The definition of oil and grease is based on the analytical procedure employed and depends on its source, the test solvent used, the sample-to-solvent ratio, the pH of the sample, and the inclusion of non-oily material. The most widely accepted methods for measurement of oil and grease are tabulated in Table 7-2 [5]. While these methods are recognized within their respective society or institute, the method applied must also conform to the regulatory agency which controls effluent quality in a specific area.

A second definition relating to oil commonly discharged from refinery and

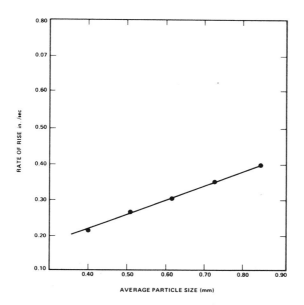

FIG. 7-5. EFFECT OF PARTICLE SIZE ON RISE RATE

petrochemical facilities can be made in terms of its phase. Oil may be free, emulsified, or soluble. A phase separation must take place prior to analyzing the oil using one of the methods cited in Table 7-2. The methods used to separate these oil phases are discussed as follows:

1. **Total Oil.** Determine the oil content of the raw wastewater sample.
2. **Free Oil.** Place a measured amount of wastewater in a separatory funnel and shake vigorously; then let the sample stand quiescently for two hours. Draw off the subnatant (aqueous layer) and determine its oil content. The oil measured is the emulsified and soluble oil fractions. The difference between the total oil content and that measured is the free oil content of the wastewater sample.
3. **Soluble Oil.** Place a measured amount of wastewater in a separatory funnel and acidify with 100 ml concentrated hydrochloric acid. Next, add 200 g/l sodium chloride and 5 g/l diatomaceous earth. Shake the mixture vigorously and let stand eight hours or more. Filter the mixture through a wet filter paper and measure the oil content of the filtrate. The oil content measured is the soluble oil fraction of the wastewater oil content.
4. **Emulsified Oil.** The difference between the oil content measured as emulsified and soluble oil and the soluble oil content is the emulsified oil content.

113

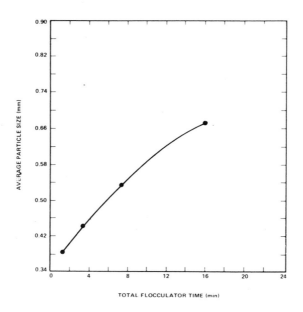

FIG. 7-6. PARTICLE DEPENDENCE ON FLOCCULATION TIME

When a significant portion of the reported oil is in the emulsified form, chemicals are required to ensure good DAF performance. For example, the effect of polyelectrolyte and bentonite clay addition on oil removal, as reported at one refinery, is shown in Table 7-3 [6].

EQUIPMENT REQUIRED

Pressurized DAF

1. 1 liter graduated cylinder
2. 1 liter chamber and related appurtenances — bench scale (see Figure 7-7)
3. 1 hand operated pump or external air pressure source (60-100 psi)
4. Pipettes and miscellaneous glassware required for sampling and analysis of float and clarified phases of test sample
5. Test coagulants and coagulant aids

Induced Air Flotation

1. 1 induced air assembly, WEMCO or equal — bench scale (see Figure 7-8)

TABLE 7-2. METHODS FOR DETERMINATION OF OIL
IN WATER AND WASTEWATER

Society or Institute	Method Name and Designation	Solvent Used	Solvent Boiling Point (°C)	Method Description	Interference Material
American Public Health Ass'n., American Water Works Ass'n., and Water Pollution Control Fed.	Oil and Grease	Petroleum ether	35-60	Direct extraction	
	Grease	n-hexane	69	Soxhlet extraction method	Elemental sulfur and organic dyes
American Society for Testing and Materials	Oily Matter in Industrial Wastewater	Benzene, carbon tetrachloride, or chloroform	60-80	Distillation of volatile oils followed by direct extraction	Phenolic type material and colloidal sulfur
American Petroleum Institute	Volatile and nonvolatile oil oily material ----------- Method 731-53	Benzene	80	Distillation of volatile oils followed by extraction	Alcohols, creosols, and organic acids
	Nonvolatile oily material ----------- Method 732-53	ethyl ether	35	Ferric hydroxide flocculation followed by direct extraction of oil from floc by solvent	Elemental sulfur and chlorophyll
Other	"A Safe Solvent for Oil and Grease Analysis"	Freon (CCl_2F-$CClF_2$)	48	Direct or soxhlet extraction - gravimetric or infrared detection (EPA is currently using gravimetric detection)	

2. 1 special glass test beaker with float withdrawal trough (see Figure 7-8)

3. Pipettes and miscellaneous glassware

Pressurized DAF — Full Flow Pressurization

1. Fill the pressure chamber with the untreated wastewater sample and pressurize the contents to the desired pressure (40 to 60 psig).

2. Shake the air-liquid mixture in the pressure vessel for one minute and allow to stand for three minutes to ensure saturation. Maintain the design pressure on the chamber during this period of time.

3. Transfer the contents from the pressure chamber to the graduated cylinder (normally one liter).

4. Measure the rise of the sludge interface in the graduated cylinder with respect to time. Correction must be applied to scale-up the height of rise in the test cylinder to the depth of a full-scale unit as shown in Figure 7-9.

115

TABLE 7-3. EFFECT OF CHEMICAL ADDITION ON DAF OIL REMOVAL

No. of Tests	Chemicals Used	Chemical Dosage (mg/l)	Inlet Oil Content (mg/l)	Outlet Oil Content (mg/l)
4	None	0	356	108
11	Anionic polyelectrolyte Bentonite clay	0.6 17	390	16
8	Cationic polyelectrolyte Bentonite clay	2 17	366	19

5. After the flotation separation in the graduated cylinder is complete, which is normally 10 to 20 minutes, the floated sludge and the clarified underflow are drawn off separately through a valve in the bottom of the graduated cylinder or through a siphon inserted in the top of the cylinder.

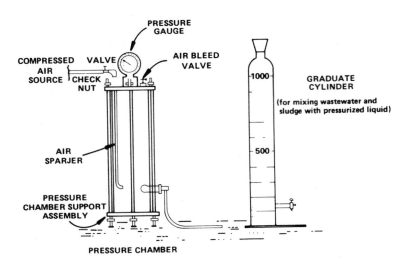

FIG. 7-7. PRESSURIZED DAF LABORATORY EQUIPMENT

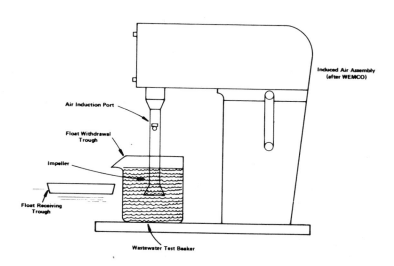

FIG. 7-8.   BENCH-SCALE INDUCED AIR ASSEMBLY

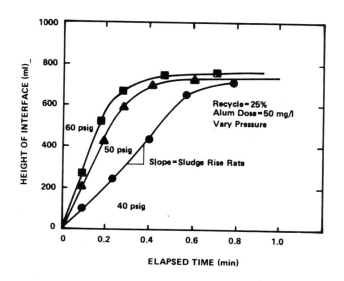

FIG. 7-9. RISE OF SLUDGE INTERFACE WITH TIME:
VARYING PRESSURE

6. Analyze the separated fractions, the float solids for suspended solids concentration, and volume, and the underflow for SS, oil, turbidity, and/or organic concentration.
7. Calculate the A/S ratio according to Equation 7-6.
8. The test can be repeated varying the solids or presure, and a relationship between A/S and percent float solids for thickening or effluent suspended solids for clarification can be established. The optimum A/S ratio in terms of process performance can be predicted from these relationships.
9. If chemicals are to be added, they should be introduced into the pressure cylinder before pressurizing the vessel.

Pressurized DAF — Recycle Pressurization [See Refs. 3 and 7]
(Assume a recirculation ratio of 33 percent)

1. Place 750 ml of representative wastewater into the graduated cylinder.
2. Fill the pressure chamber approximately 75 percent full with a liquid simulating recycle flow. (This may be done by repeated flotation of several different portions of raw waste). Pressurize the contents to the desired pressure (40 to 60 psig).
3. Shake the air-liquid mixture in the pressure vessel for one minute and allow to stand for three minutes to ensure saturation. Maintain the desired pressure on the chamber during this period of time.
4. Release a volume of pressurized effluent to the graduated cylinder and mix with the wastewater or sludge. The volume to be released is computed from the desired recycle ratio (for example, 250 ml of pressurized recycle to 750 ml of wastewater or sludge for a recycle ratio of 0.33). The velocity of release through the nozzle should be of such magnitude as not to shear the suspended solids in the feed mixture, but to maintain adequate mixing and air-liquid contact.
5. Repeat steps 5 and 6 as indicated in the "full-flow pressurization" procedure above.
6. Calculate the A/S ratio according to Equation 7-7.
7. Repeat step 8 as in the "full-flow pressurization" procedure above.
8. Should chemical flocculation with flotation be desired, the chemical may be added into the raw waste after step "1" is completed, flocculation may be carried out, for convenience, in another vessel. Care should be taken not to break up the floc when transferring the waste to the cylinder. Enough time for flocculation should be allowed before introducing the air-charged recycle water. Under appropriate conditions, a floc may be formed by gentle agitation of the waste after the chemical is added.

Because of the peculiarities of some floc formations, they will break up readily upon any excessive agitation after being formed. This is most noticeable when a liquid with a preformed floc is transferred from the cylinder used in the jar mixing test to the cylinder used in the flocculation test. If the floc does break up and does not reform immediately, it is suggested that the transfer to the flotation graduated cylinder not be made and that flotation be accomplished in the vessel where the floc was originally formed.

It may not be necessary to establish an optimum A/S ratio for a specific application. If this is the case, the test can be terminated following Step 6 in the "full-flow pressurization" procedure and Step 5 as in the "recycle flow pressurization" procedure as described above.

Induced Air Flotation [8, 9]

The bench-scale WEMCO unit or equal along with the specially designed mixing beaker are the only bench-scale equipment requirements. This apparatus is shown in Figure 7-8. However, it is useful to have sample bottles and several of the candidate chemicals available. The procedure follows:

1. Add the representative wastewater to the beaker to the three-liter mark.
2. Close the air valve.
3. Add the appropriate amount of chemical with a micropipette (Some polymers cannot be diluted with water because of the possibility of hydrolyzing and therefore very small amounts of pure polymers are added).
4. Mix the chemical and wastewater for 15 to 30 seconds with the air valve off. Both mixing and aerating are performed at 1,200 rpm (at full-scale, 300 rpm is used); however, the tip speed of the rotor is the same in both cases.
5. Open the air valve and mix for three minutes (air is introduced under the atmospheric pressure and is induced due to the negative pressure caused by the rotor ports).
6. During the mixing, scum and oil are removed from the surface by hand with a brush; these lost materials are retained for analytical examination.
7. Once the three minute mix period has been completed, a sample of the underflow is taken and observed for clarity.
8. Repeat steps 1 through 7 until a clear effluent is obtained.

Once the appropriate chemical(s) are chosen, samples are taken of the influent and effluent for analytical determinations, and the performance of an induced air flotation system evaluated.

CORRELATIONS AND RESULTS

Data for a series of batch laboratory flotation thickening experiments are shown in Table 7-4. The A/S ratio is calculated for each experiment by Equation 7-7.

In correlating laboratory data, the air solubility correction factor, f, is assumed to have a value of 1.0 since air solubility is approached. Such is not the case with full-scale equipment and a value of 0.8 will be conservatively achieved by most retention tanks.

An example calculation is presented below for the first entry in Table 7-4:

$$\frac{A}{S} = \frac{R\,C_s\,[f(\frac{P}{14.7}+1)-1]}{Q\,S_i} \tag{7-7}$$

where:

R/Q = 2.3 or 230 percent
P = 40 psig
S_i = 9,000 mg/l
C_s = 24.3 mg/l at 20°C from Table 7-1

$$\frac{A}{S} = \frac{2.3(24.3)\,[1.0(\frac{40}{14.7}+1)-1]}{9,000} \quad \frac{\text{lb air}}{\text{lb solids}}$$

= 0.0169 lb air/lb solids

For DAF application as a thickener, the float solids concentration is related to the A/S ratio as shown in Figure 7-10 for the data from Table 7-4 when DAF is used for clarification, the effluent suspended solids is related to the A/S ratio as shown in Figure 7-11 for the data from Table 7-4. The parameter of concern (float solids concentration or effluent quality) is related to the surface loading rate as shown in Figure 7-12. The surface loading rate is calculated from the slope of the linear portion of the sludge interface rise from Figure 7-9.

LIMITATIONS AND SCALE-UP

The results of DAF performance as determined in the laboratory are excellent indicators of what can be expected in a full-scale unit. This is underscored by the fact that most DAF manufacturers will guarantee performance of their unit in the field to the efficiency obtained in the bench-scale testing program. One of the best ways to predict process performance, however, is to review the data

TABLE 7-4.   LABORATORY FLOTATION RESULTS

Influent Solids, (mg/l)	Pressure, (psig)	Recycle, (%)	Float Solids, (%)	Effluent Suspended Solids (mg/l)	A/S, Air-to Solids Ratio, (lb air/lb solids)
9,000	40	230	3.6	217	0.0169
9,000	40	100	2.6	324	0.0073
6,000	40	100	3.2	243	0.0110
7,000	50	230	3.8	100	0.0272
7,000	60	230	3.9	75	0.0326
4,400	40	100	3.6	153	0.0150
6,000	50	100	3.2	215	0.0138

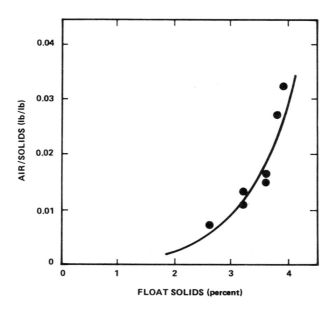

FIG. 7-10. EFFECT OF AIR/SOLIDS ON FLOAT CONCENTRATION

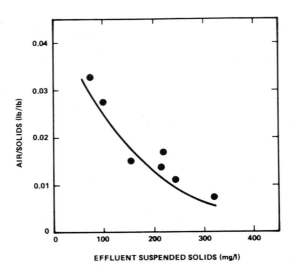

FIG. 7-11. EFFECT OF AIR/SOLIDS ON EFFLUENT SUSPENDED SOLIDS

TABLE 7-5.   DAF PERFORMANCE AS THICKENERS

Location	Feed	Influent SS(mg/l)	Effluent SS(mg/l)	SS Removal %	Float Solids %	Loading (lb/hr-sq ft)	Flow gpm/sq ft
Bernardsville, N.J.	R.S.*	17,000	196	98.8	4.3	4.3	0.5
Hatboro, Pa.	R.S.	7,300	300	96.0	4.0	2.9	0.8
Omaha, Nebr.	R.S.	19,660	118	99.8	5.9	7.6	0.8
Belleville, Ill.	R.S.	18,372	233	98.7	5.7	3.8	0.4
Indianapolis, Ind.	R.S.	2,960	144	95.0	5.0	2.1	1.47
Warren, Mich.	R.S.	6,000	350	95.0	7.0	5.2	1.75
Frankenmuth, Mich.	M.L.**	9,000	80	99.1	7.0	6.5	1.3
Oakmont, Pa.	R.S.	6,250	80	98.7	8.0	3.0	1.0
Columbus, Ohio	R.S.	6,800	40	99.5	5.0	3.3	1.0
Levittown, Pa.	R.S.	5,700	31	99.4	5.5	2.9	1.0
Nassau Co., N.Y. (Bay Park)	R.S.	8,100	36	99.6	4.4	4.9	1.2
Nashville, Tenn.	R.S.	15,400	44	99.6	12.4	5.1	0.66
Fort Worth, Texas	W.S.***	9,000	20	99.8	4.5	4.5	1.0
Toledo, Ohio	W.S.	8,200	200	99.6	7.3	3.7	0.45
Cleveland, Ohio (Easterly)	R.S.	4,550	32	99.3	4.5	3.2	1.40

*R.S. - Return Sludge   **M.L. - Mixed Liquor   ***W.S. - Waste Sludge
The above results are based on the use of chemical aids.

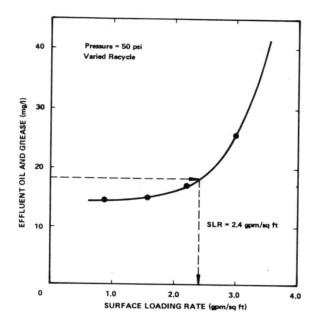

FIG. 7-12. EFFECT OF SURFACE LOADING RATE ON EFFLUENT QUALITY

from existing units. For this reason, data have been obtained from operating DAF units used for various applications, and is tabulated herein.

Thickening of activated sludge by DAF has been applied in many treatment systems. This includes feeding the return sludge, mixed liquor, or excess activated sludge to DAF units for thickening and disposal. The performance of DAF systems as thickeners is cited in Table 7-5.

Clarification of different wastewaters by removal of suspended solids has been effected through DAF application. The suspended solids removal efficiency will depend not only on DAF process parameters, but also on the nature of the suspended material contained in the wastewater. A tabulation of DAF performance data in terms of SS removal from various categories of wastewater is shown in Table 7-6.

The removal of oil in DAF units can be documented by referring to case histories where pressurized DAF units are being used to treat refinery oily wastewaters. Based on wastewater surveys within refineries having DAF units, a statistical analysis of DAF process efficiency was made when sufficient data were available. The first case history is graphically represented in Figure 7-13 where

123

TABLE 7-6.   DAF PERFORMANCE AS CLARIFIERS

Type of Application	Influent SS(mg/l)	Effluent SS(mg/l)	SS Removal (%)	Reference
Domestic Sewage	180	63	65	9
Domestic Sewage	145	70	52	9
Domestic Sewage	130	59	55	9
Domestic Sewage	158	93	41	9
Domestic Sewage	171	65	62	9
Domestic Sewage	142	66	53	9
Domestic Sewage	148	54	64	9
Domestic Sewage	103	44	57	9
Domestic Sewage	128	54	58	9
Domestic Sewage	185	80	57	9
Domestic Sewage	177	40	74	9
Domestic Sewage	183	82	56	9
Refinery	58	14	76	6
Refinery	59	32	46	6
Paper Mill	5,700	400	93	2
Aircraft Mn.	70	25	65	2
Meat Packing	4,360	170	96	2
Meat Packing	3,830	270	93	2

a rectangular DAF unit has been in operation in series with an API separator for several years. As noted, the DAF unit reduces the total oil from 68 mg/l to 15 mg/l at a 50 percent probability, and from 105 mg/l to 26 mg/l at a 90 percent probability. The separator influent oil concentration is 1,020 mg/l (50 percent) and 2,150 mg/l (90 percent). The second case history where sufficient data were collected to perform a statistical analysis is shown in Figure 7-14. This refinery has two circular DAF units preceded by an API gravity separator. Because of in-plant segregation, the oil content in the feed water is higher than normally expected. The DAF units reduce the oil from 580 mg/l to 68 mg/l (50 percent) and 1,930 mg/l to 128 mg/l (90 percent).

A search for additional DAF oil removal data was conducted to augment the two case histories previously cited. Although literature reported data are usually

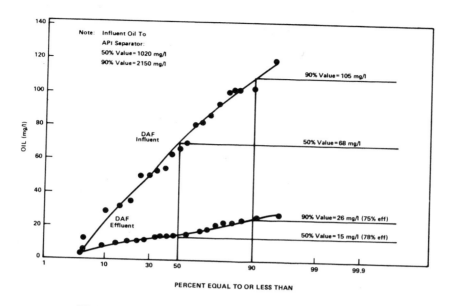

FIG. 7-13. DAF OIL REMOVAL PERFORMANCE

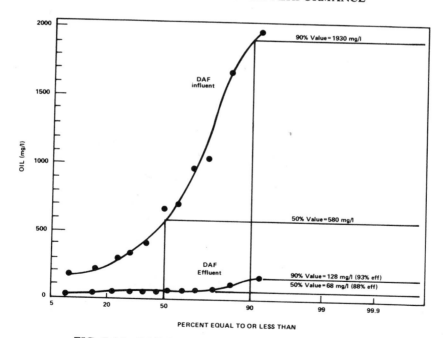

FIG. 7-14. DAF OIL REMOVAL AS A FUNCTION OF
INFLUENT OIL CONCENTRATION

125

insufficient to make a statistical analysis, reported average values are indicative of DAF oil removal capacities over a wide range of influent oil concentrations. A tabulation of this reported data is given in Table 7-7. DAF efficiency in terms of

TABLE 7-7.   DAF OIL REMOVAL PERFORMANCE

Influent oil (mg/l)	Effluent oil (mg/l)	Oil Removal (%)	Chemicals*	Configuration
580	68	88	Yes	Circular
105 (90%)	26 (90%)	78	Yes	Rectangular
68 (50%)	15 (50%)	75	Yes	Rectangular
125	30	71	Yes	Circular
100	10	90	Yes	Circular
133	15	89	Yes	Circular
94	13	86	Yes	Circular
638	60	91	Yes	Rectangular
153	25	83	Yes	Rectangular
75	13	82	Yes	Rectangular
61	15	75	Yes	Rectangular
360	45	87	Yes	Rectangular

*Alum most common, 100-130 mg/l
Polyelectrolyte, 1-5 mg/l occasionally added

oil removal is a function of many factors; namely, design overflow rate, retention time, recycle volume, pressurization level, air-solids ratio, type and volume of chemical addition, and the concentration and form of the effluent oil. The data tabulated in Table 7-7 account for these variables to the maximum extent possible. For example, all cases cited use chemicals with one exception, design overflow rates fall within the accepted design spectrum of 0.5 to 2.9 gpm/sq ft, and all use pressurized recycle. Assuming the systems are properly operated, a most significant factor with respect to process capacity and efficiency is the influent oil concentration. This effect is underscored when the data from Table 7-7 are plotted in a manner which shows effluent oil concentration and oil removal efficiency as a function in influent oil concentration. As

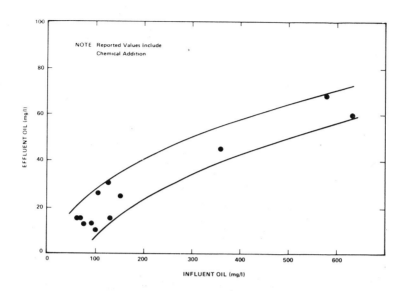

FIG. 7-15. DAF OIL REMOVAL AS FUNCTION OF INFLUENT OIL CONCENTRATION

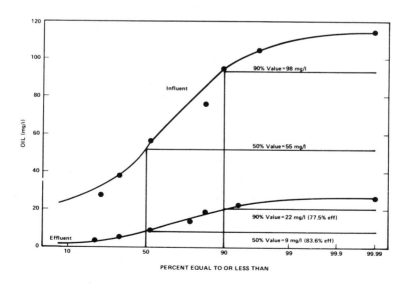

FIG. 7-16. INDUCED AIR FLOTATION PERFORMANCE — OIL REMOVAL

127

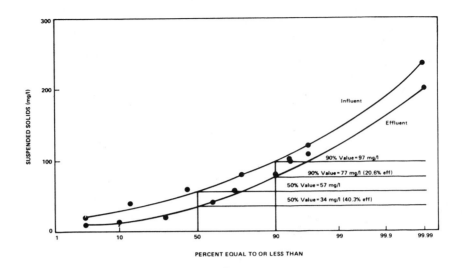

**FIG. 7-17. INDUCED AIR FLOTATION PERFORMANCE —
SUSPENDED SOLIDS REMOVAL**

**TABLE 7-8. PERFORMANCE DATA - INDUCED AIR
FLOTATION (BENCH-SCALE)**

Test Series	Chemical Additive	Conc. (mg/l)	pH	Influent COD (mg/l)	COD Rem. %	Influent Oil (mg/l)	Effluent Oil (mg/l)	Oil Rem. %	Sulfides (mg/l)	Sulfides Rem. %
No. 1	(Raw Wastewater)	--	9.0	1,378	--	111	--	--	318	--
2	None	0	9.0	1,060	23	58	30	48	238	25
3	Polyelectrolyte	25	9.0	1,171	15	42	16	62	256	20
4	Polyelectrolyte	6	9.0	988	28	41	15	63	256	20
5	Polyelectrolyte	12.5	9.0	868	37	41	15	63	--	--
6	Polyelectrolyte	12.5	9.0	892	35	44	17	60	223	30
No. 2	(Raw Wastewater)	--	6.6	1,369	--	207	--	--	128	--
1			8.0	883	35	115	--	46	16	87

*Based on one sample, 25 percent BOD removal was noted.

observed from Figure 7-15, effluent oil levels of 10 to 30 mg/l can be expected if the influent concentration remains below 150 to 200 mg/l total oil.

The performance data from induced air flotation units are not as complete as that reported for pressurization units based on case histories available. Data from a comprehensive testing program at a refinery using a full scale 150 gpm induced air system, however, indicate process efficiency. These performance data, in terms of oil removal, are shown in Figure 7-16 while the suspended solids removal is indicated in Figure 7-17. Bench-scale data for the induced air treatment of a refinery wastewater are shown in Table 7-8. This information was developed using the bench-scale apparatus shown in Figure 7-8.

REFERENCES

1. *Manual on Disposal of Refinery Wastes,* Volume on Liquid Wastes, 1st Ed., American Petroleum Institute, Washington, D. C. (1969).
2. Boyd, J. L. and Shell, G. L., "DAF Application to Industrial Wastewater Treatment," Eimco, BSP Div., Envirotech Corp., Salt Lake City, Utah (1972).
3. Eckenfelder, W. W., Jr. and Ford, D. L., *Water Pollution Control: Experimental Procedures for Process Design,* Pemberton Press, Austin, Texas (1970).
4. Katz, W. J., "Adsorption — Secret of Success in Separating Solids by Air Flotation," *Wastes Engineering,* July (1959).
5. Boyd, J. L., Shell, G. L., and Dahlstrom, D. A., "Treatment of Oily Wastewaters to Meet Regulatory Standards," Water — 1971, AICHE Symp. Series, 68:124, 393-401 (1972).
6. Simonsen, R. N., "Oil Removal by Air Flotation at SOHIO Refineries," Proc., 27th meeting, API Division of Refining, San Francisco, Calif. (May 1962)
7. Rex Chainbelt Demonstration Procedure, Data Sheet 315, 10.801-805.
8. Private Correspondence, Tretolite Division of Petrolite Corporation, St. Louis, Missouri (March 1971).
9. Hay, T. T., "Air Flotation Studies of Sanitary Sewage," Jour. Water Pollution Control Federation, 28, 100-106 (1956).

8

HYDRAULICS AND MIXING CHARACTERISTICS

DISCUSSION OF PRINCIPLES

The hydraulic and mixing characteristics of selected unit processes incorporated within a wastewater treatment system are of primary importance, as the process effectiveness is highly dependent on hydraulic and mixing efficiency. This is particularly true for gravity separation units with respect to hydraulic efficiency and aerobic biological basins in terms of mixing characteristics.

There are many ways to mathematically and graphically describe dead space, plug flow (momentum, but no mixing), complete mixing (no concentration gradient), and the degree of mixing which can logically be defined as a hybrid of these in a process unit. Generally, a relative measure of mixing between two or more systems evolves since the extremes of plug flow and complete mixing represent mathematically the difference between unity and infinity [1]. The model used in the aforementioned reference for an aerobic, biological reactor is graphically shown in Figure 8-1. The tracer used in this case is BOD_5 and is fed continuously to the reactor. This varies from most studies which employ conservative tracers which are introduced into the system in intermittently or slug-fed doses. There are four conditions illustrated in Figure 8-1 which indicate the ratio of the reactor BOD_5 concentration, C_x, at various points along the length of the reactor, X/L, and the influent BOD_5 concentration, C_i. The negatively sloped linear relationship shows a zero-order plug flow system and can be expressed by the following equation:

$$C_x = C_i - mC_i(\frac{X}{L})$$

(8-1)

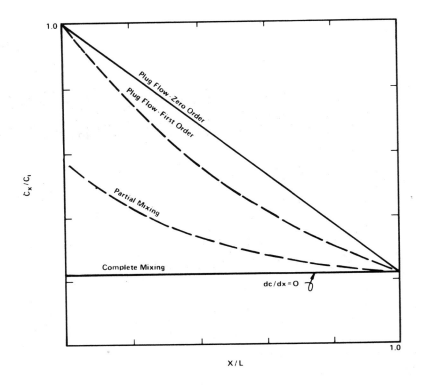

FIG. 8-1. CONCEPTUAL MIXING PROFILES

where:

C_x = BOD_5 at point X in the reactor, mg/l

C_i = BOD_5 entering the reactor, mg/l

m = 'rate of reaction

It is recognized that the BOD_5 reaction can also be considered as a cumulation of many differing zero order reactions which approximate a first order reaction as graphically shown in Figure 8-1 as a first order, plug flow regime. This can be expressed by:

$$\ln C_x/C_i = \ln (1.0) - k(\frac{X}{L}) \tag{8-2}$$

or:

$$C_x = C_i e^{-k(\frac{X}{L})} \tag{8-3}$$

132

where:

k = first order reaction rate constant (day $^{-1}$)

If the system is completely mixed in terms of BOD_5 — namely, no BOD_5 concentration gradient within the aeration basin — then $dc/dx = 0$, and a completely mixed system prevails as shown in Figure 8-1. Most systems, however, fall somewhere between complete mixing and plug flow as indicated by the "partial mixing" line. In mechanically aerated basins, for example, pumping action produces both forward and back-mixing. The degree of mixing is thus dependent on the nature of the aeration system, the placement of the units, and the basin geometry. The basin geometry is particularly significant in dictating the mixing regime based on studies relating design features of surface aerators to the size and shape of aeration tanks [2]. This is illustrated in Figure 8-2 [3]. The flow velocity in an aeration tank to keep mixed liquor suspended solids in suspension is approximately 0.5 fps. Relating velocity to momentum, which is the product of the mass of the fluid and its velocity, it is shown that the power level (hp/1,000 gal) required to maintain this velocity is a function of the basin geometry. The basin geometry is expressed by a geometrical parameter which is the volume of the liquid in the reactor divided by the wetted area. As noted by Figure 8-2, lower power levels can achieve complete mixing at higher volume-to-wetted area

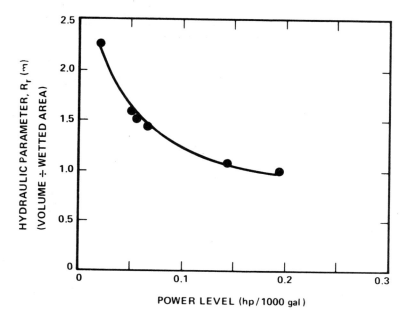

FIG. 8-2. GEOMETRY EFFECTS ON MIXING CHARACTERISTICS

ratios. The influence of power levels and basin geometry as expressed by the length-to-width ratio of the basin on the mixing regime can be expressed in other forms. For example, BOD_5 and MLSS levels in aerated lagoons of varying power levels were analyzed statistically and the extreme variation coefficient was determined in each case. This value, which is the difference between the 90 and 10 percentile values of probability divided by the mean, was then plotted as a function of the power level as conceptually shown in Figure 8-3 [2]. The magni-

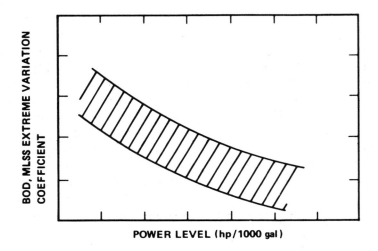

FIG. 8-3. EFFECT OF MIXING INTENSITY ON EXTREME VARIATION COEFFICIENT

tude of the extreme variation coefficient will, of course, approximate zero as the regime approaches complete mixing at two constant influent concentrations. Another expression of the geometry-power level relationship is presented in Figure 8-4 [1]. Although this is conceptual in nature, it does interrelate basin geometry in terms of length-width ratios with power levels to resultant regimes of mixing. The performance of aeration systems, such as mechanical aerators, diffused systems, and static aerators in terms of oxygenation capacity and mixing ability is highly dependent not only on basin geometry but also liquid depth [4].

An approach in evaluating the hydraulic efficiency of units, particularly gravity clarifiers, is by the slug addition of a conservative dye to the influent and measuring the effluent concentration with respect to time. A typical response

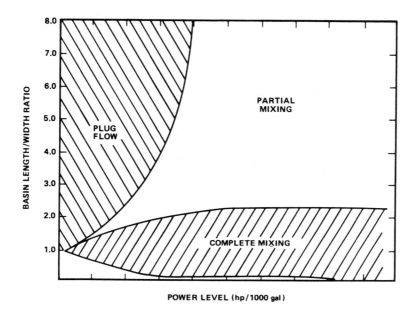

**FIG. 8-4. EFFECT OF BASIN GEOMETRY AND
POWER LEVEL ON MIXING**

curve is shown in Figure 8-5. The nomenclature shown on Figure 8-5 is defined as follows:

t_i = time lapse from dye addition to first detection

t_p = time required for concentration to reach maximum observed value

t_{10} = time at which 10 percent of the area under the concentration curve is reached

t_{90} = time at which 90 percent of the area under the concentration curve is reached

t_g = time at which the centroid of the area under the concentration curve is reached

T = theoretical flow through time = volume/flow

The hydraulic efficiencies in a relative sense can be determined from various process units using the following parameters:

1. t_i/T = 0 for ideal mixing
   1.0 for ideal settling

2. $1 - t_p/t_g$ = 0 for ideal settling
   1.0 for ideal mixing

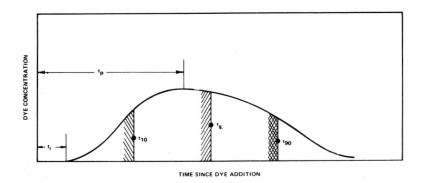

FIG. 8-5.   TYPICAL DYE RESPONSE CURVE

3. $\dfrac{t_{90} - t_p}{t_p - t_{10}}$ = 1.0 for perfect symmetry which is indicative of good settling design

The purpose of any study related to defining the hydraulic and mixing characteristics is to determine the relative amounts of complete mixing, plug flow, and dead space occurring in each unit process and comparing the actual results with the desirable values. Although complex models have been applied to defining real systems with some degree of success, a more simplistic approach has been developed and is used herein [5]. According to this approach, the mixing characteristics of a system can be predicted by establishing the manner and degree of deviation from complete mix. Two hydraulic phenomena which can limit the degree of complete mixing are sections of dead space or plug flow. Theoretical expressions such as those in Table 8-1 have been used to describe the mixing characteristics of various systems. It can then be theoretically shown that approximately 63 percent of the dye added to a completely mixed system can be recovered after one theoretical detention time:

$$\text{Percent Recovery} = 100\,(1\text{-}e^{-t/T}) = 100\,(1\text{-}e^{-1.0}) = 63 \qquad (8\text{-}4)$$

where:

   t = actual measured time interval
   T = detention time

The models used in this approach are shown as Figures 8-6, 8-7, and 8-8. In order to determine the amount of dead space in a completely mixed system, it is necessary only to determine at what fraction of a detention time 63 percent of the dye is recovered. The remaining fraction is then equal to the fraction of dead

TABLE 8-1. THEORETICAL DYE RECOVERY EXPRESSIONS FOR VARIOUS MIXING MODELS

Mixing Model	Theoretical Expression
Complete Mix	Recovery $= 1 - e^{-t/T}$
Complete Mix with Dead Space	Recovery $= 1 - e^{-t/(1-D)T}$
Complete Mix with Plug Flow	Recovery $= 1 - e^{-[1/1-P]\,[(t/T)-P]}$
Complete Mix with Dead Space and Plug Flow	Recovery $= 1 - e^{-[1/M(1-D)]\,[t/T - P(1-D)]}$

Note: t is time; T is theoretical flow through time; M is percent complete mix; P is percent plug flow; and D is percent dead space.

space in the vessel. As shown in Figure 8-6, if 63 percent of the dye is recovered at t/T = 0.75, the amount of dead space is 0.25 or 25 percent.

The effect of plug flow on a completely mixed system is shown in Figure 8-7. In this case, all of the curves pass through 63 percent dye recovery at t/T = 1.0, but the curves originate at various points on the abscissa. For example, a completely mixed system having 50 percent plug flow would have a recovery curve originating at t/T = 0.50, as shown in Figure 8-7.

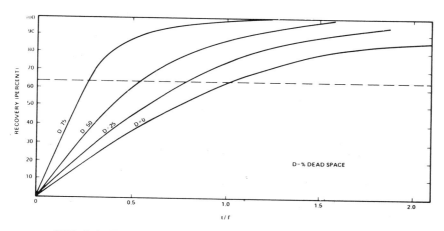

FIG. 8-6. THEORETICAL DYE RECOVERY CURVES FOR A COMPLETELY MIXED SYSTEM WITH VARYING AMOUNTS OF DEAD SPACE

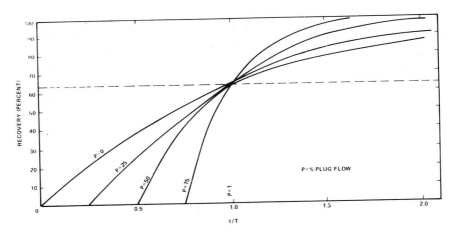

**FIG. 8-7. THEORETICAL DYE RECOVERY CURVES FOR A
COMPLETELY MIXED SYSTEM WITH VARYING
AMOUNTS OF PLUG FLOW**

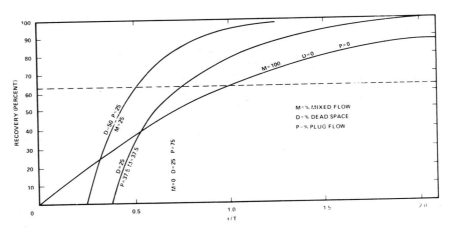

**FIG. 8-8. THEORETICAL DYE RECOVERY CURVES FOR A
COMPLETELY MIXED SYSTEM WITH VARYING
AMOUNTS OF DEAD SPACE AND PLUG FLOW**

Various combinations of plug flow and dead space on a completely mixed system are shown in Figure 8-8. The determination of the relative amounts of the three characteristics proceeds exactly as for the individual cases. For example, a system having 25 percent dead space would show 63 percent dye recovery at $t/T = 0.75$. If, in the same system, the remaining volume, i.e., the effective volume, were divided evenly between completely mixed and plug flow, the curve would originate at $t/T = 0.375$, or one-half of $(1.0 - 0.25)$.

EQUIPMENT REQUIRED

The equipment requirements to perform the hydraulic and mixing analyses using the procedure outlined herein are minimal. They include:
1. Fluorometer, Turner Model 111 or equal — equipped with 546 primary filter and 590 secondary filter. The fluorometer needs to be calibrated using serial dilutions at a specified temperature (normally $20°C$ or $25°C$).
2. Test Dye — Pontage brilliant pink B, Rhodamine B, or Rhodamine B-WT are commonly used. Tests for background and/or interference should be conducted before final dye selection is made.
3. Ancillary containers, appurtenances, and glassware for introducing dye to the unit influent as well as sampling and measuring the effluent concentration.

EXPERIMENTAL PROCEDURE

1. The dye is selected, mixed with the wastewater in question, and evaluated in terms of its "measurability." Factors which would justify selection of another dye would include interference or bacterial decay. The selection of the proper dye is important as low dye recoveries adversely affect the accuracy of the test.
2. Add a measured amount to the influent of the unit process being evaluated. The desired initial concentration (C_o) will depend on the volume of flow, dye available and instrument sensitivity. The range of C_o will usually vary from 0.1 to 0.4 mg/l.
3. Measure the dye concentration in the unit process effluent at various time intervals. The frequency of sampling will depend on several factors but, as a general rule, increments of 10 percent of the theoretical detention time up to 200 percent is appropriate. If dye is still detected after two detention times, sampling and measurement should be continued until the level approaches that of complete dissipation.
4. For ease of analysis, both concentration and time can be "normalized"

139

by plotting C/C_o as the ordinate and t/T as the abscissa where:

C = dye concentration at time "t"

C_o = initial dye concentration

T = detention time = volume/flow rate

The actual percent recovery of dye is then equal to the area under the curve of C/C_o versus t/T. The percent recovery versus time curve can be established by integrating the curve for cumulative time intervals. The percent recovery plot is constructed by assuming that the area under the concentration versus time curve is equal to 100 percent dye recovery rather than the actual dye recovery. An example of this formulation is shown in Figure 8-9.

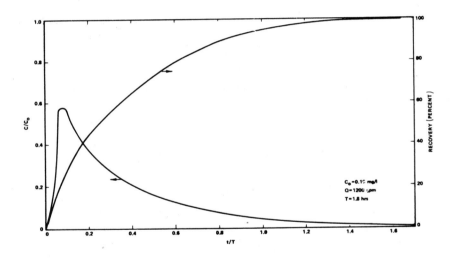

FIG. 8-9.   TYPICAL DYE RECOVERY CURVES

5. Determine the t/T value at which 63 percent of the dye was recovered and, using Figure 8-6, estimate the dead space. The fraction of plug flow is determined by the t/T value of the recovery curve starting point on the abscissa, using Figure 8-7. The balance is complete mixing. Figure 8-8 can be used to determine the relative amounts of the three characteristics, which is the same procedure used in the individual cases.

6. If various unit processes within a treatment system are evaluated in this manner, a tabulation of the results can be expressed as follows:

Process Unit	Initial Dye Concentration	General Conditions	Flow Characteristics (%)		
			Mixed	Plug	Dead Space

LIMITATIONS AND SCALE-UP

The procedure as described herein can be applied to bench, pilot or full-scale units. Attempts should not be made, however, to scale-up from one to the other. The main application using this approach is evaluation of full-scale units.

The test should be conducted so as to obtain maximum dye recovery. Inordinately low peak C/C_o values, such as less than 0.5, limit the accuracy of the test. The careful selection of dyes and the use of judicious sampling and measurement techniques will ensure test accuracy.

REFERENCES

1. "A Study of Mixing Characteristics of Aerated Stabilization Basins," National Council of the Paper Industry for Air and Stream Improvement, Inc., Tech. Bulletin No. 245, New York (1971).
2. Knop, E. and Kalbskopf, K. H., "Energy and Hydraulic Tests on Mechanical Aeration Systems," Proc., Fourth International Conference on Water Pollution Research, Prague (1969).
3. Ford, D. L., "Discussion of Energy and Hydraulic Tests on Mechanical Aeration Systems," Proc., Fourth International Conference on Water Pollution Research, Prague (1969).
4. Kalinske, A. A., "Scale-up Problems Relating to Aeration of Activated Sludge in Waste Treatment," Proc., 150th National Meeting, American Chemical Society, Atlantic City, N. J. (1965).
5. Wolf, D., and Resnick, W., "Residence Time Distribution in Real Systems," Industrial & Engineering Chemistry, Fundamentals, 2, 287-293 (1963).

9

OXYGEN TRANSFER
AND AERATION
EQUIPMENT SELECTION

DISCUSSION OF PRINCIPLES

The supply of oxygen to an aerobic biological treatment system is one of the critical aspects of proper design and operation. Oxygen, which is a sparingly soluble gas in water, is transferred from the gas phase to the liquid phase by diffusion and convection to a concentration in accordance with Henry's Law:

$$C_s = K_s P \qquad (9\text{-}1)$$

where:

C_s = saturation concentration of oxygen in water
K_s = Henry's Law constant
P = Partial pressure of oxygen in the gas phase

Under turbulent flow conditions assuming that the resistance of the liquid film controls oxygen transfer rate, transfer of oxygen from the gas to the liquid phase is a function of the overall transfer coefficient, $K_L a$, and the oxygen deficit:

$$\frac{dC}{dt} = K_L a (C_s - C) \qquad (9\text{-}2)$$

The rearranged and integrated form, converted to logarithm based on 10, yields:

$$K_L a = \frac{2.303 \log [(C_s - C_1) / (C_s - C_2)]}{t_2 - t_1} \qquad (9\text{-}3)$$

where:

C = concentration of D.O. at any time, t

$K_L a$ = overall mass transfer coefficient, time^{-1}

C_s = saturation D.O. concentration of the liquid at a specified temperature, barometric pressure, and salinity

C_1 = D.O. concentration at time, t_1

C_2 = D.O. concentration at time, t_2

The overall mass transfer coefficient, $K_L a$, can be physically measured as described in subsequent sections of this chapter, and includes the effects of changes in the liquid film coefficient, K_L, and the interfacial area per unit volume, A/V. The liquid film coefficient, as defined by Danckwerts [1] and Higbie [2], is the square root of the product of the molecular diffusion coefficient, D_L, and the rate of surface renewal, r:

$$K_L = \sqrt{D_L r} \qquad (9\text{-}4)$$

The surface renewal rate, r, is the average frequency with which the interfacial film is replaced with liquid from the body of solution. In the turbulent regime which prevails in most aerobic biological systems, the oxygen transfer rate is a function of surface renewal. The overall mass transfer coefficient is therefore equal to:

$$K_L a = K_L A/V \qquad (9\text{-}5)$$

and can be determined in the laboratory or field using Equation 9-3. From Equation 9-5 it is obvious that $K_L a$ is a function of both K_L, which is dependent on the surface tension and molecular characteristics which prevail at the gas-liquid interface of a given fluidized system, and A/V, which depends on the turbulence and bubble patterns in an aeration system.

One of the most significant factors which affect $K_L a$, based on changes in diffusivity and viscosity, is temperature. This temperature effect can be defined by the relationship:

$$K_L a_{(T)} = K_L a_{(20°)} \, \theta^{(T-20)} \qquad (9\text{-}6)$$

The θ value has been reported to vary from 1.016 to 1.037 [3, 4]. Values of 1.020 to 1.028 are normally used for bubble systems, while a value to 1.024 is considered appropriate for mechanical aeration systems [5].

When oxygen is supplied to fluidized systems treating wastewaters with aerobic biological oxidation, it is necessary to define a correction factor which relates the oxygen transfer to the nature of the waste. Using the transfer of oxygen to tap water as the datum, the parameter, alpha (α), serves as this correction factor. Specifically, it is the ratio of the overall mass transfer coefficient ($K_L a$) of the wastewater to that of tap water:

$$\alpha = \frac{K_L a \text{ (wastewater)}}{K_L a \text{ (tap water)}} \qquad (9\text{-}7)$$

Although α is represented in the mathematical relationships describing diffused, turbine, and surface aeration system performance, there are many variables which affect its magnitude. These include:

1. Temperature of the mixed liquor;
2. Nature of dissolved organic and mineral constituents in the wastewater;
3. Characteristics of the aeration equipment (diffused or mechanical);
4. The liquid mixing intensity which affects the surface renewal rate; and
5. The liquid depth and geometry of the aeration basin.

The temperature effect is attributable to the temperature dependence of the liquid film coefficient (K_L). Alpha (α) might be expected to increase, decrease, or approach unity during the course of biological oxidation since dissolved organic material affecting the transfer rate is being removed in the biological process. Alpha generally increases with the degree of treatment as conceptually shown in Figure 9-1.

The mixing intensity affects the magnitude of alpha, particularly using surface aeration systems as indicated in Figure 9-2 [6]. Under quiescent or moderately turbulent conditions, the presence of surface active agents inhibits molecular diffusion of oxygen through the gas-liquid interface and there is a decrease in surface renewal. However, α may approach or even exceed unity at high mixing intensities as high surface renewal and increased surface contact areas are associated with turbulent conditions. Determination of α based on bench-scale experiments is only an approximation because of the difficulty of accurately representing field mixing conditions in the laboratory reactor. It is difficult to scale-up diffused or mechanical aeration equipment operating characteristics

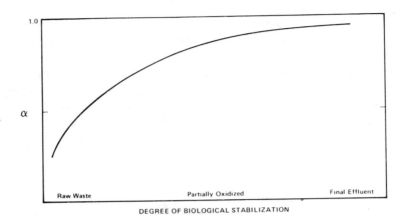

1.0

α

Raw Waste   Partially Oxidized   Final Effluent

DEGREE OF BIOLOGICAL STABILIZATION

FIG. 9-1. EFFECT OF BIOLOGICAL STABILITY ON ALPHA

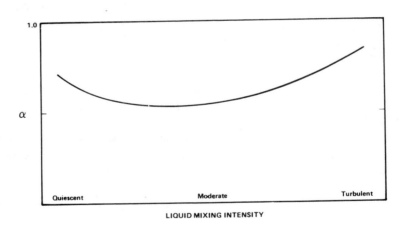

1.0

α

Quiescent   Moderate   Turbulent

LIQUID MIXING INTENSITY

FIG. 9-2. EFFECT OF MIXING INTENSITY ON ALPHA

from bench-scale to full-scale. Recognizing these constraints, a bench or pilot-scale determination of α does give an indication of its magnitude and can be used to estimate diffused, turbine, or surface aeration requirements for an aerobic biological system.

The coefficient, β, is defined as the ratio of oxygen saturation level for studied wastewater to the oxygen saturation for tap water as shown in Equation 9-8:

$$\beta = \frac{C_s \text{ (wastewater)}}{C_s \text{ (tap water)}} \qquad (9\text{-}8)$$

For the purpose of this discussion, aeration equipment is categorized into three systems: namely, diffused aeration, turbine aeration, and mechanical aeration. These systems are illustrated schematically in Figure 9-3 and discussed as follows.

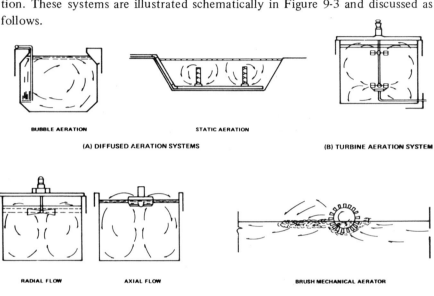

BUBBLE AERATION   STATIC AERATION

(A) DIFFUSED AERATION SYSTEMS   (B) TURBINE AERATION SYSTEM

RADIAL FLOW   AXIAL FLOW   BRUSH MECHANICAL AERATOR

(C) MECHANICAL AERATION SYSTEMS

FIG. 9-3. SCHEMATICS OF SELECTED AERATION EQUIPMENT

Diffused Bubbler Aeration Systems

Diffused aeration devices are commercially available in several basic types. Small orifice devices are constructed of silicon dioxide or aluminum oxide held in a porous mass with a ceramic binder, or in tubes or bags wrapped with Saran or nylon material. The size of bubbles released from this type of diffuser ranges from 2.0 to 2.5 mm. The absorption efficiency (oxygen absorbed/oxygen supplied) depends on the size of the air bubbles released and the turbulence generated in the system. Another type of air diffuser uses a large orifice device such as the sparjer. The sparjer contains four short tube orifices at 90° centers from which the air is emitted at high velocity. Tank turbulence tends to redivide large bubbles into smaller bubbles. The orifice diameters normally range from 0.20 in.

to 0.25 in. Other commercial units in this category include the hydraulic shear diffuser, the Venturi diffuser, and the INKA diffuser.

There are several factors which affect the transfer characteristics of diffusion units. The transfer efficiency is first a function of the gas flow as indicated in the following equation:

$$N = C G_s^n \qquad\qquad (9\text{-}9)$$

where:

N = oxygen transfer efficiency, lb O_2/hp-hr
G_s = air flow rate, standard cfm
C,n = constants which are a function of the diffuser equipment design

The effect of the liquid depth above the diffusers and the width of the tank on transfer efficiency has been previously assessed and is applied to Equation 9-9:

$$N = C G_s^n \left(\frac{H^m}{W^p}\right) \qquad\qquad (9\text{-}10)$$

where:

H = depth of aeration tank, ft
W = width of aeration tank, ft
p = width correction exponent (≈ 0.36)
m = depth correction exponent ($\approx 0.72 - 0.88$)

Incorporating the oxygen deficit or driving force, the temperature correction, and the transfer correction coefficient, Equation 9-10 becomes:

$$N = CG_s^n \; \frac{H^m}{W^p} \; \frac{(C_{sm} - C_L)}{C_s} \; \theta^{(T-20)} \, (\alpha) \qquad\qquad (9\text{-}11)$$

where:

C_{sm} = saturation concentration of dissolved oxygen at tank mid-depth, mg/l
C_L = operating dissolved oxygen concentration in aeration tank, mg/l

The C_{sm} value can be calculated according to:

$$C_{sm} = \beta \, C_s \left(\frac{P_b}{29.4} + \frac{O_t}{42}\right) \qquad\qquad (9\text{-}12)$$

where:

   P_b = absolute pressure at the depth of air release, psia

   O_t = oxygen in the exit gas, percent

Reported oxygen transfer efficiencies of bubbler diffused aeration systems range from 0.9 to 1.5 lb O_2/hp-hr.

Static Aeration Systems

Static aeration systems consist of vertical cylindrical tubes placed at specified intervals in an aeration basin and containing fixed internal elements. A central compressor supplies an air source through a sparjer at the bottom of the tubes, and an air-water mixture is forced through the cylinder. There is an intimate air-water contact as the mixture travels up through the elements within the static mixer cylinder. Most of the oxygen transfer occurs within the cylinder, although there is additional transfer at the surface turbulent area where the air-water mixture is discharged from the cylinder. The transfer efficiency of static aeration systems is reported to be higher than that obtained from the conventional diffused air-sparger or orifice system [7]. The exact transfer obtained using a static aeration system is a function of several design features; namely:

1. The bottom sparger design;
2. Diameter of the cylinder;
3. Length of the cylinder;
4. The air flow rate;
5. The liquid submergence;
6. The liquid velocity and mixing intensity; and
7. The design of the fixed elements and associated pressure drop through the cylinder.

The air flow per mixer cylinder normally varies from 12 to 30 scfm with a delivered air pressure in the range of 10 to 15 psig.

To date, static aeration systems have been used primarily in aerated lagoons carrying relatively low concentrations of biological suspended solids. This application affords several advantages, including low annual costs and relatively high transfer efficiencies. Static aerators have also been applied as mixers in small mechanical or neutralization rapid mix tanks. The oxygen transfer efficiencies of 2.0 to 3.0 lb O_2/hp-hr have been reported for static diffuser systems.

Turbine Aeration Systems

In turbine aeration, air is discharged from a pipe or sparge ring beneath the rotating blades of an impeller. The air is broken into bubbles and dispersed throughout the tank contents. Present commercial units employ one or more submerged impellers and may utilize an additional impeller near the liquid surface for oxygenation from induced surface aeration. In addition to air flow the diameter and speed of the impeller will affect the bubble size and velocity, thus influencing the overall transfer coefficient, $K_L a$. The transfer equation for turbine aeration systems is:

$$N = C\, G_s{}^n\, d_t{}^y\, R^x\, \frac{(\beta C_s\text{-} C_L)}{C_s}\, \theta^{(T\text{-}20)}\, (\alpha) \qquad (9\text{-}13)$$

where:
d_t = impeller diameter, ft
R = impeller peripheral speed, fps
y, x = exponents

A significant correlation between oxygen transfer efficiency and the power supplied to the system from the rotor (hp_R) and the compressor (hp_C) has been demonstrated [8] specifically:

$$N = C P_d{}^n \qquad (9\text{-}14)$$

where:
P_d = power split, hp_R / hp_C
C, n = constants

It was further shown that oxygenation efficiency can be related to P_d by differentiating the oxygenation efficiency with respect to P_d, equating the differential to zero, and solving for the optimum power distribution. The value is a function of the exponent "n" in Equation 9-14:

$$P_d{}^* = \left(\frac{n}{1\text{-}n}\right) \qquad (9\text{-}15)$$

in which $P_d{}^*$ is the power distribution for the optimum oxygenation efficiency.

In most cases, $P_d{}^*$ occurs near 1.0. (This implies an equal power expenditure by the turbine and the compressor.) At extremely high air rates ($P_d \ll 1.0$), large bubbles and flooding of the impeller yield poor oxygenation efficiencies, while at very low rates ($P_d \gg 1.0$), too much turbine horsepower is being expended in fluid mixing without associated oxygen transfer.

Variation in oxygen demand in the system can most easily be adjusted by varying the air rate under the impeller. This in turn will change P_d. The anticipated range of operation should cover the maximum range of oxygenation efficiency as related to P_d.

Available data indicate that the oxygenation efficiency of turbine aerators in water should vary from 1.7 to 2.4 lb O_2/hp-hr (including motor and reducer losses.)

Mechanical Aeration Systems

Mechanical aerators have become increasingly popular in recent years, particularly in industrial treatment applications. There are three basic classifications of mechanical aerators; specifically, the radial flow slow speed aerator, the axial flow high speed unit, and the brush mechanical aerator. A brief discussion of each follows.

The radial flow, slow speed aerator is essentially a low head, high volume pump. Assuming an exit liquid velocity of 8 fps and impeller submergence of 6 in., for example, the total dynamic head would be only 1.5 ft. The volume pumped per unit hp (nameplate) is a function of the motor size as indicated in

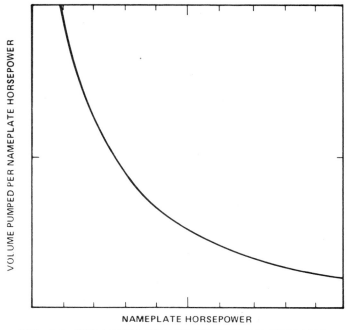

FIG. 9-4. RELATIONSHIP BETWEEN PUMP SIZE AND
PUMPING EFFICIENCY

151

Figure 9-4 and ranges from 2 to 15 cfs/hp [9]. Oxygen transfer is accomplished primarily through entrainment associated with an induced hydraulic pump. The primary component of these units are the motor, gear reducer, and impeller. The impellers vary in diameter from 3 to 12 ft, and motor sizes range from 3 to 150 hp. The output speed ranges from 30 to 60 rpm. These aerators are generally capable of mixing the contents of large aeration basins varying in depth from 3 to 18 ft. This depth can be increased by utilizing draft tubes or increasing the impeller submergence depth. These units usually are affixed to bridges or platforms.

The axial flow, high speed aerator is widely used and consists of a motor and propeller assembly which is usually float-mounted. The major components are a non-submersible motor, riser tube, fiberglass or stainless steel float, and propeller deflector. They have a lower pumping capacity per unit hp than the radial flow units, but impart a higher velocity to the liquid (12 to 18 fps). As the radial flow slow speed units, they are low head, high volume pumps working at a total dynamic head of 3 to 6 ft. Most of the oxygen transfer occurs in the spray pattern, although transfer also occurs in the turbulent area in the outer peripheral area of the spray. These units range in size from 1 to 150 hp, and the rotational speed is in the 900 to 1,400 rpm range. The liquid depths required for proper operation vary from 3 to 15 ft, depending on the aerator size.

The brush aerators, which are the mechanical aeration devices used in aeration ditches, transfer oxygen from the gas to the liquid phase in a manner similar to that of the aforementioned mechanical aerators; namely, through spray contact and air entrainment. These units rotate in the 30 to 60 rpm range with a wide range of reported oxygen transfer efficiencies. The exact efficiency depends on the type of brush, rotational speed, submergence, and aeration conditions.

The oxygen transfer efficiencies of mechanical aeration systems will depend on the inherent design of the equipment, such as the impeller diameter and configuration, deflecter plate, and speed and submergence depth of the rotating element. The reported efficiencies have ranged from 2.5 to 4.0 lb/O_2 hp-hr, although 2.5 to 3.5 lb O_2/hp-hr is probably a more accurate range.

The traditional design equation for mechanical aerators is:

$$N = N_o \left(\frac{\beta C_s - C_L}{C_s}\right) \theta^{(T-20)} (\alpha) \qquad (9\text{-}16)$$

where:

N   = oxygen transfer efficiency, field conditions, lb O_2/hp-hr,

N_o = oxygen transfer efficiency, test tank conditions, lb O_2/hp-hr

If the power level (hp/1,000 gal) is shown to affect N_o during the test series, as is the case in Figure 9-5 then:

$$N_o = K + S (P.L.) \qquad\qquad (9\text{-}17)$$

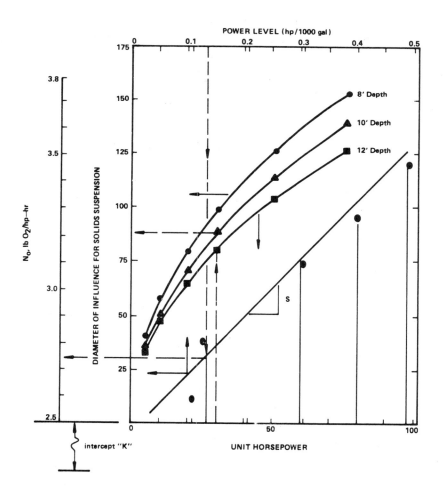

FIG. 9-5.   SURFACE AERATOR CHARACTERISTICS

153

where:

K = intercept (N_o at an infinitely low power level)

S = slope

P.L. = power level, usually expressed as hp/1,000 gal

and Equation 9-16 must be modified accordingly. This, of course, requires a trial and error solution by assuming a power level and using the corresponding N_o value to calculate N. If the resultant power level is different than that first assumed, then the calculation must be repeated until the two values coincide [10]. It should be noted that Figure 9-5 applies to one aerator type only and cannot be applied for all designs. The influence of power level on transfer efficiency will depend on aerator spacing, tank geometry, and overall mixing and circulating patterns.

A generalized summary of the characteristics and applications for the various types of aeration equipment as discussed herein is given in Table 9-1 [11].

EXPERIMENTAL PROCEDURES

The need for accurately evaluating aeration equipment in terms of oxygen transfer capability is well recognized both by manufacturers and by design engineers. The three most commonly accepted techniques used to determine transfer efficiency of aeration equipment are:

1. The non-steady state reaeration of deoxygenated "pure" water in a test tank or actual aeration basin;
2. The steady state evaluation in an activated sludge basin; and
3. The non-steady state evaluation in an activated sludge basin.

Each of these procedures and their limitations are discussed as follows.

Non-Steady State Reaeration of Deoxygenated Water

This is the most common method of evaluating aerator transfer performance and has generally been adopted as a standard. It involves reaeration of "pure" water which has been deoxygenated by the addition of sodium sulfite and a cobalt catalyst. This reaction stoichiometrically requires 7.9 ppm of Na_2SO_3 per ppm of dissolved oxygen although a 20 to 30 percent excess is normally used. Concentrations of the cobalt ion should be a minimum of 0.5 ppm and should not exceed 1.5 ppm. The predissolved chemicals are added to the test basin and the aeration equipment is turned on to mix the chemical-water mixture until the dissolved oxygen is completely depleted. Once this condition prevails, the test for reaeration can be initiated. The aeration equipment is started and dissolved

TABLE 9-1. SUMMARY OF CHARACTERISTICS AND APPLICATIONS FOR VARIOUS TYPES OF AERATION EQUIPMENT

Equipment Type	Equipment Characteristics	Processes Where Used	Advantages	Disadvantages	Reported Transfer Efficiency* (lb O_2/hp-hr)
Diffused Aeration: (Bubbler)					
Porous Diffusers	Produce fine or small bubbles. Made of ceramic plates or tubes, plastic-wrapped or plastic-cloth tube or bag.	Large, conventional, activated sludge processes.	High oxygen transfer efficiency; good mixing; maintain high liquid temperature. Varying air flow provides good operational flexibility.	High Initial and maintenance costs; tendency to clog; not suitable for complete mixing.	0.9-1.5
Nonporous Diffusers	Made in nozzle, valve, orifice or shear types, they produce coarse or large bubbles. Some made of plastic with check-valve design.	All sizes of conventional activated sludge process.	Nonclogging; maintain high liquid temperature; low maintenance cost.	High initial cost; low oxygen transfer efficiency; high power cost.	
(Static)	Produces high shear and entrainment as water-air mixture is forced through vertical cylinder containing static mixing elements. Cylinder construction is metal, plastic, or poly-ethylene.	Primarily aerated lagoon applications.	Economically attractive; low maintenance; high transfer efficiencies for diffused air systems. Well suited for aerated lagoon applications.	Ability to adequately mix aeration basin contents in high rate biological systems unconfirmed.	2.0-3.0

TABLE 9-1. SUMMARY OF CHARACTERISTICS AND APPLICATIONS FOR VARIOUS TYPES OF AERATION EQUIPMENT (continued)

Equipment Type	Equipment Characteristics	Processes Where Used	Advantages	Disadvantages	Reported Transfer Efficiency*
Mechanical Aeration:					
Radial Flow Slow Speed	Low output speed; large diameter turbine, usually fixed-bridge or platform mounted. Used with gear reducer.	All sizes of conventional, activated-sludge and aerated lagoon processes.	High oxygen transfer efficiency; tank design flexibility; good transfer efficiency. High pumping capacity.	Some icing in cold climates. Initial cost higher than axial flow aerators. Gear reducer often causes maintenance problems.	
Axial Flow High Speed	High output speed. Small diameter propeller. They are direct, motor-driven units mounted on floating structure.	Aerated lagoons and activated sludge processes.	Low initial cost; simple to install and operate; good transfer efficiency; adjust to varying water level. Flexible operation.	Some icing in cold climates; poor maintenance accessibility.	2.5-3.5
Brush Aeration	Low output speed; used with gear reducer.	Oxidation ditch applied either as an aerated lagoon or as an activated sludge process.	Relatively low initial cost, easy to install and operate, good maintenance accessibility, moderate transfer efficiency.	Subject to operational variables which may affect efficiency.	
Turbine Aeration:	Units contain a low speed turbine and provide compressed air on sparge ring. Fixed-bridge application.	Conventional, activated sludge process.	Good mixing; high capacity input per unit volume; deep tank application; moderate efficiency; wide oxygen input range; operational flexibility.	Require both gear reducer and compressor; tendency to foam; high total power requirements.	1-7-2.4

*Test conditions and procedures not documented.

oxygen levels at various points in the basin are monitored. Both an oxygen probe and a Winkler dissolved oxygen analysis should be used. If a discrepancy between the probe and Winkler data exists, then the Winkler analysis should be considered to be the more accurate.

Reaeration should continue until 75 to 90 percent of saturation is observed. The oxygen deficit is plotted with respect to time on a semi-log plot as shown in the example in Figure 9-6. The C_s value for the measured temperature of the "pure" test water can be taken from the standard oxygen saturation value shown in Table 9-2. This value can be corrected for atmospheric pressure and test water quality differences from "pure" water "as required" according to Equation 9-18:

$$C_s = C_s' \, (P/29.92) \, (\beta) \qquad\qquad (9\text{-}18)$$

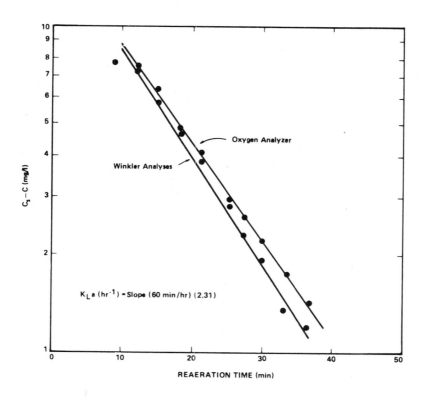

FIG. 9-6.   GRAPHICAL DETERMINATION OF K_La

where:

P	=	atmospheric pressure (in. of Hg)
β	=	saturation of test water/saturation of pure water
C_s'	=	uncorrected D.O. saturation value

TABLE 9-2. OXYGEN SATURATION VALUES (C_5) FOR DISTILLED WATER AT STANDARD CONDITIONS .

$T(^\circ F)$	$T(^\circ C)$	mg O_2/l	$T(^\circ F)$	$T(^\circ C)$	mg O_2/l
32	0	14.6	78.8	26	8.2
33.8	1	14.2	80.6	27	8.1
35.6	2	13.8	82.4	28	7.9
37.4	3	13.5	84.2	29	7.8
39.2	4	13.1	86.0	30	7.6
41.0	5	12.8	87.8	31	7.5
42.8	6	12.5	89.6	32	7.4
44.6	7	12.2	91.4	33	7.3
46.4	8	11.9	93.2	34	7.2
48.2	9	11.6	95.0	35	7.1
50.0	10	11.3	96.8	36	7.0
51.8	11	11.1	98.6	37	6.9
53.6	12	10.8	100.4	38	6.8
55.4	13	10.6	102.2	39	6.7
57.2	14	10.4	104.0	40	6.6
59.0	15	10.2	105.8	41	6.5
60.8	16	10.0	107.6	42	6.4
62.6	17	9.7	109.4	43	6.3
64.4	18	9.5	111.2	44	6.2
66.2	19	9.4	113.0	45	6.1
68.0	20	9.2	114.8	46	6.0
69.8	21	9.0	116.6	47	5.9
71.6	22	8.8	118.4	48	5.8
73.4	23	8.7	120.2	49	5.7
75.2	24	8.5	122.0	50	5.6
77.0	25	8.4			

The overall mass transfer coefficient can then be calculated as the slope of the line in Figure 9-6 according to Equation 9-3. As the test standard is $20°C$, K_La can be corrected to this temperature using Equation 9-6. The oxygenation capacity (O.C.) can then be calculated as follows:

$$\text{O.C.} = K_La_{(20°C)} (9.2) (8.34/10^6) \text{ (vol of test tank, gal)} \qquad (9\text{-}19)$$

The transfer efficiency (T.E.) in terms of nameplate horsepower (NPHP) is then:

$$\text{T.E.} = (\text{O.C.}/\text{NPHP}) \qquad (9\text{-}20)$$

The T.E. can be expressed in terms of wire to water horsepower ($hp_{w/w}$) by the following calculation:

$$(hp_{w/w}) = [\text{line voltage] [line amperage] [power factor]} \qquad (9\text{-}21)$$
$$[\text{conversion hp/watts] [(motor efficiency) (gear efficiency)]}$$

This non-steady state reaeration approach is valid only when the entire liquid content of the test basin is completely mixed and K_La is a constant and time-independent. There are several limitations to this method of evaluation, the most obvious of which is power level. As indicated in Figure 9-5, N_o is a function of power level and because of the lack of a "standard" power level in the aeration test it is misleading to compare aeration equipment rated under different conditions. The test should be conducted at the design power level. Another effect which influences the transfer efficiency of an aerator is the basin geometry of the test tank. As the transfer efficiency is dependent on flow patterns, the exact T.E. value can be related to various geometrical parameters such as a diameter/depth ratio, wetted area/basin volume, and/or length to width ratio. This aspect limits precise translation of T.E. values determined from test tanks to application in a field basin of different configuration, even though power levels, temperature, and alpha correction factors are properly considered. The effect of increasing sodium sulfate and cobalt concentrations inherent in the non-steady state test on T.E. values also has been reported [5, 12]. Strong evidence has indicated that sodium sulfate values above 2,000 ppm increases the T.E., probably due to a reduction in surface tension with an increasing interfacial area and K_La value. Moreover, an increase in T.E. with cobalt concentrations exceeding 1 to 1.5 ppm has been implied [13].

It is apparent that the non-steady state test has many shortcomings and idiosyncrasies. However, if more standard test conditions can be established and testing procedures clearly defined and followed, it does offer an acceptable method for rating and comparing aeration equipment [14].

Steady State Reaeration of Activated Sludge

There are obvious incentives to field test aerators in the activated sludge basin. As the equipment is performing under actual field conditions, the problem of translating "clean water" test results to the "field situation" is circumvented. This does force, however, a delay in aerator evaluation until the plant has been put "on line" and is working properly. Nevertheless, aeration equipment can be assessed *"in-situ"* once a quasi-steady state condition has been established in the aeration basin. Once this is obtained, Equation 9-2 can be modified:

$$\frac{dC}{dt} = K_L a(C_s - C) - r_r \qquad (9\text{-}22)$$

where:

r_r = average oxygen uptake rate in the basin by the activated sludge, mg/l-hr

Under quasi-steady state conditions, dC/dt approaches zero, and $K_L a$ can be determined as follows:

$$K_L a = r_r/(C_s - C) \qquad (9\text{-}23)$$

The oxygen uptake rate should be measured at various points within the basin to ensure uniformity and statistical accuracy. The $K_L a$ value obtained includes the effects of alpha, temperature, and solids concentration and is specific only to the particular wastewater and particular system. It is important that the wastewater treatment system be stabilized with respect to a constant organic loading, feed composition, and basin dissolved oxygen level during the test.

Non-Steady State Reaeration of Activated Sludge

Another approach in evaluating $K_L a$ under process conditions is the non-steady state reaeration of activated sludge. This involves stopping wastewater flow to the system and assuming the oxygen uptake rate will become relatively constant during the ensuing 0.5 to 1.0 hour of aeration time. Within this period, the aeration is stopped for a sufficiently long period of time for the activated sludge to deplete the liquid contents of dissolved oxygen, then the system is reaerated and the oxygen level monitored. The mass transfer coefficient, $K_L a$ can be evaluated without actually measuring the oxygen uptake rate using the following approach: (Equation 9-22 is reexpressed as follows)

$$\frac{dC}{dt} = [K_L a C_s - r_r] - K_L aC \tag{9-24}$$

If the dissolved oxygen level is monitored following aeration start-up as described above, then the profile would approximate that shown in Figure 9-7. By taking tangents at various points on the curve, dC/dt values for corresponding C levels (at the point of tangency) can be determined. These data can be replotted as shown in Figure 9-8 according to Equation 9-24. $K_L a$ is the slope of the line and can be determined accordingly. One advantage of this approach is the fact that the oxygen uptake rate, which is difficult to accurately determine, is included in the intercept and does not have to be physically measured.

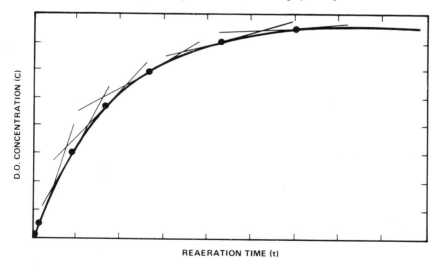

FIG. 9-7.   REAERATION D.O. PROFILE

Field Performance

Manufacturers of aeration equipment are normally required to furnish a guarantee of transfer efficiency. Although this guarantee, based on standard test conditions in a clean water test tank, can be easily defined, it may or may not relate to field oxygen supply requirements. For this reason, some vendors are basing performance guarantees on BOD removal and oxygen driving force in the actual basin. It is first shown that the T.E. is a function of the D.O. in the incoming water to the basin as depicted in Figure 9-9 [11]. Secondly, if one assumes that

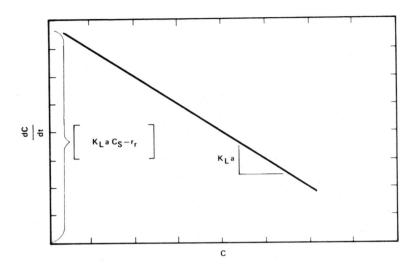

**FIG. 9-8. GRAPHICAL DETERMINATION OF K_La FROM
NON-STEADY STATE REAERATION OF ACTIVATED SLUDGE**

the oxygen utilized is proportional to the BOD removed and constant, then:

$$X = y'N = K\Delta C \qquad (9\text{-}25)$$

where:

X = lb BOD removed /hp-hr
y' = lb BOD removed/lb O_2
K = constant

This relationship is shown in Figure 9-10 and would serve as a basis for guaranteeing process performance based on oxygen residuals. This is reasonable because in the final analysis, the residual D.O. in the aeration basin is the important process consideration. For example, a guarantee of mechanical aeration performance in terms of oxygen transfer could be specified based on the concept shown in Figure 9-11. However, it should be recognized that even this approach has some limitations. From a process point of view, the oxygen utilized per lb of BOD removed in fact may not be constant due to varying substrate characteristics and oxygen demanding inorganic constituents. If the operating D.O. level falls below one mg/l there will most probably be a drop in BOD removal efficiency because of a diminution of biochemical reaction rates at low oxygen tension. Alpha values which deviate from the design prediction would also affect this approach.

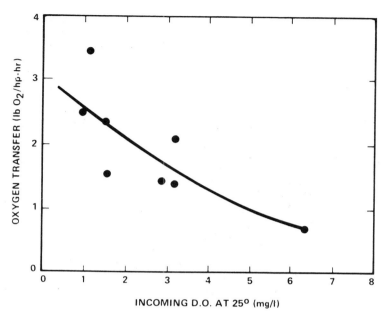

FIG. 9-9. EFFECT OF INCOMING D.O. ON OXYGEN
TRANSFER EFFICIENCY

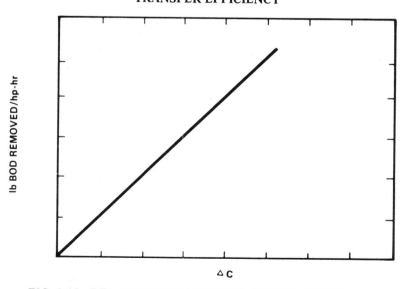

FIG. 9-10. RELATIONSHIP BETWEEN OXYGEN UTILIZATION
AND ORGANIC REMOVAL

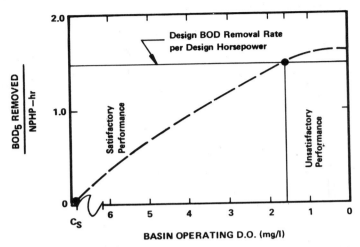

FIG. 9-11. MECHANICAL AERATION PERFORMANCE CRITERION

Laboratory Procedure for Determination of the Oxygen Transfer Coefficient (Alpha)

The equipment used for this procedure is:

1. Galvanic cell oxygen analyzer and probe, properly calibrated (chemicals and equipment necessary for performing Winkler analysis of dissolved oxygen may be used as an alternative).

2. Aeration source, either mechanical aeration device or compressed air line with diffuser. A tachometer is required with mechanical aerators and a rotameter or wet test meter would be required for a diffused air system.

3. Water receptacle, with volume of two liters to 55 gallons, depending on desired scale of alpha evaluation test.

4. Deoxygenation equipment – nitrogen source with feed line and diffuser, or deoxygenating chemicals (Na_2SO_3 + cobalt catalyst).

The following procedures can be used in the bench-scale determination of the oxygen transfer coefficient, α, and oxygen saturation coefficient, β.

1. Vessels similar to those shown in Figure 9-12 can be used. Mechanical or diffused aeration devices can be employed as desired. If a diffused system is used, an air measuring rotameter should be installed for control. When a mechanical surface aerator is used, the mixing intensity can be controlled with a variable speed motor and a rheostat.

2. The container is filled with a defined volume of tap water and the temperature recorded. The water is then deoxygenated chemically using

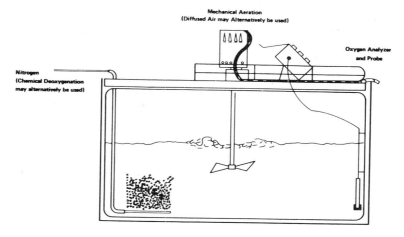

FIG. 9-12. LABORATORY APPARATUS
FOR DETERMINATION OF ALPHA α

sodium sulfite and a cobalt catalyst (approximately 8 to 12 mg/l of sodium sulfite per mg/l of dissolved oxygen) or stripping the oxygen from solution with an inert gas such as nitrogen. In the laboratory unit, the latter is preferred in order to eliminate any possible chemical interferences.

3. Once the contents have been deoxygenated, the water is reaerated at a controlled diffused air flow or mechanical rotational speed. The oxygen concentration for various time intervals is recorded at the predetermined level of liquid turbulence. The oxygen deficit at various aeration times is then plotted on semi-log paper, the slope taken as the coefficient K_La. This step can be repeated for various mixing intensities and temperatures. The use of tap water can be repeated, substituting a mechanical aeration device for the diffused air system:

    Mechanical Aeration:

        Rotation Speed = as desired
        Temperature   = 20°C, 33°C
        Deoxygenation = nitrogen stripping
        Liquid contents = tap water

Aerate until the dissolved oxygen concentration is constant. This is the saturation value.

4. Following the deoxygenation and reaeration of tap water for the various test conditions, steps 2 and 3 should be repeated, using the same volume of wastewater. As the transfer coefficient, α, is a function of the degree of

biological stabilization, every effort should be made to use a wastewater similar to the mixed liquor anticipated in the prototype aeration basin. For example, the effluent from the bench-scale biological reactors should be used in the alpha test when a completely mixed system is contemplated. There may be some problem with interferences of the wastewater with the Winkler Method *(Standard Methods)* of determining dissolved oxygen. A properly calibrated galvanic cell oxygen analyzer and probe is therefore a practical and reliable method of determining the oxygen concentration throughout the testing period.

5. The K_La values as determined in step 4 can then be compared to the K_La values for tap water at the same temperature and mixing conditions and α can be calculated in accordance with Equation 9-7 and β can be calculated in accordance with Equation 9-8.

Once the α values for a range of temperature and mixing conditions are determined, the controlling magnitude for the most critical design condition can be used as a basis for sizing aeration equipment.

LIMITATIONS AND SCALE-UP

The problems of transferring aerator performance from test conditions to field conditions have been discussed previously. To truly develop similitude, one should apply the principles of fluid mechanics; specifically, the Reynolds Number, the Froude Number, and the Weber Number as defined below:

$$Re = (V_p d\rho/\mu) \text{ or } (Nd^2 \rho/\mu) \tag{9-26}$$

$$Fr = V_p^2/gd \text{ or } N^2 d/g \tag{9-27}$$

$$We = V_p^2 d\rho/\sigma \text{ or } N^2 d^3 \rho/\sigma \tag{9-28}$$

where:

V_p = peripheral velocity of aerator
d = aerator diameter
N = rpm of aerator
g = gravity constant
ρ = fluid density
μ = fluid viscosity
σ = fluid surface tension

The attainment of true dynamic similarity would require that all three numbers be the same for all aerator sizes, and geometric similarity must prevail [12]. As this is difficult, if not impossible, to establish, empirical data such as flow patterns, velocity magnitudes and vectors, and oxygen dispersion, must be established to evaluate the similarity or dissimilarity of test and field conditions.

REFERENCES

1. Danckwerts, P. V., "Significance of Liquid Film Coefficients in Gas Adsorption," *Ind. Engr. Chem.,* 43, 1460-1467 (1951).
2. Higbie, R., "The Rate of Absorption of a Pure Gas into a Still Liquid during Short Periods of Exposure," *Trans. Amer. Inst. Chem. Engr.,* 31, 365-389 (1935).
3. Eckenfelder, W.W., and Barnhart, E.L., "Designing for Oxygen Transfer," *Wastes Engineering,* 34, 80-83 (1963).
4. Eckenfelder, W. W., and Ford, D. L., "New Concepts in Oxygen Transfer and Aeration," *Advances in Water Quality Improvement,* E. F. Gloyna and W. W. Eckenfelder, Eds., Univ. of Texas Press, Austin, Texas (1968).
5. Crocker, J. D., "Analysis of Relative Mixing Abilities of Various Mechanical Aerator Types," Unpublished Report (1972).
6. Eckenfelder, W. W., and Ford, D. L., *Water Pollution Control: Experimental Procedures for Process Design,* Pemberton Press, Austin, Texas (1970).
7. Epstein, A. C., and Glover, C., "Full Scale Aeration Studies of Static Aeration Systems," Permutit Corporation Report of Kenics Corp. (1971).
8. Quirk, T. P., "Optimization of Gas-Liquid Contacting Systems," Unpublished Report (1962).
9. "A Study of Mixing Characteristics of Aerated Stabilization Basins," National Council of the Paper Industry for Air and Stream Improvement, Inc., Tech. Bulletin No. 245, New York (1971).
10. Eckenfelder, W. W., and Ford, D. L., "Engineering Aspects of Surface Aeration Design," Proc., 22nd Industrial Waste Conference, Purdue Univeristy, West Lafayette, Ind. (1967).
11. Nagaj, R. J., "Selecting Wastewater Aeration Equipment," *Chemical Engineering,* 79:8, 95-102 (1972).
12. Kalinske, A. A., "Hydraulics of Localized Mechanical Aerators in Waste Treatment Basins and Flowing Streams," Proc., 37th Annual Meeting, WPCF Bal Harbour, Florida (1964).

13. Conway, R. A., and Kumke, G. W., "Field Techniques for Evaluating Aerators," Jour. San. Eng. Div., ASCE, 92, SA2, 21-42 (1966).
14. Ferrell, J. F., and Ford, D. L., "Select Aerators Carefully," *Hydrocarbon Processing,* 51:10, 101-102 (1972).

10

ACTIVATED SLUDGE

DISCUSSION OF PRINCIPLES

The activated sludge process is a continuous system in which aerobic biological growths are mixed with wastewater then separated in a gravity clarifier. A portion of the concentrated sludge is recycled and mixed with additional wastewater. This process should provide an effluent with a soluble BOD_5 of 15 to 40 mg/l, although the organic concentration of the effluent in terms of COD in the industrial sector may be as high as 500 to 1,000 mg/l, depending on the concentration of nonbiodegradable compounds originally in the wastewater.

There are many impurities in industrial wastewaters that must be removed or altered by preliminary operations (pretreatment) before subsequent activated sludge treatment can be considered. Experimental procedures relevant to pretreatment requirements are discussed in Chapter 3.

High concentrations of influent suspended solids discharged directly to secondary biological processes can decrease overall process efficiency, either by reducing the active biological solids fraction or by creating a sludge less amenable to sludge handling. Therefore, gravity sedimentation or flotation units are used to remove suspended material. If the wastewater happens to be high in colloidal materials, it can also be treated by chemical coagulation prior to sedimentation or flotation.

Removing oil by gravity separation is required in many industrial plants because oily waters have a deleterious effect on most secondary and tertiary treatment processes, and because effluent quality criteria restrict the discharge of oily materials to the receiving environment. Since free oils are generally easier to remove if their concentration is high, oily wastestreams are treated prior to dilution with non-oily wastewaters. Adding chemicals is often required to enhance separation, particularly when emulsions are present.

If the wastestream is alkaline or acidic, it usually must be neutralized. Carbon dioxide produced by microbial respiration will neutralize some caustic alkalinity, but free mineral acidity usually requires specific neutralization treatment.

Extreme variations in organic loadings, as well as sludge discharges of various organic and inorganic materials, can have adverse effects on the activated sludge process. When such conditions are anticipated, equalization facilities are required.

Continuous-flow and batch biological reactor systems are used in the laboratory to assess the treatability and predict the process kinetics of an activated sludge system. The continuous-flow laboratory system is designed to provide a steady supply of raw wastewater through a biological reactor and to permit a

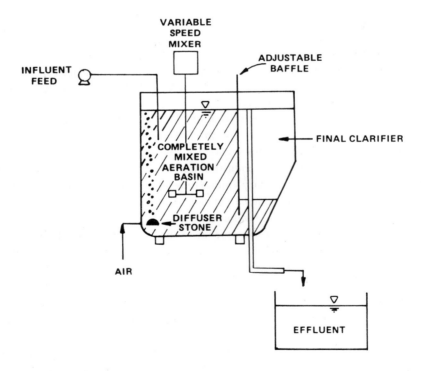

FIG. 10-1. CONTINUOUS-FLOW BENCH-SCALE ACTIVATED SLUDGE UNIT

continuous withdrawal of the treated effluent. A continuous-flow reactor (lab-scale) is shown in Figure 10-1. The batch system is based upon the addition of the sample wastewater to a vessel containing an acclimated culture of active bio-mass (seed). The mixed contents are aerated and bio-degradation of the organic constituents proceeds to completion without a continuous exchange of the mixed liquor and feed in the reactor. Parallel batch reactor units are shown in Figure 10-2.

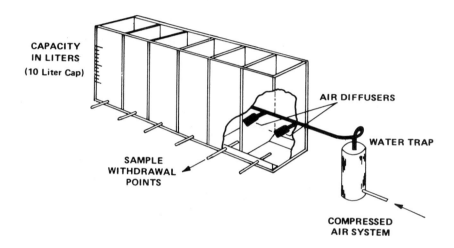

FIG. 10-2. BATCH ACTIVATED SLUDGE UNITS

The mechanisms of the activated sludge process are schematically shown in Figure 10-3 [1]. It is desirable to represent a biological oxidation system by a mathematical expression, determining the coefficients necessary for establishing basic design criteria from bench or pilot-scale biological reactors. This includes an evaluation of substrate removal, sludge production, and oxygen requirements.

Organic Removal

There is an increasing use of the completely mixed system, particularly in the activated sludge treatment of industrial wastes. In this case, the soluble BOD in the effluent is equal to that in the aeration tank. BOD removal in the activated sludge process results from several mechanisms. The BOD in the form of suspended solids is removed by physical enmeshment in the biological flocs. Colloidal organics are flocculated and adsorbed in the biological flocs. Most soluble

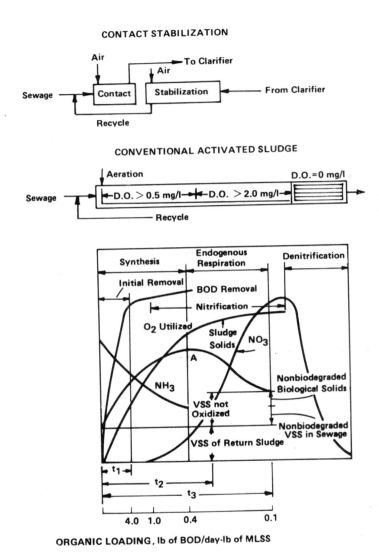

CONTACT STABILIZATION

CONVENTIONAL ACTIVATED SLUDGE

ORGANIC LOADING, lb of BOD/day-lb of MLSS

FIG. 10-3. MECHANISMS OF THE ACTIVATED SLUDGE PROCESS

organic compounds are removed as a zero order reaction. In a multicomponent wastewater a number of zero order reactions are occurring concurrently, and the sum of these reactions approximates a first order reaction. The overall reaction under batch oxidation conditions can frequently be expressed as an exponential of the form:

$$S_e/S_o = e^{-kX_v t/S_o} \qquad (10\text{-}1)$$

where:

S_o = influent BOD, COD, TOC, mg/l
S_e = effluent soluble BOD, COD, TOC, mg/l
X_v = average concentration of MLVSS, mg/l
t = aeration time, days
k = removal rate coefficient, day^{-1}

Equation 10-1 describes the batch bio-oxidation process. A mass balance around a completely mixed reactor yields the following equation for a constant-strength waste [1] :

$$\frac{S_o - S_e}{X_v t} = kS_e \qquad (10\text{-}2)$$

However, for most industrial wastes the influent organic strength is highly variable and the design relationship has been shown to be [2] :

$$\frac{S_o(S_o - S_e)}{X_v t} = kS_e \qquad (10\text{-}3)$$

In most cases where COD, TOC or TOD are used to measure the organic substrate, a non-degradable organic residual remains even with high degrees of treatment. This residual level of organics is reflected by modifying Equation 10-3 to:

$$\frac{(S_o - S_e)}{X_v t} = k(S_e - y) \qquad (10\text{-}4)$$

Equation 10-3 implies that, as the concentration of organics remaining in the reactor decreases, the rate of removal also decreases since that remaining is progressively more difficult to remove. The reaction rate coefficient, k, can be determined for a specific waste by correlating the left hand side of Equation 10-4 with the soluble effluent organic concentration as shown in Figure 10-4.

It is well established that the rate coefficient, k, varies with temperatures as shown below:

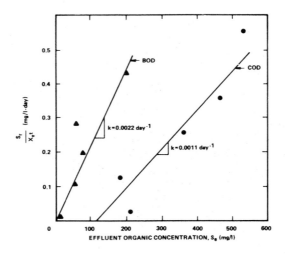

**FIG. 10-4. DETERMINATION OF ORGANIC REMOVAL RATE
COEFFICIENT**

$$k_2 = k_1 \theta^{(T_2 - T_1)} \qquad (10\text{-}5)$$

where:

k_1, k_2 = BOD removal rate coefficients at temperatures, T_1 and T_2, respectively, day^{-1}

θ = temperature correction coefficient

The temperature coefficient, θ, should be determined for each wastewater by operating experimental systems at different temperatures and correlating the data as shown in Figure 10-5.

Oxygen Requirements

It has been shown previously that the total oxygen requirements in a biological system are related to the oxygen consumed to supply energy for synthesis and the oxygen consumed for endogenous respiration [1]. This assumes that oxygen must be supplied to the system in order to satisfy the following demands:

1. Biological organic removal ($a'S_r$).

174

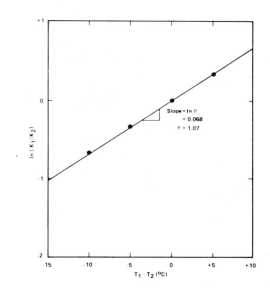

FIG. 10-5. DETERMINATION OF TEMPERATURE COEFFICIENT

2. Endogenous respiration where cells lyse and release soluble oxidizable organic compounds $(b'xX_v)$.
3. Chemical oxidation as measured by the immediate oxygen demand (R_c).
4. Ammonia which is oxidized to nitrate (R_n).

This expression is:

$$R_r = a'S_r + b'xX_v + R_n + R_c \qquad (10\text{-}6)$$

where:

R_r = total oxygen utilization, lb O_2/day
S_r = BOD removed, lb/day
a' = oxygen utilization coefficient for synthesis, lb O_2 utilized/lb organics removed
b' = oxygen utilization coefficient for endogenous activities, lb O_2 utilized/day-lb MLVSS
R_c = chemical oxygen demand as measured by the immediate oxygen demand test, lb O_2/day

R_n = oxygen utilized in the oxidation of ammonia to nitrate, lb O_2/day
X_v = average MLVSS in the aeration basin, lb
x = biodegradable fraction of MLVSS

Considering only that oxygen used for BOD removal, Equation 10-6 can be rearranged:

$$\frac{R_r}{xX_v} = a'\frac{S_r}{xX_v} + b' \tag{10-7}$$

Consequently, the coefficients, a' and b', can be determined by correlating the specific oxygen uptake, R_r/xX_v, in lb O_2 utilized/day-lb MLVSS versus the BOD removal rate, S_r/xX_v, in lb BOD removed/day-lb MLVSS. This determination is shown in Figure 10-6.

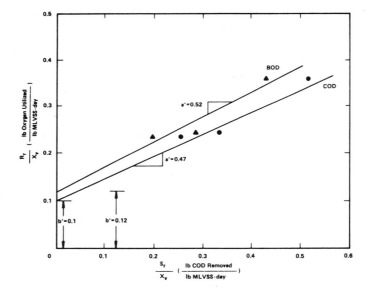

FIG. 10-6. DETERMINATION OF OXYGEN UTILIZATION COEFFICIENTS

Sludge Production

Sludge accumulation in the activated sludge system from the biological oxidation of wastewaters can be estimated using a similar approach. The components of a mathematical relationship would be the following:

1. An increase in sludge attributable to non-biodegradable influent SS, fX_i
2. An increase in sludge due to cellular synthesis, aS_r
3. A decrease in sludge due to cellular oxidation of endogenous respiration, bxX_v
4. A decrease in net sludge due to effluent SS, X_e

The expression for computing excess biological volatile sludge production, ΔX_v, is:

$$\Delta X_v = aS_r - bxX_v \qquad (10\text{-}8)$$

The expression for computing total excess sludge production, ΔX, is:

$$\Delta X = fX_i + \frac{\Delta X_v}{f'} - X_e \qquad (10\text{-}9)$$

where:

ΔX_v = excess biological volatile sludge production, lb VSS/day

a = sludge synthesis coefficient, lb VSS produced per lb organics removed

b = sludge auto-oxidation coefficient, lb VSS oxidized/day-lb MLVSS in the aeration basin

ΔX = total excess sludge production, lb SS/day

f = non-biodgradable fraction of influent suspended solids

X_i = influent suspended solids, lb SS/day

f' = volatile fraction of MLSS in aeration basin, lb MLVSS/lb MLSS

X_e = effluent suspended solids, lb SS/day

By considering only biological sludge production and correcting for the loss of effluent suspended solids, Equation 10-8 can be expressed as:

$$\frac{\Delta X_v}{xX_v} = a\,\frac{S_r}{xX_v} - b \qquad (10\text{-}10)$$

Therefore, a and b can be developed by correlating the observed sludge production, $\Delta X_v/xX_v$, as lb VSS produced/day-lb MLVSS in the system versus the BOD removal rate, S_r/xX_v, as lb BOD removed/day-lb MLVSS in the system as shown in Figure 10-7.

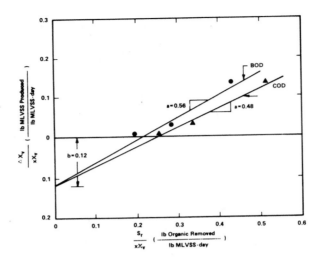

**FIG. 10-7. DETERMINATION OF SLUDGE PRODUCTION
COEFFICIENTS**

Organic Loading

The organic loading or food-to-microorganism ratio, F/M, to the activated sludge process is defined by the relationship:

$$F/M = \frac{S_o}{X_v t} \qquad (10\text{-}11)$$

where:

S_o = influent BOD, mg/l
X_v = average concentration of MLVSS, mg/l
t = detention time, days
F/M = food-to-microorganism ratio, lb BOD applied/day-lb VSS

and the sludge age by the relationship:

$$G = \frac{X_v}{\Delta X_v} = \frac{X_v}{aS_r - bxX_v} \qquad (10\text{-}12)$$

where:

S_r = BOD removal, lb/day

178

X_v = average MLVSS in the aeration basin, lb

G = sludge age, days

The performance of the activated sludge process and the characteristics of the sludge in the process are related to the organic loading to the system, F/M, and to the sludge age, G, in the process as shown in Figure 10-8. High loadings (low sludge ages) can lead to dispersed or filamentous sludge with poor settling properties. Low loadings (high sludge ages) can result in floc oxidation and dispersion.

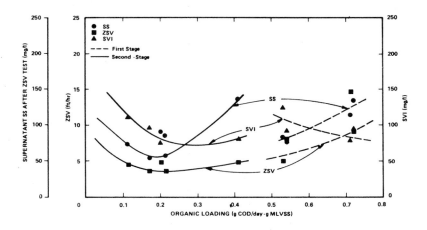

FIG. 10-8. EFFECTS OF ORGANIC LOADING ON ACTIVATED SLUDGE PERFORMANCE

The biomass generated in the process is composed of approximately 77 percent biodegradable material and 23 percent non-biodegradable organic material (volatile solids). As the sludge age in the process is increased (organic loading decreased), the non-degradables accumulate and the degradable fraction, x, of the volatile suspended solids decreases. The relationships between the degradable fraction, x, and F/M are shown in Figure 10-9.

The biodegradable fraction, x, can be determined experimentally or computed using the following relationship:

$$x = \frac{aS_r + bX_v - \sqrt{(aS_r + bX_v)^2 - (4bX_v)(0.77aS_r)}}{2bX_v} \qquad (10\text{-}13)$$

The extended aeration system, which is a modification of the activated sludge process, provides a detention time sufficiently long to allow oxidation of biological solids, thus minimizing the amount of sludge for disposal. The sludge is theoretically non-biodegradable residue. However, when it is withdrawn from continuous reactors, it also contains an active biological fraction. Excess sludge from extended aeration plants, therefore, requires additional digestion, as well as dewatering and disposal.

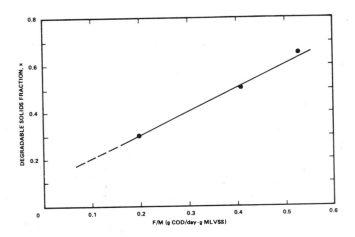

FIG. 10-9. RELATIONSHIP OF ORGANIC LOADING AND ACTIVE MASS

Biological Nitrification

Biological nitrification may be defined as the biological conversion of ammonia and some organic nitrogen forms to nitrite and nitrate nitrogen forms by a specific set of microorganisms, *Nitrosomonas* and *Nitrobacter.* These organisms are strictly aerobic autotrophs, i.e., they obtain their carbon needed for metabolic activities from inorganic sources such as carbon dioxide and bicarbonates, and they do not employ the same metabolic mechanisms as those organisms which assimilate organic BOD materials. Nitrification occurs in two steps. The first is the oxidation of ammonia nitrogen to nitrite and the second is oxidation of nitrite to nitrate.

$$NH_4 + 3/2\ O_2 \xrightarrow{\text{Nitrosomonas}} NO_2^- + 2H^+ + H_2O \qquad (10\text{-}14)$$

$$NO_2^- + 1/2\,O_2 \xrightarrow{\quad\text{Nitrobacter}\quad} NO_3^- \qquad (10\text{-}15)$$

The nitrifiers have lower reproduction rates than the organic-assimilating organisms and have a difficult time competing in the same environment. In a high rate activated sludge system, the nitrifiers, because of their lower reproduction rate, may be wasted from the system faster than they can reproduce thereby inhibiting successful nitrification. Consequently, insufficient nitrification will result unless the wastage rate is lowered to accommodate the nitrifiers requirements. The wastage rate is usually controlled to maintain a sufficient sludge age in the system for the desired degree of nitrification.

A design approach is suggested which uses the results of pilot investigations to predict varying degrees of nitrification based on detention time and VSS concentration. A first order relationship has been suggested as [3] :

$$\frac{N_e}{N_o} = e^{-k_n X_v t} \qquad (10\text{-}16)$$

where:

N_e = desired effluent ammonia concentration, mg/l
N_o = influent ammonia concentration, mg/l
k_n = gross nitrification rate coefficient, l/mg-day
X_v = concentration of VSS in aeration basin, mg/l
t = hydraulic detention time, days

Generally, when ammonia wastes are treated in the presence of carbonaceous materials, there is some lower value of $X_v t$, or sludge age, below which the slow growth rate of the nitrifiers results in their "washout" from the system. This washout causes any slight degree of nitrification to proceed at rates much lower than those predicted by Equation 10-16. Consequently, in a system removing both ammonia and carbonaceous BOD, Equation 10-16 can be modified for the limiting value of $X_v t$ by:

$$\frac{N_e}{N_o} = e^{-k_n (X_v t - X_L)} \qquad (10\text{-}17)$$

where:

X_L = limiting value of $X_v t$ below which nitrification is negligible.

This approach has been applied to both low and high strength ammonia wastes. Pilot and field data can be correlated as shown in Figure 10-10 to determine the rate coefficient, k_n, for various wastes [3]. The efficiency of the nitrifiers is dependent on many factors, including pH, dissolved oxygen level, presence of inhibitors as well as other factors, and it is recommended that the rate coefficient be developed for each situation.

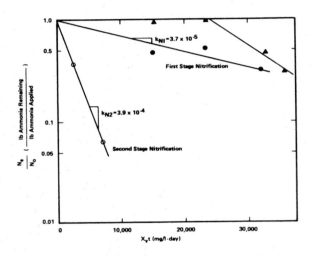

FIG. 10-10. DETERMINATION OF NITRIFICATION RATE COEFFICIENT

The theoretical oxygen requirements, based on the biochemical equations of nitrification (Equations 10-14 and 10-15) have been defined as 4.57 lb O_2 required/lb ammonia-nitrogen nitrified. Generally, it is assumed that this oxygen demand must be satisfied by atmospheric molecular oxygen, furnished and dissolved by conventional aeration equipment. However, since the nitrifiers are autotrophic and obtain their carbon requirements from inorganic sources such as carbon dioxide or bicarbonates, the oxygen contained in these compounds may also be available for metabolism. Thus, depending on the alkalinity of the wastewater, the actual oxygen which must be furnished by aeration equipment may be lower than the theoretical 4.57 ratio. If excess alkalinity is available, it can be reasonably assumed that the external oxygen requirements will be appro: lately 4.3 lb O_2 required/lb ammonia removed. Discounting the ammonia required for BOD removal, the nitrifiers will also utilize a fraction of the available nitrogen for synthesis of cellular components. It has been estimated that this ammonia demand is equivalent to 0.7 oxygen equivalents so that the theoretical oxygen ratio of 4.57 would be reduced to about 3.9 based solely on influent and effluent ammonia concentrations [4].

It is very difficult to experimentally distinguish between that oxygen required for nitrification and that oxygen required for organic BOD oxidation. The oxygen uptake rate as measured by the D.O. probe will reflect total oxygen requirements for both BOD and ammonia oxidation. Consequently, Equation 10-6 is not adequate for distinguishing between the two uses of oxygen. A model has been developed [3] which will allow a graphical determination between the two uses of oxygen as shown below:

$$[\frac{lb\ O_2}{day}]\ Total = [\frac{lb\ O_2}{day}]\ BOD + [\frac{lb\ O_2}{day}]\ Ammonia \qquad (10\text{-}18)$$

$$[\frac{lb\ O_2}{day}]\ Total = a''\ [\frac{lb\ BOD_r}{day}] + c\ [\frac{lb\ N_r}{day}] \qquad (10\text{-}19)$$

$$\frac{(lb\ O_2)\ Total}{lb\ BOD_r} = a'' + c\ [\frac{lb\ N_r}{lb\ BOD_r}] \qquad (10\text{-}20)$$

where:

a'' = overall oxygen required per unit of BOD removal, mg O_2/mg BOD_r

c = oxygen required per unit of ammonia oxidized, mg O_2/mg ammonia oxidized

Thus, by measuring the total oxygen used by conventional methods (D.O. probe) and knowing the degree of BOD and ammonia oxidation, the coefficients, a'' and c, can be graphically estimated by correlating the data as shown in Figure 10-11. The slope of the correlation will be the coefficient, c, and the intercept on the y-axis will be the coefficient, a''. It must be emphasized that the coefficient, a'', will vary with organic loading and sludge age so that the exact oxygen requirements for BOD removals should be estimated by Equation 10-7.

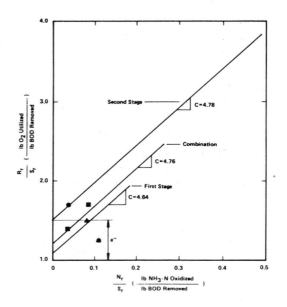

FIG. 10-11. DETERMINATION OF OXYGEN REQUIREMENTS FOR NITRIFICATION

EQUIPMENT REQUIRED

The equipment required for satisfactory testing and developing of design criteria for the activated sludge process consists of an aeration chamber and a settling compartment plus associated apparatus to monitor organic removal efficiencies, oxygen uptake, settleability, and excess sludge production. The monitoring requirements are the same whether bench-scale or pilot-scale systems are examined.

Bench Scale Activated Sludge Systems

1. **A Single-Stage Combined Reactor-Clarifier (Figure 10-1).** The system shown in Figure 10-1 combines both aeration chamber and upflow clarifier into a single unit and has been found to be very useful in laboratory and bench-scale experimentation because it eliminates a separate clarifier and an additional pump to control the return sludge. For larger bench-scale applications or for on-line investigation, a 55-gal drum may be converted into a combined aeration chamber-upflow clarifier as shown in

Figure 10-12. It is essential that the source of aeration (diffused air) be located so that air bubbles will not enter the clarifier section and cause disruptive turbulence.

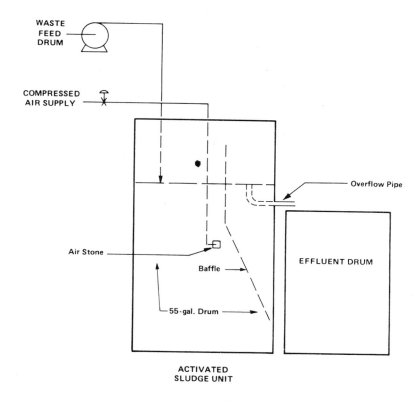

FIG. 10-12. SCHEMATIC ILLUSTRATION OF ACTIVATED SLUDGE UNITS

2. **Multi-Stage Activated Sludge System (Figures 10-13 and 10-14).** The multistage aerobic system incorporating activated sludge may take one of two forms. One system, shown in Figure 10-13, consists of two aeration basins in series with sludge return from the second stage to the first stage. The second system, shown in Figure 10-14, incorporates a flow-through first stage with no return sludge and a second stage activated sludge system with self-contained recycle. In the second system, since sludge is not

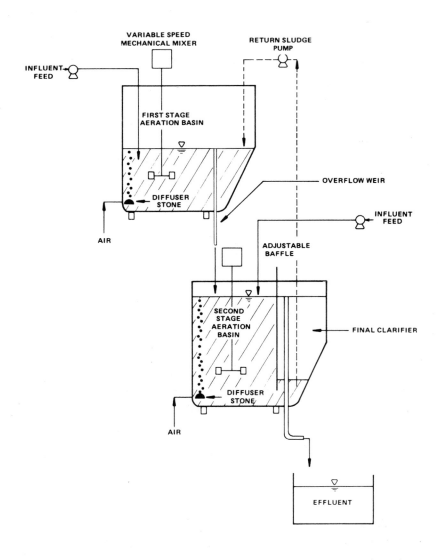

FIG. 10-13. BENCH-SCALE TWO-STAGE ACTIVATED SLUDGE SYSTEM

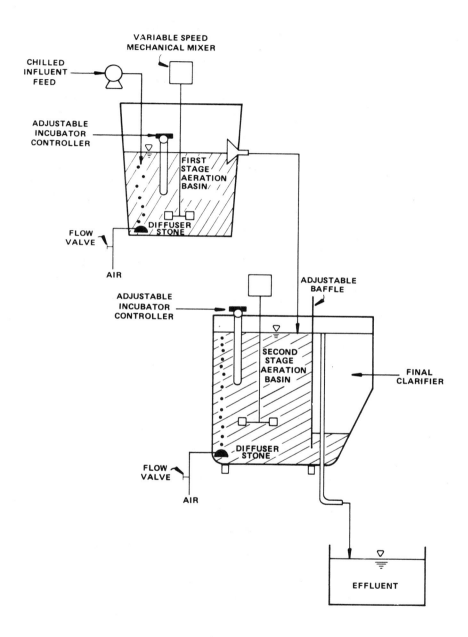

**FIG. 10-14. BENCH-SCALE AERATED LAGOON ACTIVATED SLUDGE
SYSTEM**

returned to the first stage, the solids level will be typical of an aerated lagoon. It has been found that a typical overflow weir used in the other laboratory systems will not suffice because suspended solids tend to accumulate in the basin. In order to minimize this non-representative accumulation of suspended solids, it is recommended that a funnel arrangement be utilized for the weir as shown in Figure 10-14.

3. **Influent Feed and Recycle Sludge Pumps.** For laboratory use, it is recommended that positive displacement pumps be utilized. This will minimize errors in pumping operation. Unfortunately, many positive displacement pumps use check valves or similar devices in their operation. With highly degradable wastes and wastewaters containing appreciable levels of suspended solids, these check valves can become clogged or altered in operation so that they do not fully close, thereby resulting in inconsistent pumping operation.

In general, it has been found that the most reliable pumps for laboratory and bench-scale operation are "peristaltic" pumps which use some form of flexible tubing to provide the pumping action. Tygon tubing is acceptable, but it should not be used more than one week at a time for pumping because the tubing collapses and the pumping efficiency deteriorates significantly. Other materials, such as viton, are more durable but are also more expensive. All raw waste pump lines should contain sufficient connections so that the pump can be disconnected to allow periodic cleaning of the lines.

A simple pumping apparatus, which may be used in situations where economics will not allow the purchase of several pumps, is illustrated in Figure 10-15 [5]. This system uses economical pressure regulators and capillary tubes to maintain a controllable pressure on liquids in the container. The container should be placed at a two to three foot differential from the aeration chamber in order to assist control.

4. **Influent and Effluent Waste Containers.** These containers may be of glass or plastic. With most raw wastes common plastic trash cans may be employed.

5. **Aeration Basin Mixers.** Variable speed mixers (see Figure 10-1) should be available for use in the aeration basins in order to provide adequate mixing without having to use excessive diffused air. By using the mixers to control the mixing and diffused air to control the dissolved oxygen level, better operation of the systems is obtained.

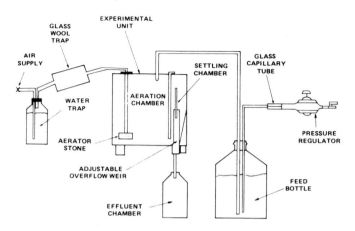

FIG. 10-15. INEXPENSIVE LABORATORY FEED
APPARATUS

6. **Diffused Air Supply.** Air is generally applied to bench-scale aeration chambers through a diffuser stone. This air supply is regulated to approximately 10 psi at flow rates in the range of 7,000 to 10,000 cc/min. These high flow rates are necessary to adequately mix the aeration basin contents and maintain high dissolved oxygen levels in solution in the absence of mixers. With the use of mixers, as described in Item 5 above, the air flow will be considerably less in a 10 to 20 liter aeration chamber. The air supply should be scrubbed with water to saturate it prior to the systems in order to minimize evaporation. This scrubbing becomes essential with low influent waste flow rates and higher operating temperatures. The water scrubbing will also serve to collect oils and other impurities which may be in certain air supplies. If possible, it is best to use an instrument air source.

7. **Heating and Cooling.** For heating, common aquarium heaters are sufficient; however, cooling a system is much more difficult. The air flow rate into the system provides the major effects on temperature. It is very difficult and usually impractical to control systems by operation in a cold temperature room. It is recommended that stainless steel coils connected to an ice or refrigerated system be placed in the aeration chamber. The temperature of the unit can then be controlled by varying the flow

rate of cold water or other coolant through the coils. The authors have found that this system is very efficient.

Pilot Scale Activated Sludge Systems

Pilot activated sludge systems may take several configurations and incorporate all types of equipment from earthen basins to steel tanks. A very important consideration in pilot systems is the method of aeration which is planned for the prototype facilities. If surface aerators are anticipated, then they should be used in the pilot system in order to simulate such phenomena as proper stripping action and cooling effects. A pilot system is shown in Figure 10-16 which consists of equalization, a roughing trickling filter, and air and pure oxygen activated sludge systems operated in parallel. Several factors are significant in ensuring the success of a pilot system and in obtaining representative data:

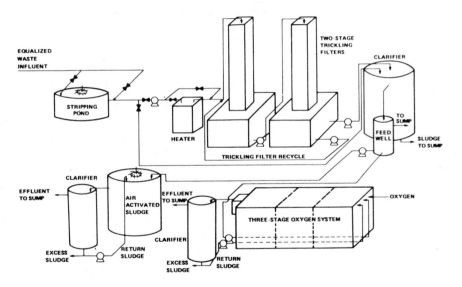

FIG. 10-16. PILOT ACTIVATED SLUDGE SYSTEM

1. **Aeration Tank.** The aeration tank should be operated at a power level of at least 100 hp/mil gal. The depth should be less than 10 ft for surface aerators of less than 5 hp size and no greater than 5 ft for 1.5 hp units. The

tank should be sufficiently baffled to ensure complete mixing and absence of vortexing effects. If a fixed surface aerator is used in the pilot system, it is recommended that a weir arrangement be constructed so that the depth can be varied within 6 to 8 inches. This capability to vary the depth will enable the investigator to correct for normal installation errors with the small-scale aerator which might cause insufficient mixing or aeration. A weir arrangement may be used or a device similar to that shown in Figure 10-17 can be installed. By raising or lowering the U-pipe, the liquid level can be varied on the aerator blade in order to control the dissolved oxygen level or mixing efficiency in the basin at the desired levels.

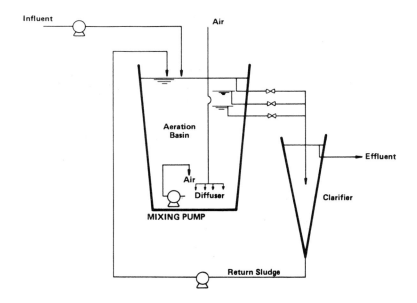

FIG. 10-17. DEVICE FOR CONTROLLING LIQUID LEVEL IN AERATION BASIN

2. **Secondary Clarifier.** The smallest manufactured clarifier which contains all components is approximately 10 ft in diameter (78.5 sq ft). Assuming normal activated sludge clarifier overflow rates in the range of 500 to 700 gpd/sq ft, this clarifier would require flow rates on the order of 27 to 38 gpm. Consequently, smaller clarifiers are usually required for most typical

pilot scale operations. If a small clarifier is needed, a model such as that shown in Figure 10-18 may be fabricated.

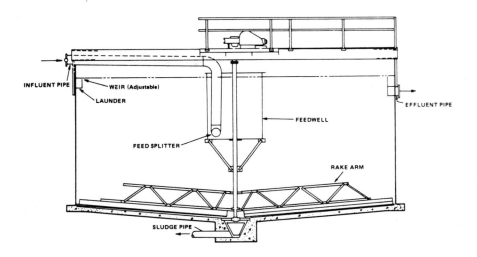

FIG. 10-18. SMALL SCALE PILOT CLARIFIER

Since it is usually desirable to operate pilot systems through a cold weather period, it is essential that all exposed piping be heat traced to prevent freezing in smaller lines. It is also essential to maintain weirs which tend to ice up and may affect flow splitting to various portions of the system.

Monitoring Equipment and Apparatus

1. **Chemicals and Materials.** Standard chemicals and materials are used for monitoring parameters such as BOD, COD, TOC, TOD, suspended solids, pH, temperature, ammonia nitrogen, total Kjeldahl nitrogen, nitrate nitrogen and phosphorus.

2. **Zone Settling Velocity Apparatus.** With activated sludge it is necessary to monitor the settleability, as indicated by the zone settling velocity test. This test consists of observing the settling of the sludge-liquid interface with time. It is necessary to stir the sludge sample at a minimum rate of

4 to 6 revolutions per hour. An apparatus which allows the operation of three systems at one time is shown in Figure 10-19.

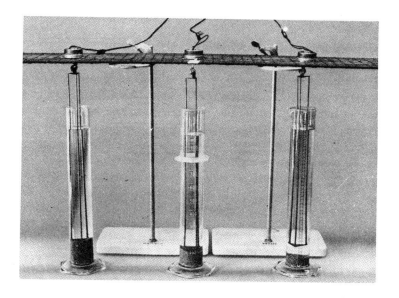

FIG. 10-19. EXPERIMENTAL APPARATUS FOR ZONE SETTLING TEST

3. **Oxygen Uptake Rate Test.** The measurement of oxygen uptake is accomplished by using a dissolved oxygen probe with stirrer as shown in Figure 10-20. There are several available probes on the market and all are suitable for this test.

EXPERIMENTAL PROCEDURES

The development of design criteria for an activated sludge system principally consists of collecting data from systems which are operating at different organic loadings (F/M). It is desirable to operate three or four of the experimental systems at the design cold weather temperature with one system operated at a warm weather situation in order to calculate the temperature coefficient, θ.

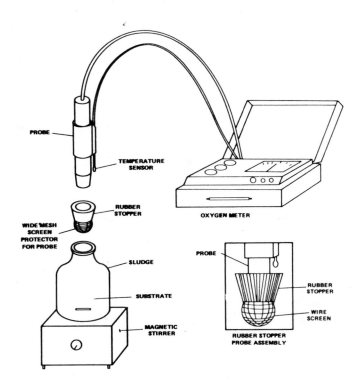

FIG. 10-20. EXPERIMENTAL APPARATUS FOR OXYGEN UPTAKE RATE TEST (RECORDER NOT INCLUDED)

However, due to difficulties in the laboratory of maintaining three to four systems under cold conditions, the procedure is generally to operate three or four systems at the laboratory room temperature (22 to 24°C) and one cold weather system. If this is impractical, literature values of θ can be assumed.

Continuous Activated Sludge Methodology

The experimental procedure for activated sludge is to develop an acclimated seed, operate several systems over a period of four to eight weeks until stabilized conditions are obtained, and closely monitor the response of the systems to the various constraints during the stabilized period of operation. Specifically, the procedures are as follows:

    1. Develop an acclimated seed in accordance with the procedures described in Chapter 3, "Screening and Toxicity Methodology."

2. Divide the acclimated seed evenly between the desired number of experimental units. It is important to begin all systems with an identical seed so that no initial difference between the parallel systems is introduced into the testing procedures. If several units have been used to acclimate the seed, the contents of all units should be mixed before dividing into the different systems at the predetermined volume (10 to 20 liters). Concentrate or dilute the acclimated seed, as required, to have an initial VSS concentration of approximately 2,500 mg/l.

3. Turn on the diffused air system and completely mix the tank contents. Adjust the sliding baffle to provide a ¼ to ½ in. slot opening at the bottom. Subsequent baffle adjustments can be made, as desired, according to the sludge blanket in the settling zone and the sludge interchange rate between the mixing and settling chambers.

4. Operate the systems at different F/M values (predetermined) within the approximate range of 0.2 to 0.8 day $^{-1}$. If exceedingly high levels of organic removal are required or nitrification is desired, F/M levels as low as 0.05 may be warranted. The F/M is usually controlled by varying the detention time. The cold weather system should normally be set up at an intermediate F/M level. For example at a BOD of 500 mg/l, an MLVSS concentration of 2,500 mg/l, and a desired F/M of 0.3 day $^{-1}$, the detention time would be:

$$F/M = S_0/X_v t$$
$$t = 500/2,500 \, (0.3) \qquad\qquad (10\text{-}11)$$
$$= 0.67 \text{ days}$$

Start the feed pump at a flow rate necessary to obtain the desired detention time. Filamentous bulking is related to the maintenance of an aerobic floc. This in turn relates dissolved oxygen to F/M. It is important to maintain the dissolved oxygen level in the test unit at the same level as that contemplated in the full scale plant. This usually requires a mixer to maintain sludge in suspension with air flow control to maintain the desired dissolved oxygen level.

5. Pretreat the raw waste as necessary. It is essential to maintain all suspended solids in the raw waste in suspension in the feed container in order to prevent settling during feeding to the system and ensure no liquid phase separation. Although diffused air can be used to mix the influent contents, a mechanical mixer is desired in order to minimize stripping and aeration

of the influent wastewater. Any desired coagulation of raw waste constituents, such as heavy metals, should be accomplished in a separate container. It is cautioned that oftentimes precipitates, such as calcium phosphate, may occur on the addition of nutrients to the raw wastewater. In
these instances, it is essential that no settling be allowed to occur in the
influent container so that these nutrient precipitates can be fed into the
aeration basin.

6. As the systems are being operated, it is necessary to frequently check all
   feedlines for clogging and biological growth. It is desirable to clean the
   lines once per week if growths develop. For concentrated wastes, greater
   than 5,000 mg/l BOD, the waste feed rates are very difficult to control and
   often two to three times the desired volume may be accidentally pumped
   through the systems. In order to prevent this undesirable laboratory upset,
   it is recommended that the feed container only contain 20 percent more
   than the desired daily volume of wastewater. Therefore, the maximum
   shock from mechanical laboratory problems would only be 20 percent.

7. Monitor the systems according to a schedule similar to that shown in
   Table 10-1. In order to minimize project costs, it is usually warranted to
   conduct a minimum monitoring program during stabilization. After the
   systems have stabilized, the monitoring program should be intensified to
   collect sufficient data for the development of design parameters. In situations where all parameters cannot be monitored due to factors such as
   temporary personnel problems or equipment breakdown, it is essential,
   at the minimum, to measure the influent parameters so that investigators
   know what was fed to the systems.   Steady-state conditions may be
   assumed once the oxygen uptake rate of the aeration basin contents
   reaches consistent levels and the TOC or COD of the effluent have stabilized. Several detention times will be required before this occurs. In order
   to measure the volatile suspended solids of the aeration basin, it is necessary to plug the effluent tube, clean the sides of the vessel, and measure
   the VSS of the completely mixed contents. In this way the total mass of
   organisms in the system can be obtained. If the baffle is left down in
   a small system it is possible to obtain erroneous results due to the interchange of solids between the clarifier and the aeration basin. A constant
   level of VSS is maintained in the system by wasting a quantity of solids
   daily which is equal to the daily accumulation. It is suggested that solids
   be measured at the beginning of each time cycle and a necessary volume of
   sludge withdrawn to bring the VSS concentration down to the predetermined level. It is possible that no solids will have to be wasted during

TABLE 10-1. SAMPLING AND MONITORING SCHEDULE FOR TREATABILITY STUDY

| Parameter | Sample Location & Frequency (samples/wk) | | |
	Inf. Waste	Eff. Waste	Aeration Basin
BOD, Total	3	1	--
Soluble	1	3	--
COD, Total	2	1	--
Soluble	1	2	--
TOC, Total	3	3	--
Soluble	3	3	--
NH_3-N	2	2	--
TKN, Total	2	1	--
Soluble	1	2	--
Total P	1	1	--
SS & VSS	2	3	5
pH	5	--	7
Temperature	--	--	7
Flow Rate	2[a]	7	--
Oxygen Uptake Rate	--	--	3
Zone Settling Velocity, Sludge Volume Index	--	--	3

[a] May desire to check influent flow on concentrated wastes to determine if evaporation is significant.

the first few days of operation. Since the procedures for determining the zone settling velocity and the specific oxygen uptake are not commonly presented in analytical manuals, they will be described below:

a. *Zone Settling Velocity Test.* In order to accurately monitor the zone settling velocity of a sludge, an apparatus similar to that shown in Figure 10-19 is recommended. A one liter cylinder is filled with sludge, the rotating mechanism connected, and the sludge-liquid interface recorded at periodic time intervals. The height of these interface levels can be plotted versus time, and the slope of the straight-line portion of the curve taken as the zone settling velocity. Settling velocities are generally recorded in ft/hr. Stirring plays an important role and is discussed in the final section, "Limitations and Scale-Up."

b. *Specific Oxygen Uptake Rates.* The oxygen uptake test is performed with a dissolved oxygen probe as shown in Figure 10-20. A BOD bottle is filled to the top with mixed liquor from the aeration chamber of the experimental unit. The probe is inserted into the bottle, ensuring that no air bubbles are trapped inside, and the contents are mixed using either a magnetic stirring bar or a self-contained stirrer present on many of the newer probes. The depletion of dissolved oxygen can be measured and plotted against time.

In collecting the sample for the oxygen uptake test, great care should be taken to ensure that the system has been subjected to consistent day-to-day operation. It is best to perform this test when the effluent weir is stoppered and the baffle raised for the suspended solids test. The influent waste flow is usually cut off during this time and the system is actually operating under batch conditions temporarily. If several systems are being run in parallel, it is difficult to consistently analyze each unit at the same time each day after the feed is cut off. However, if this is not done the system will vary in oxygen uptake rate simply because of variation in equilibrium substrate level under a batch condition. Thus, it is essential to perform the oxygen uptake test at exactly (± 10 min) adhering to the same time interval after each day the baffle is raised and the feed cut off.

The slope of the resulting straight-line is taken as the true oxygen uptake rate and is expressed in mg of oxygen utilized per liter/min. This value can be divided by the biological solids (MLVSS) to get the specific oxygen uptake rate which is expressed in g of oxygen used/day-g MLVSS. If many oxygen uptake tests are to be run, it is recommended that the probe be connected to a recorder so that the dissolved oxygen depletion can automatically be plotted against time. The probe should be calibrated daily and the membrane replaced every 2 weeks or sooner, if necessary.

8. At the end of the testing, mixed liquor from each unit should be aerated (without the addition of feed) and the VSS measured daily until a constant residual VSS is obtained. The degradable fraction, x, of the biomass at each loading can then be computed as shown in Figure 10-21.

9. If the wastewater contains volatile organic constituents, a unit must be

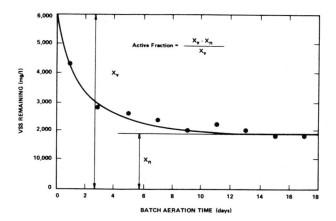

**FIG. 10-21. DETERMINATION OF ACTIVE FRACTION OF
BIO-MASS**

operated at the same detention time and air flow rate to define the BOD
removal for stripping. A batch run should also be made at the same air
flow rate and temperature to define a stripping rate coefficient, k_s. Due
to the potential interferences by stripping mechanisms, it is recommended
that mixers always be used in the small scale aeration basins and the air
flow be maintained at that level needed to control the dissolved oxygen in
a range of 2 to 4 mg/l.

10. Many wastewaters, particularly those from multi-product industrial operations will exhibit a highly variable composition. This variable composition
will significantly influence the reaction rate coefficient, k. Under applicable circumstances, the experimental units should be operated under variable wastewater conditions (or a pilot plant operated on variable feed) to
define a statistical distribution of k. These procedures will permit definition of the variability in effluent composition from the process. An
engineering decision will consider increased equalization of the wastewater
to reduce the variability in k and therefore effluent quality.

Batch Activated Sludge Methodology

The degradability of a wastewater can be evaluated using a series of batch
reactors, although such an approach should not be used for process design of

199

continuous, completely mixed systems. The set up and operation of batch systems have been thoroughly described in Chapter 3, "Screening and Toxicity Methodology."

CORRELATION OF RESULTS

The experimental systems are operated until stabilized conditions are obtained. After stabilization, the systems should be continued in operation for at least two weeks under the stabilized operating period. The data for the stabilized period are averaged and treated as a single point in the design correlations. The correlations of the experimental results are oriented toward determining the design parameters and coefficients discussed in the first section of this chapter.

1. Develop chronological plots of the significant parameters as illustrated in Figures 10-22 and 10-23. These plots are very important and should be

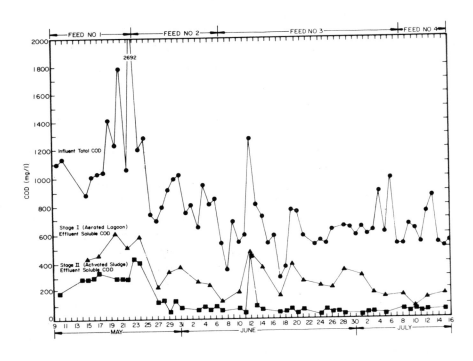

FIG. 10-22. CHRONOLOGICAL RESPONSES OF TWO-STAGE ACTIVATED SLUDGE SYSTEM

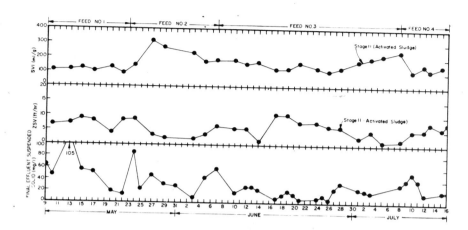

**FIG. 10-23. CHRONOLOGICAL VARIATIONS IN SVI, ZSV AND FINAL
EFFLUENT SUSPENDED SOLIDS FOR SYSTEM I**

used as indicators throughout the experimental phase of the study. These
correlations are more useful than summary data tables for observing the
performance of the units and to confirm upset conditions and stabilized
periods of operation. Stabilized periods should be indicated as shown in
Figure 10-22.

2. Average all the parameters during the stabilized periods of operation and
summarize as shown in Table 10-2. These averages are then used for the
design correlations. Daily values should never be used in the design correlations since the effluent quality observed for one day is generally not a
function of the same influent waste for that day unless the detention time
is less than 4 to 6 hr. It is recommended that weekly averages be the
minimum average periods that are used for developing the design correlations.

3. Plot the soluble effluent BOD, COD, TOC, or TOD concentration as a
function of the organic removal rate and initial organic concentration as
shown in Figure 10-4. Determine the slope of the line as the reaction rate
coefficient, k. If a residual effluent organic concentration persists indicating the presence of relatively nondegradable organics, as shown in Figure
10-4 the intercept on the x-axis should be noted. Cold and warm weather
data can be plotted in the same manner and the different reaction rate
coefficients determined for each temperature can be used to calculate the
temperature coefficient, θ.

201

TABLE 10-2. SUMMARY OF BIOLOGICAL TREATABILITY STUDY

System	I	IIa	IIb	III	IVa	IVb
Operational Parameters						
F/M (lb BOD/day-lb MLVSS)	0.20	0.198	0.0265	0.286	0.443	0.104
Detention Time (days)	20	13.3	10.6	8.3	5.4	2.7
MLVSS (mg/l)	1,766	2,413	728	2,811	2,785	1,012
Oxygen Uptake (lb O_2/day lb MLVSS)	0.13	0.231	0.21	0.24	0.358	0.304
SVI (ml/g)	80	190	99	302	288	223
ZSV (ft/hr)	9.6	4.6	12.8	0.5	0.06	4.9
Influent Quality Parameters						
BOD (mg/l)	7,400	6,368	128	6,666	6,666	285
COD (mg/l)	7,976	8,233	413	8,341	8,341	533
TOC (mg/l)	2,108	2,260	153	2,260	2,260	289
NH_3-N (mg/l)	471	436	127	420	419	199
NO_3-N (mg/l)	<1	<1	136	<1	<1	4.5
Phenol (mg/l)	3,316	3,366	<0.1	3,266	3,266	1.92
Cyanide (mg/l)	3.2	2.7	0.10	3.5	3.5	0.1
Effluent Quality Parameters						
BOD (mg/l)	26	76	18	64	201	53
COD (mg/l)	87	361	214	468	533	182
TOC (mg/l)	26	128	85	256	227	95
NH_3-N (mg/l)	44	135	8	213	197	73
NO_3-N (mg/l)	122	136	227	3.2	4.5	121
Phenol (mg/l)	<1.0	<0.1	<0.1	0.55	1.92	0.4
Cyanide (mg/l)	<1.0	0.10	0.04	0.09	0.11	0.09
Organic Removal Efficiencies						
BOD (percent)	99.6	98.8	85.9	99.0	97.0	81.4
COD (percent)	98.9	95.6	48.2	94.4	93.6	65.3
TOC (percent)	98.7	94.3	44.4	88.7	89.9	67.1

4. Determine the oxygen utilization coefficients by plotting the specific oxygen uptake rate versus the organic removal rate as shown in Figure 10-6. If nitrification is occurring, a′ will be significantly high (greater than 0.7 to 1.0). In the case of nitrification, the data can be correlated in accordance with Figure 10-11 to distinguish between the oxygen requirements for BOD removal and nitrification. If very low values of a′ result, it is possible that significant air stripping of degradable compounds occurred, thereby resulting in substantially higher BOD removal than the oxygen utilization would indicate by biological mechanisms.

5. The sludge production coefficients are determined by correlating Equation 10-10 as shown in Figure 10-7. Influent suspended solids should be corrected out of the sludge production so that only biological sludge production is represented by the term X/xX_v in Equation 10-10.

6. The temperature coefficient, θ, can be calculated by inserting the values of the reaction rate coefficients determined from Figure 10-4 into the following equation:

$$k_2 = k_1 \theta^{(T_2 - T_1)}$$

$$\ln \theta = \frac{\ln(k_1/k_2)}{(T_1 - T_2)}$$

If several temperatures have been examined, the rate coefficients can be determined and correlated as shown in Figure 10-5 to determine θ.

7. The zone settling velocity and sludge volume index can be correlated to the various organic loadings to evaluate the loading level at which the optimum sludge settling occurs. Typical correlations are shown in Figure 10-8 for a two-stage activated sludge system. The aeration volume requirements will be controlled by either BOD removal rate or F/M depending on the BOD removal and settleability requirements. Highly degradable wastewaters may be degraded in a relatively short detention time or high F/M. However, due to settleability constraints, a lower F/M is usually necessary. It is also desirable to correlate effluent suspended solids to organic loading. At the design F/M, it is desirable to construct a probability plot of the zone settling velocities observed during operation of this system. Such a plot is shown in Figure 10-24. The design settling velocity can then be taken as the 50 percent value from this curve. For extreme conservatism, the 10 percent number may be selected. The overflow rate can then be calculated by multiplying the zone settling velocity (ft/hr) times a conversion

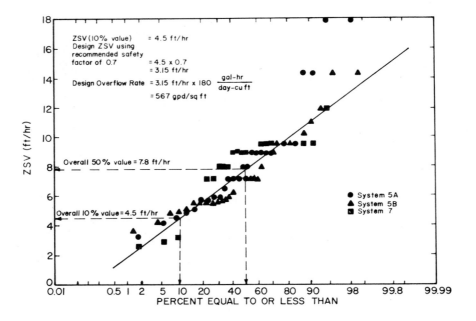

FIG. 10-24. STATISTICAL PROBABILITY OF ZONE SETTLING VELOCITY

factor of $\dfrac{180 \text{ gpd/sq ft}}{\text{ft/hr}}$ as shown below:

$$\text{Overflow rate} = \text{ZSV (ft/hr)} \times 7.48 \text{ (gal/cu ft)} \times 24 \text{ (hr/day)}$$

$$= \text{ZSV(ft/hr)} \left(\frac{180 \text{ gpd/sq ft}}{\text{ft/hr}}\right)$$

In addition, thickening characteristics of the clarifier will need to be checked. The procedures and correlation of data for thickening requirements of a clarifier are identical to those for design of a gravity thickener. The investigator is thereby referred to Chapter 19, "Gravity Thickening of Sludges," for the information.

8. The correlation of Equation 10-4 in Figure 10-4 relates to soluble effluent organic concentration. The final effluent in the plant, however, will contain suspended solids carryover from the secondary clarifier. The BOD contributed from these solids must be added to the anticipated soluble

organic concentration in order to obtain the total BOD in the effluent. The BOD of filtered and unfiltered samples and the suspended solids content has been obtained from the schedule presented in Table 10-1. These data are then correlated as shown in Figure 10-25. Consequently, at the design organic loading the anticipated effluent suspended solids can be obtained and the BOD content of these solids can be estimated from Figure 10-25.

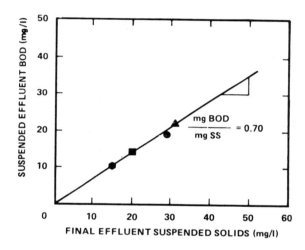

FIG. 10-25. BOD CONTENT OF EFFLUENT SOLIDS

9. For nitrification, the influent and effluent ammonia concentrations can be correlated to the product of volatile suspended solids and detention time $(X_v t)$, which is a measure of the sludge age, as shown in Figure 10-10. The nitrification rate coefficient, k_n, is defined by the slope of this correlation. Operation of warm and cold systems will define the nitrification temperature coefficient, θ, which can be determined similar to the temperature coefficient for BOD removal.

10. In some situations with specific wastewaters, it may be desirable to correlate specific parameters such as cyanides or phenols with organic loading as shown in Figure 10-26.

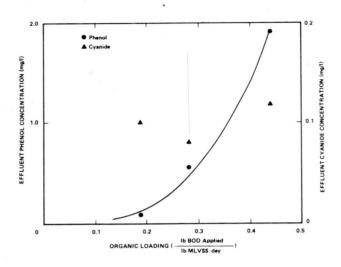

**FIG. 10-26. RELATION OF EFFLUENT PHENOL AND CYANIDE LEVELS
TO F/M**

LIMITATIONS AND SCALE UP

It is possible to design a prototype activated sludge facility based on experimental results obtained from bench-scale systems. However, there are several significant factors which must be considered by the designer in scaling up from small units to an actual field system. The two most important factors in scale up involve mixing and final clarification. Generally, most laboratory systems achieve complete mixing whereas improperly designed full-scale systems may not be truly completely mixed. Consequently, great caution should be applied in making sure that the full-scale system is completely mixed.

Most bench-scale systems are imperfect, relative to sedimentation, and usually result in a nonrepresentative higher suspended solids overflow than will be experienced in actual field operation. Monitoring the suspended solids after the zone settling velocity test is generally more representative than using the values which are monitored in the actual effluent from the bench-scale units. The supernatant resulting after the zone settling velocity test is more representative of the field operation. However, it still must be cautioned that these values might not be truly representative of field performance. The settling velocities monitored in the lab will closely approximate those in the field. However, it is essential that the settling tests be conducted properly under laboratory conditions. A large source of error in laboratory settling experiments is the influence of cylinder diameter. After several series of tests, it was found that the effect of a smaller diameter is to increase the velocity for lesser concentrated suspensions and to decrease the settling velocity for more concentrated sludges, with very little effect in the 5,000 to 6,000 mg/l range [6]. These results may help explain why high and low velocities may be reported for small diameter cylinders even though both results may be true, since the influence of cylinder diameter depends on the concentration of sludge. Much of the influence of cylinder size can be removed by stirring mechanisms. It is recommended that most laboratory-determined results indicate extremely high settling velocities (greater than 7 or 8 ft/hr), it is recommended that conventional settling rates on the order of 500 to 700 gpd/sq ft be used for design.

It is not feasible to scale up the aeration equipment from laboratory systems, so that these considerations must be separately designed and spaced as explained in Chapter 9, "Oxygen Transfer and Aeration Equipment Selection." It is also necessary to be aware of the degree of stripping which might occur under laboratory conditions. With highly volatile wastewater it is possible that the laboratory systems will generate results which are not representative of field conditions. At the higher power levels generally observed in the laboratory, it is possible to obtain higher degrees of stripping thereby inferring higher levels of removal of biodegradable material than might actually occur under field situations. Therefore, it is emphasized that the proper use of laboratory mixers, as described in this chapter, be implemented at all times. It is important to control the dissolved oxygen level in the range of 2 to 4 mg/l since this is the level which will usually be achieved under field situations. At higher dissolved oxygen levels, it is possible to simulate conditions which might occur in a pure oxygen system, thereby giving slightly higher settling results.

Further considerations involved in scale-up involve equalization requirements which may be observed in the laboratory but deviated from in the field. Most laboratory systems receive a 24-hr equalized wastestream for practicality. This may be non-representative of field conditions without equalization and might be significantly influential on systems with short detention times. Therefore, in the absence of a pilot system, sufficient equalization should be considered. It is essential to make sure that the experimental program has encountered all the wastewater constituents which will be expected in the prototype system, especially inhibitory materials such as heavy metals or certain organic compounds. Finally, since temperature significantly influences the reaction rate coefficient, it is important to accurately predict the temperature of the aeration basin under field conditions. During the early part of the investigation it is desirable to make rough estimations of the detention time of the field system and calculate the approximate cold weather temperature so that this level may be simulated in the laboratory. A detailed explanation of this design approach is available in the literature [7].

REFERENCES

1. Eckenfelder, W. W., Jr., *Water Quality Engineering for Practicing Engineers,* Barnes and Noble, Inc., New York (1970).

2. Adams, C. E., Jr., Eckenfelder, W. W., Jr., and Hovious, J. C., "A Kinetic Model for Design of Completely-Mixed Activated Sludge Treating Variable Strength Industrial Wastewaters," *Water Research,* 9, 37-42 (2975).

3. Adams, C. E., Jr., and Eckenfelder, W. W., Jr., "Nitrification Design Approach for High Strength Ammonia Wastewaters," *J. Water Pollution Control Federation,* 49, 413-421 (1977).

4. McCarty, P. L., "Biological Processes for Nitrogen Removal — Theory and Application," Proc., 12th Sanitary Engineering Conference, University of Illinois, Urbana, Illinois (1970).

5. Adams, C. E., Jr., "The Response of Activated Sludge Systems to Transient Loading Conditions," Ph.D. Dissertation, The University of Texas, Austin, Texas (January 1969).

6. Vesilind, P. A., Discussion, "Evaluation of Activated Sludge Thickening Theories," *Jour. San. Eng. Div.,* ASCE, 94, 185-191 (1968).

7. Adams, C. E., Jr., and Eckenfelder, W. W., Jr., "Response of Activated Sludge to Transient Loading Conditions," Center for Research in Water Resources Report No. 37, University of Texas, Austin, Texas (1967).

11

AERATED LAGOON

DISCUSSION OF PRINCIPLES

An aerated lagoon is a treatment system utilizing artificial aeration in a basin where biological organisms are allowed to grow and proliferate. Oxygen may be supplied to the basin by either mechanical or diffused aeration units. There are two types of aerated lagoons: the aerobic lagoon, in which dissolved oxygen is maintained throughout the basin; and the aerobic-anaerobic or facultative lagoon, in which oxygen is maintained in the upper layer of liquid in the basin only. These basins are depicted in Figure 11-1.

In the aerobic lagoon, all solids are maintained in suspension, and this system may be thought of as a "flow-through" activated sludge system without solids recycle. Thus, the effluent suspended solids concentration will approximate the aeration basin solids concentration. In most cases, separate sludge settling and disposal facilities are required. The aerobic lagoon can readily be modified to the activated sludge process by the addition of sludge separation and recycle facilities.

In the facultative lagoon, a portion of the suspended solids settle to the bottom of the basin where they undergo anaerobic decomposition. The anaerobic by-products are subsequently oxidized in the upper aerobic layers of the basin. The facultative lagoon can also be modified to yield a more highly clarified effluent by the inclusion of a separate or baffled settling compartment.

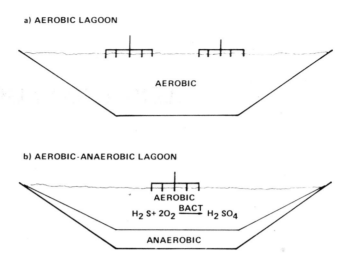

a) AEROBIC LAGOON

AEROBIC

b) AEROBIC-ANAEROBIC LAGOON

AEROBIC

$H_2 S + 2O_2 \xrightarrow{BACT} H_2 SO_4$

ANAEROBIC

**FIG. 11-1. COMPARISON OF ALTERNATIVE AERATED
LAGOON SYSTEMS**

BOD Removal Characteristics

As in the completely-mixed activated sludge process, organic removal is primarily a function of detention time, biological solids concentration, temperature, and the nature of the wastewater. Organic removal in completely-mixed lagoons can be determined using the following relationship:

$$\frac{S_o - S_e}{X_v t} = kS_e \qquad (11\text{-}1)$$

where:

S_o = influent total BOD, COD, or TOC, mg/l
S_e = effluent soluble BOD, COD, or TOC, mg/l
X_v = average or equilibrium concentration of VSS in aeration basin, mg/l
t = detention time, days
k = specific organic removal rate coefficient, l/mg-day

Thus, at a constant basin detention time, the equilibrium biological solids concentration and overall rate of organic removal can be expected to increase as the influent organic concentration increases. For a soluble waste, the equilibrium biological solids concentration, X_v, can be predicted from the following relationship:

$$X_v = \frac{X_{ov} + aS_r}{1 + bt} \qquad (11\text{-}2)$$

where:

X_{ov} = influent biological volatile suspended solids concentration, mg/l

a = sludge synthesis coefficient, mg VSS produced/mg organics removed or lb VSS produced/lb organics removed

S_r = organics (BOD, COD or TOC) removed $(S_o - S_e)$, mg/l

b = sludge auto-oxidation coefficient, mg VSS destroyed/day-mg VSS or lb VSS destroyed/day-lb VSS in the aeration basin

Assuming no influent biological volatile suspended solids ($X_{ov} = 0$), Equations 11-1 and 11-2 can be combined and the effluent soluble organic concentration can be defined as follows:

$$S_e = \frac{1 + bt}{akt} \qquad (11\text{-}3)$$

Equation 11-3 can be linearized as:

$$S_e = \frac{1}{akt} + \frac{b}{ak} \qquad (11\text{-}4)$$

The specific organic reaction rate coefficient, k, can thus be determined from a plot of S_e versus $1/t$ as shown in Figure 11-2. From Equation 11-3 it may be concluded that the effluent soluble organic concentration is independent of the influent organic concentration. For lagoons with fixed detention times, this conclusion is justified because higher influent organic concentrations will result in higher equilibrium biological solids levels, and, therefore, higher overall BOD removal rates. It should be emphasized, however, that the unit organic removal rate remains proportional to soluble organic concentration in the lagoon as shown in Equation 11-1. The minimum detention time for the use of Equation 11-3 occurs as S_e approaches S_o. This minimum detention time can be determined using the following relationship:

$$t_m = \frac{1}{ak\text{-}b} \qquad (11\text{-}5)$$

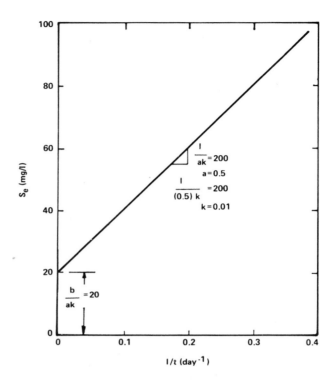

FIG. 11-2. DETERMINATION OF REMOVAL RATE COEFFICIENT

where:

t_m = minimum detention time for biological organisms to multiply to equilibrium levels, days

The specific organic reaction rate coefficient, k, is highly temperature dependent. The following relationship can be used to correct k for temperature.

$$k_2 = k_1 \theta^{(T_2 - T_1)} \tag{11-6}$$

where:

k_2 = specific organic reaction rate coefficient at T_2 °C, 1/mg-day
k_1 = specific organic reaction rate coefficient at T_1 °C, 1/mg-day
θ = temperature correction coefficient, assumed to be 1.035 for aerated lagoons

Depending on the aeration power level and the nature of the solids, a portion of the solids may deposit on the bottom of the basin. At low organic and suspended solids levels, the biological growth is dispersed and tends to remain in suspension even at very low levels.

Solids deposited on the bottom of facultative lagoons will undergo anaerobic degradation. This degradation results in a feedback of soluble organics to the upper aerobic layer. For these conditions, Equation 11-1 should be modified as follows:

$$S_e = \left(\frac{S_o}{1+kX_v t}\right)F \qquad (11\text{-}7)$$

where:

F = organic feedback coefficient due to benthal activity, dimensionless

The degree of anaerobic activity is highly temperature dependent and the coefficient, F, may be estimated to vary from 1.0 to 1.4 under winter and summer conditions, respectively.

Oxygen Requirements

For completely-mixed aerobic lagoons, oxygen requirements can be computed in a manner similar to that for activated sludge. The relationship is:

$$R_r = a'S_r + b'X_v \qquad (11\text{-}8)$$

where:

R_r = total oxygen utilization, lb O_2/day
a' = oxygen utilization coefficient for synthesis, lb O_2 utilized/lb organics removed or mg O_2 utilized/mg organics removed
S_r = organics (BOD, COD or TOC) removed (S_o - S_e), lb/day
b' = oxygen utilization coefficient for endogenous respiration, lb O_2 utilized/day-lb VSS in the aeration basin or mg O_2 utilized/day-mg VSS in the aeration basin
X_v = average of equilibrium VSS in the aeration basin, lb

In facultative aerobic-anaerobic lagoons, biological solids are maintained at a lower level and soluble organics are fed back to the liquid as anaerobic degradation of the settled solids proceeds. In this instance, the oxygen requirements can be related to organic removal and estimated from the following relationship:

$$R_r = F'S_r \qquad\qquad (11\text{-}9)$$

where:

$F' = $ overall oxygen utilization coefficient for facultative lagoons, dimensionless

The results obtained for various industrial wastes indicate that the value of F' is a function of the degree of organic feedback. This feedback depends on the basin temperature, and F' can be estimated to vary from 0.8 to 1.1 during winter operation when anaerobic activity in the bottom of the basin is low and from 1.2 to 1.5 during summer operation when anaerobic activity in the bottom of the basin is at a maximum. Oxygen requirements should generally be designed for summer operation since the rates of organic removal and benthal feedback will be the greatest during the warmer months of the year.

Multiple basins may be effectively used in aerated lagoon systems under the proper conditions. Although it can be shown from Equation 11-1 that there is no advantage to series basin operation at a given temperature in terms of effluent organic concentration, there are two considerations which may favor series operation. First, series operation may be desired when land availability is a concern. A minimum total basin volume can be obtained by employing two basins. The first basin volume is minimized to maintain a high temperature and a resulting high BOD reaction rate. Second, series operation may be favored when more stringent effluent suspended solids standards must be met. In the case where a low solids effluent is required, a primary, completely-mixed basin is followed by a secondary facultative basin. The facultative basin at low power (mixing) levels will permit partial solids settling. An optimization procedure can be utilized to determine the smallest total basin volume and the lowest aeration horsepower for a specified effluent quality.

Sludge Production

During the process of organic removal in a conventional aerated lagoon, organisms grow and reproduce, thereby resulting in an accumulation of suspended solids in the aeration basin. In order to obtain the highest effluent quality from an aerated lagoon system, the biological solids should be separated from the effluent. In completely-mixed, single-stage systems, solids separation is generally accomplished by installing a settling basin following the aerated lagoon. In partially-mixed, single-stage systems and two-stage systems where aerobic and facultative lagoons are operated in series, solids separation occurs due to settling of the solids on the bottom of the facultative lagoon. The rate of solids buildup on the bottom of facultative lagoons should be estimated so that the lagoon solids accumulation can be cleaned out before the treatment efficiency is impaired.

The amount of excess biological volatile sludge produced is a function of the sludge produced via organic removal less that sludge which is destroyed through endogenous respiration. Excess biological volatile sludge production can be determined using the following equation:

$$\Delta X_v = aS_r - bX_v \qquad (11\text{-}10)$$

where:

ΔX_v = excess biological volatile sludge production, lb VSS/day
S_r = organics (BOD, COD or TOC) removed $(S_o - S_e)$, lb/day
X_v = average or equilibrium VSS in aeration basin, lb
a = sludge synthesis coefficient, mg VSS produced/mg organics removed
b = sludge auto-oxidation coefficient, mg VSS destroyed/day-mg VSS in basin

The total excess sludge production is a function of the influent suspended solids concentration, the biodegradable fraction of the influent suspended solids, the excess biological sludge produced, and the effluent suspended solids concentration . Total excess sludge production can be determined by using the following equation:

$$\Delta X = fX_o + \frac{\Delta X_v}{f_v} - X_e \qquad (11\text{-}11)$$

where:

ΔX = total excess sludge production, lb SS/day
f = non-biodegradable fraction of influent suspended solids
X_o = influent suspended solids, lb SS/day
X_e = effluent suspended solids, lb SS/day
f_v = volatile fraction of equilibrium basin suspended solids, mg VSS/ mg SS

Final Settling Basin

The final settling basin should be designed with four major considerations in mind:

1. Sufficiently long detention time to realize the desired suspended solids removal;
2. Adequate volume for sludge storage;
3. Minimization of development of algae;
4. Minimization of odor development from anaerobic benthal activity.

Unfortunately, these objectives in design are not always compatible. At times the short detention times required to minimize algal growth are insufficient to obtain proper settling. Moreover, adequate volume must remain above the sludge deposits at all times to prevent the escape of odorous gases of decomposition. Thus sludge storage volume is taken out of service. Different locales will dictate requirements. For example, algal colonies and high degrees of anaerobic feedback are more predominant in warmer climates than colder climates. In most cases, the following guidelines are applicable:

1. A minimum detention time of one day is required to settle the majority of the settleable suspended solids. Thus, the settled sludge should not be allowed to accumulate to depths which would result in less than a one-day detention time of the supernatant liquid. A calculated one-day detention time may be too short for proper settling if uneven distribution of solids has occurred and channeling has developed.
2. If algal growth poses potential problems, a maximum detention time of one to two days is recommended. This short detention time should prevent the algal colonies from proliferating thus causing blooms and associated problems. Algal growth may result in deteriorated effluent quality during certain periods of the year. Consequently, when the basin is empty, the maximum detention time should be two days for algal control.
3. For odor control, it is recommended that a minimum water level of 3 ft be maintained above the sludge deposits at all times. In most climates, this layer is deep enough to oxidize reduced sulfur compounds, thereby minimizing odor potential. In addition, the 3-ft water layer assists in oxidizing soluble organics generated during anaerobic decomposition of the sludge deposits. In cases of high summer temperatures or excessive sulfide concentrations, it may be necessary to maintain water layers of up to 6 ft to prevent odorous conditions from developing.
4. Care should be exercised in minimizing fetch distances along the axis of prevailing winds. Even with this practice, it should be recognized that strong winds create velocities which may increase effluent total suspended solids and settleable solids concentrations.

A certain percentage of the deposited volatile solids will degrade each year and may be estimated in the range of 40 to 60 percent degradation per year. The sludge accumulation, therefore, will be equal to the deposited volatile solids which have not degraded plus the deposited inert or non-volatile suspended solids.

Nutrient Requirements

Biological volatile solids in aerated lagoon systems usually contain up to 12.3 percent nitrogen and 2.6 percent phosphorus, and each nutrient must be present in quantities sufficient for organism growth and synthesis. These nutrients are contributed to the system by the influent wastewater or by cell lysis accompanying endogenous respiration. Wastewaters are often deficient in one or both nutrients; therefore, the addition of each nutrient may be required. Maximum nitrogen and phosphorus requirements for aerated lagoon systems may be calculated using the following equations:

$$\text{lb N/day} = 0.123 \, \Delta X_v \qquad\qquad (11\text{-}12)$$

$$\text{lb P/day} = 0.026 \, \Delta X_v \qquad\qquad (11\text{-}13)$$

EQUIPMENT REQUIRED

Since aerated lagoons are flow-through systems, the experimental equipment is simpler to set up and operate than activated sludge laboratory systems. The aerated lagoons may be simulated by any container as shown in Figure 11-3. It is recommended that a small laboratory funnel be installed horizontally in order to prevent non-representative accumulation of suspended solids in the basin. More explanation of this potential accumulation is provided in Chapter 10, "Activated Sludge."

Attempts have been made to duplicate the conditions of the facultative lagoon, namely, partial solids settling, by installing the air diffuser about 1 to 2 ft off the bottom of the aeration chamber. However, it should be emphasized that it is practically impossible to duplicate field power levels in the laboratory so that these efforts are, for the most part, non-representative.

EXPERIMENTAL PROCEDURES

In order to develop the kinetic parameters required for design, several aerated lagoons are operated in parallel at various detention times. The systems are operated until stabilized conditions are achieved and continued for at least two

FIG. 11-3. CONTINUOUS-FLOW AERATED LAGOON

weeks under the stabilized situation. The data collected during the stabilized period are averaged for each unit and used as a single point in the design correlations.

1. Develop an acclimated seed in accordance with the procedures described in the Chapter 3, "Screening and Toxicity Methodology." In order to collect enough seed to operate several aerated lagoon systems, it may be practical to acclimate under activated sludge conditions so that a greater quantity of sludge can be developed.

2. Divide the acclimated seed into 3 to 4 containers and dilute to the desired volume. It is generally preferable to begin each unit with a higher concentration of VSS than will result after equilibrium conditions are obtained. It can be assumed that 0.3-0.5 mg/l of VSS will result at equilibrium for each mg/l of BOD removed.

3. Monitor the influent and effluent streams for total and soluble BOD and TOC (or TOC, BOD, and TOD), total and volatile suspended solids, nitrogen, phosphorus, pH and other characteristics, such as phenols or cyanides which may be unique to the wastewater being studied. The aeration basin contents should be monitored for specific oxygen uptake expressed in mg O_2 utilized/day-mg of VSS in the basin.

4. The final settling chamber supernatant should be monitored for VSS and then the contents stirred in order to determine the total VSS for sludge production estimates.

CORRELATION OF RESULTS

The specific design parameters required for use in the equations of the first section of this chapter can be developed by correlating the data obtained during the experimental investigations.

1. Average the stabilized periods of data for each system.
2. Determination of sludge production coefficients, a and b. Correlate the excess biological volatile sludge production with the BOD removal. The excess sludge is equivalent to that sludge which enters the final settling basin. Plot $\triangle X_v/X_v$ versus S_r/X_v on the Y and X axes, respectively, as shown in Figure 11-4. The slope of the resulting straight line is equal to a, and the Y axis intercept is equal to b.

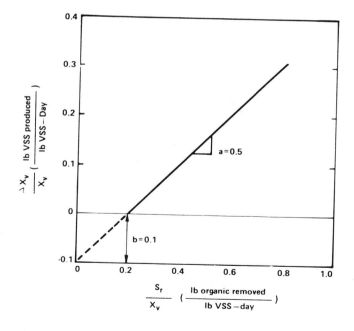

FIG. 11-4. DETERMINATION OF SLUDGE PRODUCTION
COEFFICIENTS

3. Determination of the specific BOD reaction rate coefficient, k. Correlate the data according to Equation 11-4:

$$S_e = \frac{1}{akt} + \frac{b}{ak} \qquad (11\text{-}4)$$

Plot S_e versus $1/t$. The slope of this plot is equal to $1/ak$ and the Y axis intercept is equal to b/ak (see Figure 11-2). The specific BOD reaction

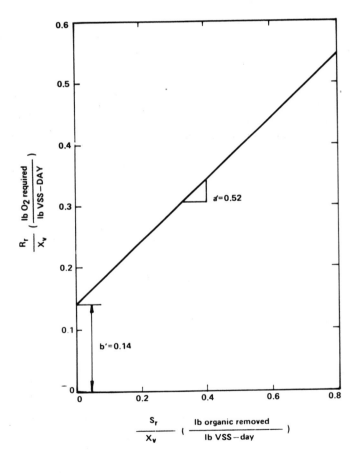

FIG. 11-5. DETERMINATION OF OXYGEN UTILIZATION
COEFFICIENTS

rate coefficient, k, can be obtained by substituting the value for "a" obtained from Figure 11-4 into the equation for the slope obtained from Figure 11-2.

4. Determination of oxygen coefficients, a' and b'. Correlate the total oxygen utilization rate with the BOD reaction rate. Plot R_r/X_v versus S_r/X_v as shown in Figure 11-5. The slope of the resulting straight line is equal to a' and the intercept equal to b'.

LIMITATIONS AND SCALE-UP

It is realistic to employ the experimentally-determined coefficients in the design of an aerobic lagoon. However, extreme caution and experienced judgment are required in design of the facultative lagoon since the equilibrium VSS in suspension is very difficult to accurately predict. It is difficult, if not impossible, to duplicate field power levels and mixing conditions in the laboratory. Thus, representative equilibrium suspended solids cannot actually be simulated

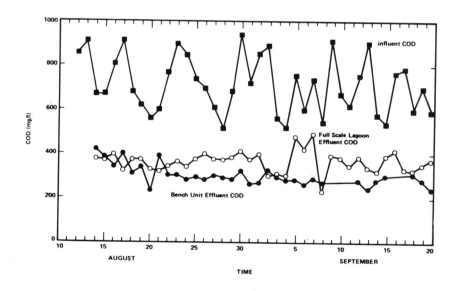

FIG. 11-6. COMPARISON OF ORGANIC REMOVAL EFFICIENCIES BETWEEN BENCH-SCALE AND FULL-SCALE AERATED LAGOONS

in the lab. Likewise it is not possible to simulate the final settling basin charac-teristics under bench-scale conditions. Additionally, since the majority of bench-scale programs are one to four months in duration, the degradation and accumu-lation of solids in the bottom of a final basin cannot be accurately measured. It is possible to obtain an indication of the settleability of the aeration basin solids by conducting simple settling tests where suspended solids are measured with time in a quiescent cylinder. In general, however, the final basin design and the estimate of solids accumulation must be based on experience.

The organic removal scale-up, however, is more accurate. If the VSS con-centrations are controlled in the laboratory to levels which approximate past field experience, and if other conditions such as pH and temperature are con-trolled, organic removal efficiencies can be predicted quite closely. One example of a parallel bench-scale reactor versus a full-scale aerated lagoon simulation study is shown in Figure 11-6 and indicates this accuracy [1].

REFERENCES

1. Adams, C. E., Jr., and Eckenfelder, W. W., Jr., Eds., *Process Design Tech-niques for Industrial Waste Treatment,* Enviro Press, Nashville, Tn., (1974).

12

TRICKLING FILTER

DISCUSSION OF PRINCIPLES

The advent of more stringent water quality control under the U. S. Federal Water Quality Amendments of 1972 (P.L. 92-500) has shifted the emphasis of trickling filter applications in both municipal and industrial wastewater treatment systems. Specifically, the "state of the art" has moved from the rock filter as a secondary and total treatment process to the synthetic medial filter specifically designed as a unit process. This process is combined with pre- and post-treatment facilities to remove organic carbon by biological oxidation or ammonia-nitrogen by biological nitrification. This does not imply that trickling filters no longer have application as total secondary treatment processes or that synthetic media will totally replace rock media simply because the filter is a low energy user, requires little operation and maintenance, and is a candidate system in developing countries and areas of low ecological sensitivity. It is probably true, however, that performance limitations in terms of BOD removal and inherent advantages of synthetic media over rock media change the perspective of trickling filter application to a significant extent.

The trickling filter consists of a bed of coarse media, natural or synthetic with an attached zoogleal slime over which wastewater flows. Soluble and colloidal organic material is transported from the wastewater to the slime and the BOD is reduced via the mechanisms of aerobic and anaerobic biochemical oxidation. The media specifications and overall filter design should allow good air circulation to minimize anaerobic biodegradation and prevent physical plugging. The liquid follows a vertical flow pattern with little lateral movement

223

and is generally considered to be plug flow. The effluent is collected in an underdrain system and conveyed to a final clarifier where filter sloughings are separated from the carrier effluent by gravity. Effluent from trickling filters treating municipal wastes seldom is below 20 to 30 mg/l BOD and the BOD removal efficiency is generally less than 88 percent BOD removal when treating higher strength wastes.

Trickling filters are operated over a wide range of hydraulic and organic loadings and the classical definitions of high and low rate systems are presented elsewhere [1]. Predicting organic removal performance as a function of hydraulic loading is only approximate and this information is therefore of·little use in the design of these systems. Relatively complex mathematical models, incorporating system design characteristics, have been formulated to predict organic removal performance. Selected mathematical approaches will be subsequently discussed.

Organic Removal Performance

There are many variables which affect trickling filter performance; the primary ones being media depth and configuration, nature of the substrate, specific surface of the media, hydraulic surface loading, and temperature. In terms of organic removal, first order reaction kinetics applied to the plug flow process have been used to approximate performance.

$$\frac{S_e}{S_0} = e^{-K A_v t} \tag{12-1}$$

where:

S_e = effluent concentration of soluble substrate, mg/l
S_0 = influent concentration of soluble substrate, mg/l
K = organic removal velocity constant, ft/day
A_v = specific surface of the medium, sq ft/cu ft
t = travel time through the depth of filter, day

This Equation can be modified by assuming flow velocity is independent of depth and redefining time as a flow per unit area of filter media:

$$t = C\left(\frac{D}{q^n}\right) \tag{12-2}$$

where:

C, n = constants which characterize the media
D = media depth, ft
q = hydraulic surface loading, gpm/sq ft

Equation 12-1 can be appropriately modified:

$$\frac{S_e}{S_o} = e^{-K_1 A_v (\frac{D}{q^n})}$$

(12-3)

where:

$K_1 = K(C) = $ modified constant

The constant, K, varies with temperature and a correction must be applied in predicting performance. The traditional correction expression is:

$$K_2 = K_1 \theta^{(T_2 - T_1)}$$

(12-4)

where:

K_1	=	organic removal velocity constant at temperature T_1
K_2	=	organic removal velocity constant at temperature T_2
$T_1 T_2$	=	water temperature, $^\circ C$
θ	=	temperature coefficient

The temperature coefficient, θ, has been reported to range from 1.035 to 1.072 with the higher values more applicable at the higher organic loading [2]. More recent investigations have indicated a range of θ from 1.10 to 1.35 with an average value of 1.21 [3]. This shows a much more pronounced temperature effect than previously predicted and should be strongly considered in trickling filter design, particularly where seasonal temperature ranges are extreme and/or where effluent requirements are stringent. Incorporating the temperature correction factor, Equation 12-3 can be modified:

$$\frac{S_e}{S_o} = e^{-K_1 \theta^{(T_2 - T_1)} A_v(\frac{D}{q^n})}$$

(12-5)

Equation 12-5 has been further modified based on recent investigations [4] to:

$$\frac{S_e}{S_o} = e^{-K_1 \theta^{(T_2 - T_1)} A_v(\frac{D}{q^n S_o})}$$

(12-6)

A graphical method for evaluating the media and organic substrate constants using experimental data is presented as follows:

Rewriting Equation 12-3:

$$\ln \frac{S_o}{S_e} = K_1 A_v (\frac{D}{q^n})$$

(12-7)

or:

$$\log \left(\ln \frac{S_o}{S_e} \right) = \log K_1 + \log A_v D \ n \log q \tag{12-8}$$

At a constant depth and specific surface in the experimental trickling filter, the hydraulic loading can be varied to give the relationship shown in Figure 12-1.

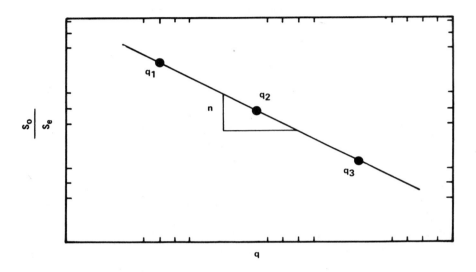

FIG. 12-1. DETERMINATION OF COEFFICIENT "n" ON LOG-LOG PAPER

According to Equation 12-8, the negative slope of the line is "n" The organic removal coefficient, K_1, may be calculated from the intercept of Figure 12-1, with factors A_v and D known, but a more precise approach presents the data in the format shown in Figure 12-2. The variable is "q" which produces a corresponding S_o/S_e value. According to Equation 12-7, the slope of such a plot is K_1, which must then be corrected as required from the test temperature to the design temperature in accordance with Equation 12-4. The data may be arranged, as shown in Figure 12-3, to determine if a more linear relationship exists. If this is the case, Equation 12-6 can be used for design purposes rather than Equation 12-5.

In most trickling filter applications, recycling the effluent is standard practice. This has the effect of diluting the organic strength of the influent and

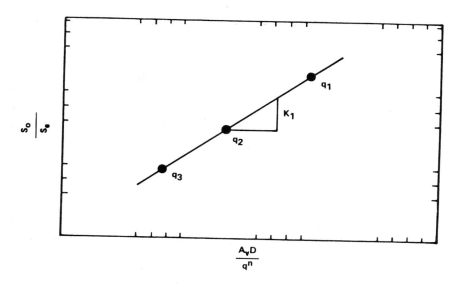

FIG. 12-2. DETERMINATION OF TRICKLING FILTER
ORGANIC REMOVAL VELOCITY CONSTANT "K_1"
ON SEMI-LOG PAPER

should be appropriately incorporated into the design formulation. Referring
to Figure 12-4 on a mass balance basis and letting "a" equal the recycle ratio
and Q equal the influent flow rate:

$$S_i = \frac{Q}{Q + aQ} (S_o) + \frac{aQ}{Q + aQ} (S_e)$$

$$S_i = \frac{Q}{Q + aQ} (S_o + aS_e)$$

$$S_i = \frac{S_o + aS_e}{a + 1} \tag{12-9}$$

After calculating S_i, the term S_e/S_i can be substituted in Equation 12-5 and
12-6. The practice of recycling is not necessarily required unless dilution of the
incoming wastewater is shown to be necessary or if it is required to maintain a
good filter slime during periods of low flow. In practice, higher hydraulic applications using high recirculation have generally resulted in a decreased efficiency
for BOD removal [5]. The recycle of sludge from the secondary clarifier which
receives the sloughings may be desirable. Although positive process control

227

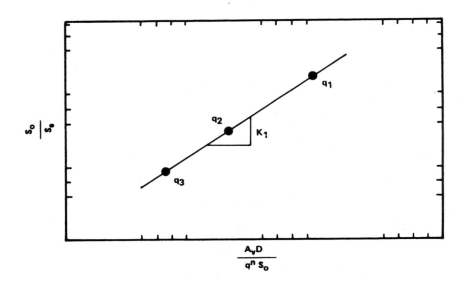

**FIG. 12-3. DETERMINATION OF MODIFIED TRICKLING FILTER
ORGANIC REMOVAL VELOCITY CONSTANT "K_1"
ON SEMI-LOG PAPER**

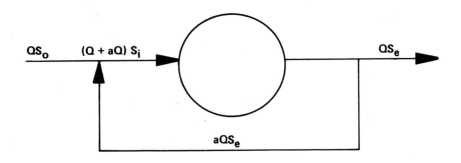

FIG. 12-4. MASS BALANCE ANALYSIS

is difficult to obtain in practice, recycling sludge may enhance removal of soluble organics and help to sustain the bacterial slime on the media during shock loads or periods of no organic inflow [6].

Ammonia Removal Performance

A more recent application of trickling filters has been in the area of biological nitrification. This has evolved from more stringent effluent requirements for ammonia-nitrogen, and the use of trickling filters to accomplish this removal via conversion to nitrates merits consideration. The effectiveness of trickling filters in nitrifying wastewater ammonia depends on hydraulic loading, temperature, pH, and the BOD concentration [7]. Based on reported results, plastic media filters are capable of achieving consistent, high level nitrification when operating on a low BOD wastewater stream [8]. Approximately 90 percent conversion was obtained with a filter charge of 15 to 30 mg/l BOD_5 and 10 to 20 mg/l NH_3-N. Applied hydraulic rates of this secondary municipal effluent ranged from 0.5 gpm/sq ft to 1.5 gpm/sq ft. The influence of recycle and seasonal temperature on effluent ammonia as a function of nitrogen loading to the tower is shown in Figure 12-5. The effect of filter depth on ammonia removal (or conversion) can be estimated by plotting an ammonia profile such as shown in Figure 12-6 [9].

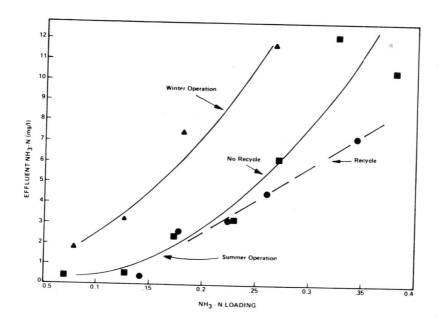

FIG. 12-5. AMMONIA LOADING VS. NH_3-N IN TOWER EFFLUENT

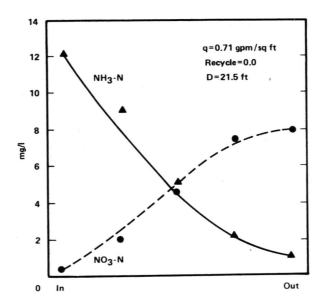

FIG. 12-6. NITROGEN PROFILE IN TOWER

There are currently no comprehensive studies which have fitted ammonia removal data into a model such as the ones described in Equations 12-5 and 12-6. Since the same variables generally influence ammonia removal and organic removal, it is ostensible that a similar approach could be used in determining the design coefficients. In the absence of such quantification, however, nitrification efficiency can be predicted from pilot studies using a defined filter media and wastewater by developing a performance curve in a format such as shown in Figure 12-7.

Summary

In general, trickling filters are most applicable as a secondary treatment process where low operation and maintenance considerations offset high quality effluent requirements. Trickling filters may be competitive with alternate forms of biological treatment systems, such as activated sludge, in a bi-modal treatment system consisting of, for example, biological treatment, post filtration, and possibly carbon adsorption. Inherent advantages of trickling filters over aeration systems in minimizing heat loss may be significant and the use of trickling filters for nitrifying secondary-treated municipal effluents has been demonstrated.

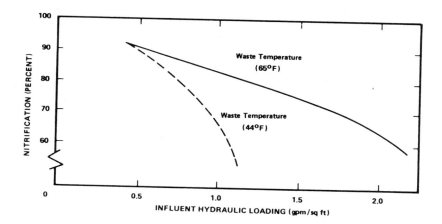

FIG. 12-7. NITRIFICATION PERFORMANCE CURVE

Trickling filters also require less land and power requirements than other candidate biological systems, which may be a consideration in the overall process selection.

The selection of media for trickling filters is an integral part of design and many configurations are available. Random media such as rock or plastic rings are available as well as sheet media such as self-supporting modules or corrugated plastic sheets, plastic pipe, or tubular material. The specific surface ranges from approximately 10 to 20 sq ft/cu ft for rock media to as high as 70 sq ft/cu ft for synthetic sheet or randomly packed media. The selected media and filter shell should be integrated into an optimum ventilation design as this is an important aspect in process performance.

Recent Modification of the Fixed-Media System

A modification of the fixed media system is a rotating disc system partially submerged in the wastewater as illustrated in Figure 12-8. The disc is usually constructed of corrugated polyethylene media which is mounted on a horizontal shaft up to 20 ft long. The disc, which may range from about 6 to 12 ft in diameter, is placed in a steel or concrete tank at approximately 40 percent submergence and rotated at 1.5 to 3.0 rpm. High levels of treatment are achieved by arranging trains of the discs in series.

Rotation of the disc alternatively contacts the biomass (attached to the disc at 2 to 4 mm thickness) with the wastewater for removal of organics or ammonia and the air for adsorption of oxygen. The disc is rotated at a peripheral velocity

231

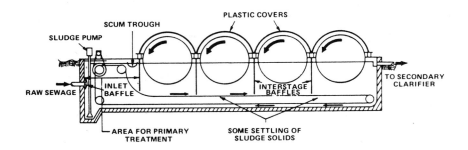

FIG. 12-8. ROTATING DISC SYSTEM

of 1.0 fps to exert shearing forces on the biomass to slough excess biological growth and deter clogging. The mixing action of the media maintains most solids in suspension so that they flow to a clarifier for separation. For anaerobic treatment and denitrification, the shaft assemblies are totally submerged in the wastewater.

Because of the low rotational speeds, power consumption may be as low as 70 to 80 percent of activated sludge systems. The capital investments are similar to other secondary treatment processes.

EQUIPMENT REQUIRED

Trickling filter studies are usually conducted using bench-scale units such as the one shown in Figure 12-9 or the larger pilot scale filter as shown in Figure 12-10. A basic equipment list consists of:

1. Filter shell with appropriate support gratings, orifices, air ports, and distribution appurtenances;
2. Feed and recycle pumps;
3. Flow measuring devices;
4. Test media;
5. Substrate and effluent reservoir receptacles; and
6. Appropriate analytical equipment for monitoring and analyzing system performance.

EXPERIMENTAL PROCEDURES

Determination of Design Coefficients–Organic Removal

Using a bench or pilot scale trickling filter as shown in Figure 12-9 and Figure 12-10, the following procedure can be used:

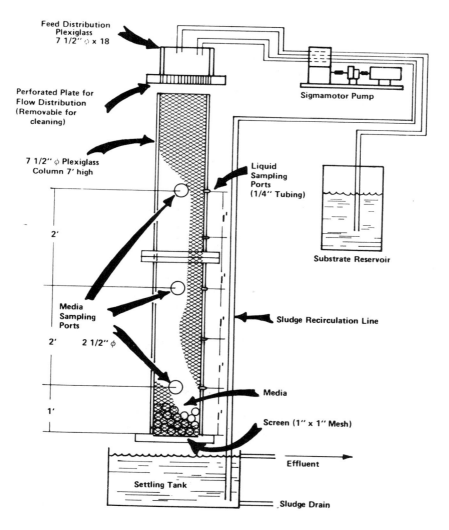

FIG. 12-9. BENCH-SCALE TRICKLING FILTER UNIT

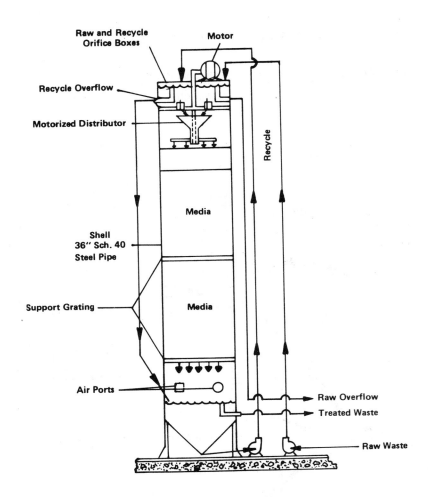

FIG. 12-10. PILOT SCALE TRICKLING FILTER

1. Generate an acclimated slime on the filter media by feeding the wastewater to the system at a control rate (less than 1.0 gpm/sq ft). A dilute activated sludge mixture applied to the system may speed the "sliming" process.

2. Select a minimum of three hydraulic flow rates. Apply the selected flow rate to the filter with a selected media depth until "quasi" steady-state conditions are established. This is defined as such time when the soluble effluent BOD_5 (or COD, or TOC) is constant with time. It may take several weeks after the acclimated slime is developed to reach this condition.

For deeper filters (greater than 10 feet) with plastic packing (an average specific surface of 20 to 30 sq ft/cu ft), the selected flow rate should fall within a range of 0.5 to 3.0 gpm/sq ft.

3. At each flow rate, sample at a minimum of three depths. Analyses should be made (filtered BOD_5, COD, or TOC) until consistent results are obtained. Additional analyses should include pH, alkalinity/acidity, temperature, and possibly the nitrogen series (if nitrification levels are of interest).

4. Plot the ln S_o/S_e (in terms of soluble BOD_5, COD, or TOC) for each applied hydraulic loading rate (q) on log-log paper as shown in Figure 12-1. If TOC or COD is used, it will be necessary to subtract the non-biodegradable fraction to linearize the data. The negative slope is taken as the "n" exponent which characterizes the media.

5. Plot S_o/S_e on semi-log graph paper for each applied hydraulic loading series using the term $[A_v D/q^n]$ as the abscissa. A typical plot is shown in Figure 12-2. The specific surface, depth and exponent "n" will be constant if data are taken from the same test series used in No. 4 above, with "q" being the only variable. The slope is taken as the organic removal velocity coefficient, K_1.

6. Additional test series can be performed, varying the depth and/or media as required. It should be recalled, however, that A_v and n are a function of the media, and K_1 is a function of both the substrate and the media.

Determination of General Design Criteria - Ammonia Removal

The same type of installation used in the previous determination can be used in nitrification test work. The following procedure can be used:

1. The primary variables to evaluate when performing nitrification studies using trickling filters are nitrogen loading (varying hydraulic application and/or nitrogen concentration in the influent), recycle, temperature, and pH. As nitrifying bacteria are extremely temperature and pH sensitive, the latter two variables are significant.

A predetermined nitrogen loading to the system is applied to a filter with an acclimated slime until the effluent NH_3-N concentration is relatively constant. A higher load is then applied and the test run repeated. The general application range is from 0.10 to 0.60 lb NH_3-N/sq ft-day. Recycle, temperature, and influent pH should be held constant for each run. Once the nitrogen loading effect on nitrification is determined for a given set of conditions, then a different set of recycle conditions and temperature can be imposed. A typical analytical schedule and format for

TABLE 12-1. PLASTIC MEDIA TRICKLING FILTER (SURFPAC) PILOT PLANT [7]

Sample Date	Total BOD$_5$ (mg/l) Raw	Final	Soluble BOD$_5$ (mg/l) Raw	Final	Susp. Solids (mg/l) Raw	Final	pH Raw	Final	Kjeldahl-N (mg/l) Raw	Final	Organic-N (mg/l) Raw	Final	NH$_3$-N (mg/l) Raw	Final	Nitrite-N (mg/l) Raw	Final	Nitrate-N (mg/l) Raw	Final
5-21-72	7.3	8.0	1.2	3.7	...	...	7.5	7.9	35.60	15.30	11.60	2.80	24.00	12.50	0.36	1.35	2.38	7.25
5-22-72	6.7	6.8	3.3	1.1	5.9	11.2	7.2	7.5	29.00	14.30	8.50	6.30	20.50	8.00	0.79	3.36	2.34	7.55
5-23-72	6.8	7.7	4.3	5.5	10.9	9.9	7.4	7.8	25.10	19.90	14.60	15.00	10.50	4.90	0.45	2.76	0.61	7.85
5-24-72	6.3	6.7	4.1	3.3	6.9	15.5	7.6	7.7	25.10	14.50	11.20	10.00	13.90	4.50	0.56	4.65	1.35	8.60
5-25-72	6.2	7.2	5.3	2.1	10.6	9.9	7.5	7.7	14.50	5.23	4.00	2.63	10.50	2.60	0.44	2.65	1.43	8.90
5-29-72	6.5	7.1	2.1	3.8	11.6	10.0	7.6	7.6	11.20	6.29	6.97	4.51	4.23	1.78	1.02	2.14	5.98	11.20
5-30-72	7.1	...	...	...	9.6	13.9	7.6	7.3	10.30	1.79	6.79	1.42	3.51	0.37	0.44	1.60	3.06	9.80
5-31-72	7.4	4.5	.2	1.3	31.7	8.9	7.2	7.4	5.91	1.49	4.13	1.39	1.78	0.10	0.17	2.65	4.98	11.00
6-1-72	5.6	6.4	.2	...	8.6	6.8	7.5	7.4	8.84	1.37	1.88	1.07	6.96	0.30	0.68	2.85	4.95	10.80
6-4-72	6.9	7.0	2.4	2.1	9.9	7.3	7.6	7.8	14.50	1.56	3.80	1.27	10.70	0.29	0.51	4.68	0.75	11.90
6-5-72	7.0	6.5	2.0	3.4	17.2	17.2	7.6	7.6	16.00	2.49	10.04	2.02	5.96	0.47	0.65	4.15	1.58	13.80
6-6-72	5.9	5.6	3.7	1.3	8.9	0.3	7.5	7.5	13.40	1.31	2.60	1.14	10.80	0.17	0.22	1.40	0.54	12.00
6-7-72*	6.6	5.8	1.1	1.6	8.6	4.9	7.5	7.7	13.40	1.31	0.20	1.16	13.20	0.15	0.35	1.55	0.70	15.60
6-8-72**	7.2	6.4	...	...	13.5	20.5	7.5	7.5	19.00	1.43	4.70	1.27	14.30	0.16	0.42	2.05	0.48	12.50
Average	6.7	6.6	2.7	2.7	11.8	10.6	7.5	7.6	17.50	6.31	6.50	3.72	10.75	2.69	0.51	2.70	2.22	10.60

* Raw COD = 39.0 mg/l Final Soluble COD = 31.2;
** Raw COD = 42.9 mg/l Final Soluble COD = 31.2;

Flows: Raw: 0.50 gpm/sf   Recycle: 0.50 gpm/sf

tabulating data is presented in Table 12-1.

2. Plot the data in a manner shown in Figure 12-5. This graphical representation can be used in predicting nitrification as a function of nitrogen loading. Samples should be withdrawn at intermediate points in the filter so a profile analysis as shown in Figure 12-6 can be presented. This may be useful in optimizing filter depths for final design. If the nitrogen concentration in the trickling filter feed remained relatively constant, then nitrification levels as a function of hydraulic loading, such as shown in Figure 12-7, can be presented.

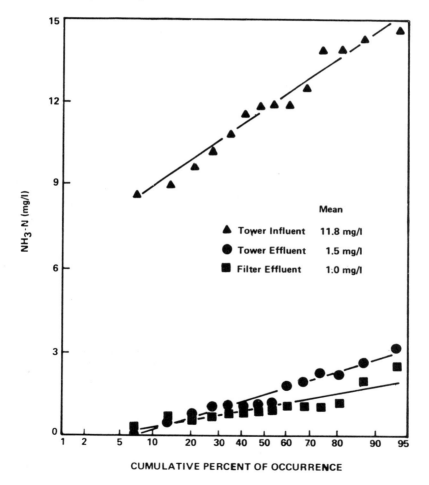

FIG. 12-11. CUMULATIVE PERCENT OF OCCURRENCE OF NH₃-N

3. Once a "quasi" steady-state condition is reached for a given test series, the influent and effluent NH_3-N concentration can be presented in a probability of occurrence as shown in Figure 12-11. This type of analysis is indicative of what range of effluent variation might be expected in a full scale system.

CORRELATION OF RESULTS

The results of the organic removal analysis in determining trickling filter design coefficients can be evaluated statistically by establishing the correlation coefficients of the plots shown in Figures 12-1 and 12-2, or 12-3. Good linearity (the correlation coefficient approaches unity) would tend to validate the mathematical approximations as expressed in Equations 12-5 and 12-6. A similar approach could be taken in attempting to resolve ammonia conversion data into the same model format, although the authors are not aware of such an attempt at this time.

Two factors should be recognized at this point. First, experimental results may not accurately fit the models posed herein, particularly where more complex industrial wastes are involved, and an appropriate modification may be in order. Secondly, even if the data can be resolved perfectly into these models, scale-up factors or changes inherent in full-scale operations as compared to the bench or pilot-scale evaluation may adversely affect its validity.

LIMITATIONS AND SCALE-UP

Experience has shown that the translation of biochemical reactions and biological process efficiency approximates unity scale-up providing the experimental process is judiciously designed. Specifically:

1. The wastewater is representative and influent variations in the bench or pilot-scale program approximate the pattern expected for a full-scale system;
2. The influence of environmental factors such as pH, temperature, alkalinity/acidity, nutrients, influent concentration, and inclusion or exclusion of potential inhibitors, is quantified;
3. No significant short-circuiting or non-homogeneity of media prevails in the bench or pilot scale units;
4. Good distribution of wastewater to the filter media in the bench, pilot,

and full-scale systems is accomplished; and

5. An acclimated slime is developed in all cases.

With these provisos, translating experimental design coefficients directly to full scale application should be sufficiently accurate. It should be noted, however, that the aforementioned models and development of coefficients was based on soluble concentrations, and exclude the effect of the suspended organic (and inorganic) fraction which will be discharged from the final clarifier. This is extremely difficult to predict using the bench or pilot-scale approach, and the solids balance around the filter should be predicted from empirical data derived from operating full scale systems.

REFERENCES

1. *Wastewater Treatment Plant Design,* WPCF Manual of Practice No. 8, Water Pollution Control Federation, Washington, D.C. (1977).
2. Eckenfelder, W. W., Jr., *Industrial Water Pollution Control,* McGraw-Hill, New York (1966).
3. Malina, J. F., Eckenfelder, W. W., Jr., Gloyna, E. F., Kayser, R., Drynan, W. R., "Design Guides for Biological Wastewater Treatment Processes." Technical Report EHE-71-2, CRWR-76, Environmental Health Engineering Research Laboratories, Center for Research in Water Resources, University of Texas, Austin, Texas (1972).
4. Oleszkiewicz, J. A. and Eckenfelder, W. W., Jr., personal communication (1974).
5. Richard, J. G. and Kingsbury, R. P., "Design Considerations for Plastic Media Biological Towers," 55th Annual Short School of the Texas Water Utilities Association, Texas A & M University, College Station, Texas (March 1973).
6. Voeller, C. J., "Treatment of Combined Domestic Creamery and Potato Waste with Plastic Media Trickling Filters," Proc., 38th Annual Meeting, Pacific Northwest Pollution Control Association, Spokane, Wash. (1971).
7. Sampayo, F.F., "The Use of Nitrification Towers at Lima, Ohio," The 2nd Annual Conference, Waste Management Association of Ohio, Columbus, Ohio. (October 1973).
8. Adams, C. E., Jr., Krenkel, P. A., and Bingham, E. C., "Investigations into the Reduction of High Nitrogen Concentrations," Proc., 5th International Conference on Water Pollution Research, San Francisco and Honolulu (July-August 1970).

9. Duddles, G. A. and Richardson, S. E., "Application of Plastic Media Trickling Filter for Biological Nitrification Systems," EPA R2-73-199, U. S. Environmental Protection Agency, Washington, D. C. (1973).

13

WASTE STABILIZATION PONDS

DISCUSSION OF PRINCIPLES

Waste stabilization ponds are relatively low cost treatment systems which utilize bacteria and algae to reduce organic constituents as well as disease-causing agents. The process effectiveness depends on bacteria to biochemically oxidize the organic materials in the influent wastewater while algae, utilizing sunlight and the simpler bacterial degradation products, produce oxygen through photosynthesis which is available to aerobic and facultative microorganisms. If the algal population can furnish sufficient oxygen to maintain an aerobic environment, the aerobic or facultative microorganisms will grow and proliferate, using a portion of the organic substrate to produce new cells and the balance as an energy source to drive subsequent reactions. If a high organic loading to a pond exerts an oxygen demand above that provided by photosynthesis and atmospheric aeration, then anaerobic or facultative bacteria will become dominant in the aquatic environment. These conditions will promote the anaerobic production of the various forms of organic acids, alcohols, and other reduced products of biological degradation.

Waste stabilization ponds are usually classified as aerobic, anaerobic, or facultative, depending on the presence or absence of dissolved oxygen. Most ponds are facultative, where the upper layers are aerobic and the lower layers are anaerobic. The organic load, intrinsic pond design, and sunlight intensity dictate how the pond is to function. A fourth classification is the maturation pond, designed as a shallow, long detention basin whose primary function is to reduce the number of disease-causing microorganisms [1].

241

When organic reduction is the primary consideration, a series connected aerobic-facultative pond is normally used. A maturation pond may be used as the last in a series connected system, particularly when pathogenic micro-organism reduction is a consideration.

Although over 15,000 species of algae have been identified, only a few are important in wastewater treatment [2]. Typical green algae found in waste stabilization ponds include *Chlamydomonas* and *Chlorella.* Blue-green algae include *Oscillatoria* and *Euglena.* The biology and chemistry of a pond will be extremely dependent on the algal activity and interactions. The factors which most affect this activity are illumination, temperature, and nutrient availability.

It is difficult to calculate light penetration in a precise manner as the pond contents are not homogeneous. Estimates can be formulated, however, using a theoretical or empirical approach. Temperature is particularly significant in waste stabilization pond design as the rate of photosynthetic oxygen production is temperature dependent. Limiting values range from 4°C to 35°C with an optimum temperature for oxygen production around 20°C [3]. The bacteria are increasingly active going from the lower temperature to the higher, indicating a higher oxygen demand with a limited photosynthetic oxygen supply during summer operations. This condition often results in anaerobic conditions prevailing during the warmer summer months in ponds designed as aerobic or facultative systems. The nutrient requirements of bacteria in waste stabilization ponds are the same as those in other biological treatment systems; specifically, nitrogen, phosphorus, and organic carbon. Most algal species use only free carbon dioxide in photosynthesis, although some algae have been reported to use the bicarbonate ion. Additionally, nitrates and phosphates are required to complete the algal synthesis cycle. The simplified photosynthetic reduction-biological oxidation equations are:

Photosynthetic Reduction.

$$aCO_2 + bH_2O + cNO_3^- + dPO_4^{-3} \xrightarrow{\text{light}} C_rH_sN_tO_uP_v + wO_2 \qquad (13\text{-}1)$$

Biological Oxidation:

$$C_rH_sN_tO_uP_v + wO_2 \longrightarrow aCO_2 + bH_2O + cNO_3^- + dPO_4^{-3} \qquad (13\text{-}2)$$

The design of waste stabilization ponds is predicated on many criteria, such as wastewater characteristics, hydrological and meteorological conditions, light, topography, public health considerations, and effluent quality limits. The physical shape of the pond will influence performance as both photosynthesis and surface oxygenation. Bacterial-substrate contact is enhanced by thermal mixing and wind action. Although this is beneficial, wind action may result in effluent quality deterioration if bottom sediments are disturbed to the point of being carried out in the final effluent flow. Although these factors all affect design and performance, detention time, temperature, and surface loading usually dictate pond sizing as currently practiced.

An aerobic pond design should be based on the concept of minimal depth with maximum algae production considering the BOD design load. The area requirement based on algal oxygen supply required to maintain aerobic conditions can be estimated by the following equation [4].

$$O_2 = 0.25 \, FI_L \qquad (13\text{-}3)$$

where:

O_2 = oxygen production, lb O_2/acre-day
F = light conversion efficiency = 4
I_L = light intensity, cal/cm^2-day

The depth of oxygen penetration necessary to maintain aerobic pond conditions has been estimated as a function of surface loading [5]. This relationship is shown in Figure 13-1.

Several concepts have been used for the design of facultative ponds. One design formulation considers the more important factors which influence the degradation of organic material by bacteria and the production of oxygen by algae. The following rational design formula based on several intrinsic assumptions was developed after observing the results of many small laboratory ponds, pilot plants, and a wide variety of field installations treating domestic wastes:

$$V = 10.7 \times 10^{-8} \, QS_0\theta^{(35-T)} ff' \qquad (13\text{-}4)$$

where:

V = pond volume, acre-ft
S_0 = influent ultimate BOD, mg/l
Q = wastewater flow rate, gpd
T = average temperature of coldest month, °C
f = algal toxicity factor, 1.0 for domestic wastes
f' = sulfide correction factor, 1.0 if $SO_4^=$ less than 500 mg/l

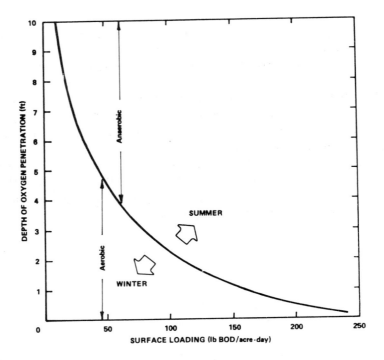

**FIG. 13-1. INFLUENCE OF BOD LOADING ON THE DEPTH
OF OXYGEN PENETRATION**

If one takes the liberty of assuming that the influent organic constituents
are oxidized in a facultative pond which is completely mixed, then:

$$\frac{S_e}{S_o} = \frac{1}{1 + K_1 t} \quad \text{(single pond)} \qquad (13\text{-}5)$$

where:

S_e = effluent BOD, mg/l
S_o = influent BOD, mg/l
K_1 = reaction rate constant at temperature T, day^{-1}
t = detention time, days

244

and:

$$\frac{S_e}{S_o} = (\frac{1}{1 + K_1 t_1}) (\frac{1}{1 + K_1 t_2}) \cdots (\frac{1}{1 + K_1 t_n}) \qquad (13\text{-}6)$$

(multiple ponds)

This assumes that the reaction rate constant is the same for each pond in the series. This most likely will not be the case and therefore:

$$\frac{S_e}{S_o} = (\frac{1}{1 + K_1 t_1}) (\frac{1}{1 + K_2 t_2}) \cdots (\frac{1}{1 + K_n t_n}) \qquad (13\text{-}7)$$

The temperature correction for the reaction rate constant can be applied as follows:

$$(K_{35}/K_T) = \theta^{(35 - T)} \qquad (13\text{-}8)$$

where:

K_T = reaction rate constant at temperature T, day^{-1}
K_{35} = reaction rate constant at 35°C, day^{-1}
θ = temperature reaction coefficient ($\doteq 1.085$)

Waste stabilization ponds, as any biological process, are susceptible to upsets and aquatic population shifts attributable to specific constituents in the incoming wastewater. There are many compounds which inhibit algae and prevent its growth and proliferation. This upsets the algal-bacterial interrelationship and the pond will not function as designed.

A shift from green to blue-green algae might be noted as conditions in the pond become more severe. The presence of sulfur compounds in the influent wastewater is significant. *Desulfovibrio,* a reducing bacteria, utilizes sulfate as an inorganic hydrogen acceptor and produces a large amount of sulfide in an anaerobic environment. If the pH remains high, then the reduced sulfur will be in the form of the hydrosulfide ion which is held in solution. Sulfide has been reported as toxic to algae in the concentration range of 6 to 7 mg/l which is a consideration in the pond treatment of sulfur-laden wastewaters [6]. There are two bacterial types which are capable of oxidizing reduced sulfur compounds. The first group consists of colorless bacteria which are strict aerobes using molecular oxygen as the hydrogen acceptor. The second group is comprised of photosynthetic sulfur bacteria. These are anaerobes and require both light and sulfides for growth, and utilize CO_2 as the hydrogen acceptor. These bacteria, which impart a red or brown color to the water, appear where anaerobic conditions exist and sulfides are present. This oxidation of reduced sulfur, which takes place in two steps, occurs as follows[1] :

$$CO_2 + 2H_2S \xrightarrow{\text{light}} (CH_2O) + H_2O + 2S \qquad (13\text{-}9)$$

$$3CO_2 + 2S + 5H_2O \xrightarrow{\text{light}} 3(CH_2O) + 2H_2SO_4 \qquad (13\text{-}10)$$

It is noted that this photosynthetic reaction forms no molecular oxygen. Moreover, no BOD reduction takes place based on the sulfur transformation and may even tend to increase the BOD concentration.

In summary, long term waste stabilization ponds, properly designed, have selected applicability in the treatment of domestic and industrial wastewaters. Aside from the wastewater characteristics, removal kinetics, and hydrological considerations, design features should include proper grading, access, maintainable embankments, proper influent, effluent, and connecting pipes, proper selection of materials, and means for insect control.

TABLE 13-1. GENERALIZED BOD LOADING PER UNIT AREA PER DAY UNDER VARIOUS CLIMATIC CONDITIONS

Surface Loading (BOD/acre-day)	Detention Time (days)	Environmental Conditions
Less than 10	More than 200	Frigid zones, with seasonal ice cover, uniformly low water temperatures and variable cloud cover.
10-50	200-100	Cold seasonal climate with seasonal ice cover and temperate summer temperatures for short season.
50-150	100-33	Temperate to semi-tropical, occasional ice cover, no prolonged cloud cover.
150-350	33-17	Tropical, uniformly distributed sunshine and temperature, and no seasonal cloud cover.

Waste stabilization ponds are seldom designed as total treatment systems in current practice as regulatory requirements are becoming increasingly more stringent. They are, however, widely used following some form of primary or secondary treatment. Surface loadings and detention times, as previously mentioned, usually dictate size. Allowable surface loadings are, of course, highly dependent on climate conditions as indicated for domestic wastes in Table 13-1 [1]. Ponds used at various positions within the treatment process train and their process effectiveness for the treatment of petrochemical wastewaters are tabulated in Table 13-2 [7].

TABLE 13-2. WASTE STABILIZATION POND TREATMENT OF PETROCHEMICAL WASTES

Flow (mgd)	BOD In (mg/l)	BOD Out (mg/l)	BOD Rem (%)	COD In (mg/l)	COD Out (mg/l)	COD Rem (%)	Organic Loading lb BOD/ acre-day	Nutrients Required	Remarks
19.1	100	50	50	350	200	43	Primary pond 91; total ponds 46	None	Pond in series after aerated lagoon, bench scale.
5	500-1,000	400-700	20-60				96	None	Anaerobic
5	400-700	25-50	88-96				164	None	Anaerobic
5	25-50	5-30	40-90				5	None	Aerobic
3.25	150	7-15	90-95	260			75	None	Facultative pond, 18 days detention; influent SO_4 = 650 mg/l
2.45	50-100	20-50	50-80	150-200	120	20-40	95		Following aerated lagoon or activated sludge; bench-scale
1.69	686	186		1,681	590	65			Facultative ponds
0.15	20			1,120-5,950	4,610 4,450	10-25	25	None	Bench-scale; facultative ponds to remove some residual COD. High non-biodegradable fraction. After activated sludge..
			95-99			75-96	100		Facultative ponds.

Increasing land cost and more stringent effluent quality controls by regulatory agencies, particularly in terms of total suspended solids (TSS), will limit new waste stabilization pond application for wastewater treatment in many areas. However, they will continue to be used in areas where conditions favor this mode of treatment based on land cost, ultimate water reuse, process effectiveness, and climatological factors. Additionally, accelerated algal systems, (ponds carrying high concentrations of algal and bacteria cells with facilities for solids-liquid separation by flotation), have shown promise [8]. If this concept can be proven in the field to be a viable and effective means of treating wastewater, then a reorientation of waste stabilization pond technology and application can be expected.

EQUIPMENT REQUIRED

1. A batch or continuous bench-scale pond system, as illustrated in Figure 13-2. Larger pond reactors, such as the one shown in Figure 13-3, can be constructed from 55 gallon drums.

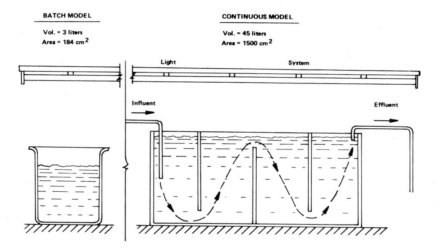

BATCH MODEL

Vol. = 3 liters
Area = 184 cm^2

CONTINUOUS MODEL

Vol. = 45 liters
Area = 1500 cm^2

Light   System

Influent   Effluent

FIG. 13-2. BENCH-SCALE POND SYSTEMS

2. Artificial lighting system with fluorescent and incandescent lights at an intensity of approximately 600-800 foot candles.
3. Control system for lighting pond system 12 out of every 24 hours.
4. Artificially compressed air system for furnishing cleansed air to surface simulating wind action.
5. Feed and effluent storage receptacles and facilities for discharging influent feed to the pond model on a continuous or semi-continuous basis at a controlled rate.

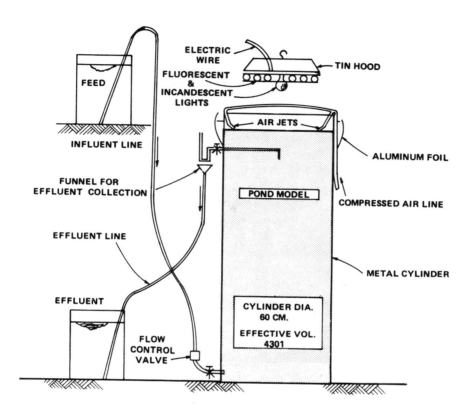

FIG. 13-3. CROSS SECTION OF MODEL WASTE STABILIZATION POND

6. Associated glassware, pipettes, chemicals, and analyzers. Samples withdrawn for the pond are normally analyzed for pH, D.O., and ORP. Additionally, the influent and effluent quality is normally analyzed for organic content and other miscellaneous constituents.

EXPERIMENTAL PROCEDURES

1. Fill the continuous or batch model stabilization ponds with the liquid contents taken from a properly functioning aerobic or facultative pond. Determine the initial COD of the contents, both filtered and total. If industrial

wastes are to be tested, then the initial seed should be from a pond treating a similar type wastewater. If this is not possible, then a longer acclimation and pond equilibration time will be required.

2. Apply the wastewater to the unit on a continuous or fill and draw basis. Select a desired surface loading and detention time. Add tap water daily to the unit to compensate for evaporation. Provide an air jet just above the surface of both units to prevent scum formation and simulate wind action.

3. Withdraw samples from each unit daily and analyze for soluble and total effluent COD. The effluent COD (or BOD) should stabilize following approximately 1.5 to 2.0 detention times. If a multiple pond series is used, the effluent from one pond will serve as the raw feed for the next.

4. Measure the pH, ORP, and dissolved oxygen of the pond contents at the end of the "lights on" cycle. Record any periods when noticeable odors are prevalent. Also note any apparent changes in the color of the pond contents (transmittance using a spectrophotometer may be used to record such a change). If the raw wastewater contains sulfate ion ($SO_4^=$) in excess of 240 mg/l, check the sulfate and sulfide concentrations in the pond on a weekly basis. Also, check the total Kjeldahl nitrogen (TKN) and diurnal

TABLE 13-3. TABULATION OF POND PERFORMANCE DATA

Time (days)	TOC (mg/l) Filtered	TOC (mg/l) Unfiltered	COD (mg/l) Filtered	COD (mg/l) Unfiltered	DO (mg/l)	pH	% Trans.
Raw Waste→ --		5,000	14,580	14,800			
7	710	790	2,440	2,990	0	3.3	--
14	630	790	2,920	2,700	0	3.6	17
21	1,100	2,450	5,250	6,320	0	6.5	5
28	1,650	1,950	6,190	6,560	0	5.8	0
35	--	--	5,560	6,170	0	5.4	0
42	--	1,950	5,300	6,440	0	5.1	0
49	--	--	4,830	4,670	0	5.5	0
56	1,800	1,900	--	--	0	5.1	0
63	--	--	--	--	0	--	--
70	1,600	1,600	4,840	4,880	0	4.9	0

changes in dissolved oxygen periodically. Data can be recorded as shown in the experimental data tabulated in Table 13-3.

5. Step 2 can be repeated using different organic surface loadings if required. The results of the test or test series in terms of pond performance can then be plotted as shown in Figure 13-4.

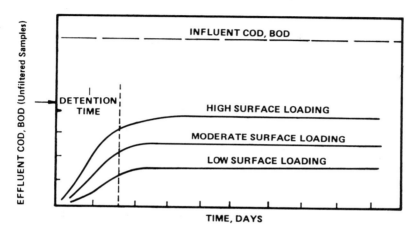

FIG. 13-4. EFFECT OF SURFACE LOADING ON EFFLUENT QUALITY

6. Determine the required pond detention time to produce the desired effluent from the graphical formulation of data shown in Figure 13-5.

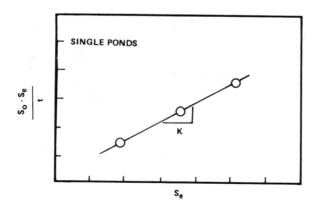

FIG. 13-5. DETERMINATION OF BIOLOGICAL RATE CONSTANT

From the average flow, the pond volume can be calculated. The reaction rate, K, should be corrected for design temperature according to Equation 13-8.

If the pond is to be designed as an aerobic facility, the areal requirements based on photosynthetic oxygen supply can be estimated from the solar energy concept (Equation 13-1). The depth can be approximated from Figure 13-1. İt should also be noted that the "K" volume will depend on the relative depth of the aerobic and anaerobic portions of the pond and this should be considered in scale-up.

LIMITATIONS AND SCALE-UP

There are obvious limitations in translating bench or pilot-scale pond data to full-scale systems. The most difficult factor to predict from these studies is the wind and mixing effect in the field, and this influence on removal kinetics and

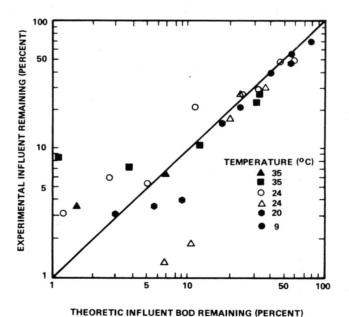

FIG. 13-6. CORRELATION OF EXPERIMENTAL AND THEORETICAL RESULTS

bottom scouring. The effluent suspended and settleable solids quality as determined in the laboratory could therefore be quite different from that experienced in the full-scale system. Moreover, the light intensity as simulated in the lab would be different both in terms of magnitude and exposure time from that experienced in the field. This would in turn affect algal synthesis and oxygen production rates.

Although these scale-up limitations would apparently mitigate the validity of extrapolating bench-scale results into design criteria, the approach as outlined herein can be applied with a relative degree of expected accuracy. For example, a correlation between the theoretical values of BOD removal for single ponds using Equation 13-5 and experimental data has been established by Gloyna [1]. This correlation is shown in Figure 13-6 and is indicative of the accuracy of the mathematical model shown as Equation 13-5. As Equation 13-4 was developed empirically from field installation, laboratory, and pilot-scale pond observations, it should be relatively accurate as a predictive equation.

In summary, there are many external factors that influence pond performance which as a practical matter cannot be incorporated into the predictive mathematical models. Experimental treatability projects can, however, be used to develop generalized pond design criteria, predict soluble organic removal and effluent quality, indicate the fate of potential pathogenic agents, and demonstrate the influence of the test wastewater on algal species.

REFERENCES

1. Gloyna, E. F., *Waste Stabilization Ponds,* World Health Organization Monograph Series No. 60, World Health Organization, Geneva, Switzerland (1971).
2. Palmer, C. M., and Tarzwell, C. M., "Algae of Importance in Water Supplies," *Public Works,* 86 (1955).
3. Gloyna, E. F., "Waste Stabilization Ponds," Lecture Series, Univ. of Texas, Austin, Texas (1967).
4. Oswald, W. J., "Fundamental Factors in Waste Stabilization Pond Design," *Advances in Biological Waste Treatment,* W. W. Eckenfelder, Jr., and B. J. McCabe, Eds., Pergamon Press, Oxford (1963).
5. Oswald, W. J., "Advances in Anaerobic Pond Systems Design," *Advances in Water Quality Improvement,* E. F. Gloyna and W. W. Eckenfelder, Jr., Eds., The University of Texas Press, Austin, Texas (1968).
6. Gloyna, E. F., and Espino, E., "Sulfide Production in Waste Stabilization Ponds," *Jour. San. Eng. Div.,* 95, 607-628 (1969).

7. Gloyna, E. F., and Ford, D. L., *Petrochemical Effluents Treatment Practices,* Water Pollution and Control Research Series, 12020, FWPCA, Ada, Oklahoma (1970).

8. Shelef, G., and Schwarz, M., "Prediction of Photosynthetic Biomass Production in Accelerated Algal-Bacterial Wastewater Treatment Systems," Proc., 6th International Conference on Water Pollution Research, Jerusalem, Israel (1972).

14

ANAEROBIC TREATMENT OF ORGANIC WASTES

DISCUSSION OF PRINCIPLES

Traditionally, anaerobic degradation of organic materials has been associated with digestion of wastewater sludges which resulted from primary sedimentation of degradable organic solids or were generated during biological oxidation of soluble and colloidal organic materials. Anaerobic processes are also very effective for treating soluble and colloidal organic materials and to biologically reduce nitrogen in the form of nitrate to harmless nitrogen gas. Since the anaerobic system can obtain 50 to 70 percent organic destruction at a relatively low energy input, it may also be utilized very effectively for pretreating soluble organic wastewaters prior to aerobic systems.

Anaerobic systems, where applicable, offer several advantages over aerobic systems:

1. The cell yield (sludge production) is much lower with anaerobic processes.
2. The solids concentrations in the contact basin are not limited to oxygen transfer rates. Consequently, higher solids levels can be used, thereby accelerating the rate of organic removal.
3. The energy requirements are substantially lower than aerobic systems where mechanical aeration must be supplied.
4. There is a possibility of recovering energy in the form of methane gas.
5. There are much lower nutrient requirements for the anaerobic system due to the lower sludge production. This can be   significant for many industrial wastewaters.

Anaerobic Treatment of Organic Wastewaters

Anaerobic treatment can be employed for the degradation and breakdown of organic solids (sludges) or soluble organics to gaseous end products as shown in Figure 14-1 [1]. The process occurs in two stages: an initial breakdown to organic acids, followed by fermentation of the organic acids to methane and carbon dioxide.

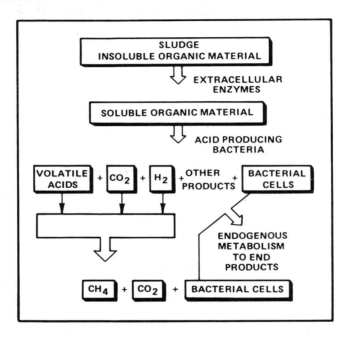

FIG. 14-1. MECHANISM OF ANAEROBIC DEGRADATION OF ORGANICS

Successful anaerobic treatment requires the proper balance between the rate of acid formation and the rate of methane formation.

One of the most significant influences on the rate of anaerobic degradation is the mixing intensity in the anaerobic contact reactor. Scale-up from laboratory data has inferred that power levels on the order of 1,500 hp/mil gal are required to achieve optimum anaerobic activity. Economic considerations and practical design have generally resulted in power levels in the range of 30 to 50 hp/mil gal in full-scale systems due to the difference in mixing intensities.

When treating soluble organic wastewaters, a higher rate of degradation may be obtained by increasing the solids concentration in the anaerobic reactor. The solids concentrations can be increased by separation of the solids from the treated effluent and returned to the anaerobic tank similar to an aerobic activated sludge system. It is usually necessary to degas the solids prior to sedimentation by either a vacuum degasifier or rapid mixing to release the gases from the suspended solids. The methane fermentation will control the overall rate of reaction so that conditions suitable for effective methane fermentation must be maintained in the process. The optimum conditions required for consistent methane fermentation are summarized in Table 14-1 [2].

TABLE 14-1. ENVIRONMENTAL CONDITIONS FOR METHANE FERMENTATION

Variable	Optimum	Extreme
pH	6.8 - 7.4	6.4 - 7.8
Oxidation - reduction potential, mv	-520 to -530	-490 to -550
Volatile acids, mg/l, as acetic	50 - 500	>2000
Total alkalinity, mg/l, as $CaCO_3$	1,500 - 5,000	1,000 - 3,000
Salts		
NH_4^+, mg/l, as N		3,000
Na, mg/l		3,500 - 5,500
K, mg/l		2,500 - 4,500
Ca, mg/l		2,500 - 4,500
Mg, mg/l		1,000 - 1,500
Gas production, ft^3/lb of VS destroyed	17 - 22 (1,060 - 1,370 l/kg of VS)	
Gas composition, % CH_4	65 - 70	
Temperature, °F	90 - 100	

The sludge age of the methane organisms must be sufficiently long in a flow-through reactor so that they will not be washed from the process. Consequently, the detention time of a flow-through system must be greater than the growth rate of the methane organisms. It should be emphasized that there are several species of methane organisms present in an anaerobic system so that the optimum detention time may vary from waste to waste even though all other conditions are constant. Various data have shown that the growth rate of the methane organisms varies from 2 to 20 days. Some data for different organic constituents are shown in Table 14-2[2]. The relationship of various components of an anaerobic system is shown in Figure 14-2 [7].

TABLE 14-2. GROWTH RATE OF METHANE ORGANISMS

Substrate	Temp. (°C)	Residence Time (days)
Methanol	35	2
Formate	35	3
Acetate	35	5
Propionate	35	7.5
Primary and activated sludge	37	3.2
Propionate	25	2.8
Butyrate	35	2.7

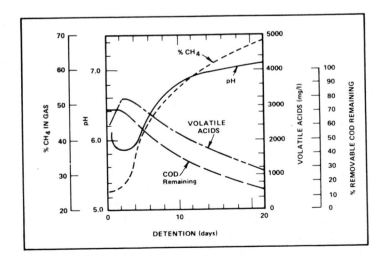

FIG. 14-2. ANAEROBIC DEGRADATION OF ORGANIC WASTE

The gas produced during anaerobic fermentation will be composed of methane and carbon dioxide with small quantities of hydrogen sulfide and hydrogen gas. The percentage of methane in the gas will depend primarily on the residence time. Higher percentages of carbon dioxide result at lower detention times with correspondingly reduced concentrations of methane organisms. The data in Figure 14-3 [3] infer approximately 7.4 cu ft of methane formed per lb of BOD removed with a meat packing waste. Lawrence and McCarty [4]

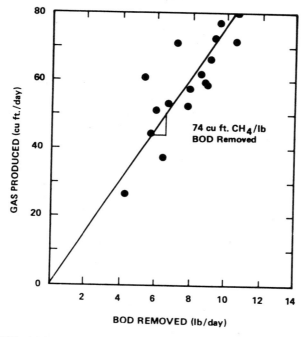

FIG. 14-3. GAS PRODUCTION FROM ANAEROBIC BOD
REMOVAL

have theoretically and experimentally shown that 5.62 cu ft of methane will be produced per lb of COD reduced.

Several variations of the anaerobic contact process are shown in Figure 14-4.a and 14-4.b. A submerged upflow column is very effective for soluble organic wastewaters or for anaerobic denitrification. Recycle may be desirable in order to dilute the incoming waste to levels amenable to the contact time afforded by the reactor. Recycle ratios as high as 20 to 1 have been used.

There are three variations of the completely mixed system. The first alternative considers only a flow-through reactor where the detention time must be

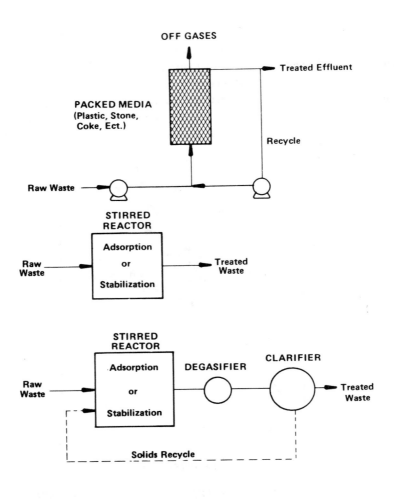

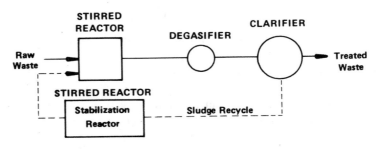

FIG. 14-4. ALTERNATIVE ANAEROBIC SYSTEMS

long enough to allow the required degradation of the organics. The sludge age is equivalent to the hydraulic detention time of the system. The second alternative allows the designer to control the sludge age, or organic loading, by concentrating and returning the solids back to the stirred reactor. The stirred reactor is sized to accomplish the desired degree of stabilization, and solids levels on the order of 5,000 to 12,000 mg/l may be carried in the reactor. The degasifier may be a vertical steel tank with approximately 20 inches of mercury applied vacuum. The third alternative for a completely mixed system employs a short detention time, unheated stirred reactor (1 to 3 hr detention time) followed by solids separation. The concentrated sludge is then stabilized in a separate reactor for a minimum detention time of 8 to 12 hr and may be heated. The third system has been found feasible for meat packing, milk, fatty acid, wood fiber, and domestic sewage wastewaters. It is most effective for wastewaters containing degradable suspended solids. It should not be employed with soluble organic wastewaters.

Treatment performance of different wastewaters with the flow-through (conventional) and contact processes is summarized in Table 14-3 [8].

Kinetics of Anaerobic Degradation

With soluble wastewaters, kinetics similar to the aerobic activated sludge process can be employed. It has been found that Monod kinetics describe the operation of anaerobic treatment of soluble organic wastes very effectively [5]. Consequently, it can be shown that a completely mixed anaerobic system can be described by a pseudo second order rate as shown below [1]:

$$\frac{S_o - S_e}{X_v t} = kS_e \qquad (14\text{-}1)$$

where:

S_o = influent BOD, mg/l
S_e = effluent soluble BOD, mg/l
X_v = mixed liquor volatile suspended solids, mg/l
t = hydraulic detention time, days
k = BOD removal rate coefficient, l/mg-day

The data from a completely mixed anaerobic system can be correlated as shown in Figure 14-5. Occasionally, a plug flow system with a column or a fixed media is more desirable particularly when recycle is employed. The advantages of a plug flow system over a completely mixed system are shown in Figure 14-6

TABLE 14-3. TREATMENT PERFORMANCE FOR ANAEROBIC SYSTEMS

Waste	Hydraulic Detention Time (Days)	Digestion Temperature (°C)	Raw Waste (mg/l)	BOD$_5$ (lb/1,000 cu ft-day) Added	BOD$_5$ (lb/1,000 cu ft-day) Removed	BOD$_5$ (lb/1,000 cu ft-day) Stabilized	Percent Removed	Reference
Conventional Process:								
Butanol	10.0	--	17,000	114	80	75	70	Buswell (1954)
Acetic Acid	30.0	35	620,000	975	965	876	99	McCarty, et al (1962)
Butyric Acid	30.0	35	400,000	1,000	980	910	98	McCarty, et al (1962)
Contact Processes:								
Maize Starch	3.3	23	6,280	110	97	85	88	Hemens, et al (1962)
Whiskey Distillery	6.2	33	25,000	250	237	164	95	Painter, et al (1960)
Cotton Kiering	1.3	30	1,600	74	50	42	67	Pettet, et al (1959)
Citrus	1.3	33	4,600	214	186	141	87	McNary, et al (1954)
Brewery	2.3	--	3,900	127	122	--	96	Newton, et al (1962)
Meat-Packing	1.3	33	2,000	110	104	77	95	Pettet, et al (1960)
Meat-Packing	0.5	33	1,380	156	142	66	91	Steffen, et al (1962)
Meat-Packing	0.5	35	1,430	164	156	--	95	Schroepfer, et al (1965)
Meat-Packing	0.5	29	1,310	152	143	--	94	Schroepfer, et al (1965)
Meat-Packing	0.5	24	1,110	131	119	--	91	Schroepfer, et al (1965)

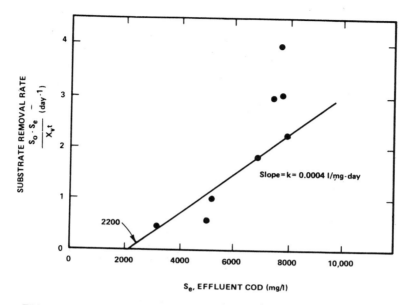

FIG. 14-5. DETERMINATION OF ORGANIC REMOVAL RATE COEFFICIENT

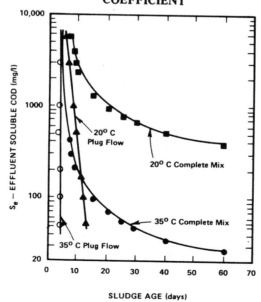

FIG. 14-6. RELATIVE REMOVAL EFFICIENCIES FOR PLUG FLOW AND COMPLETELY MIXED SYSTEMS

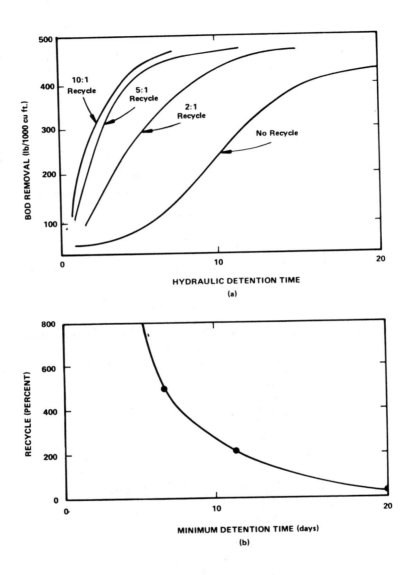

FIG. 14-7. TYPICAL DATA CORRELATIONS FROM PLUG FLOW COLUMN REACTORS

[5]. However, a plug flow reactor should always be preceded by sufficient equalization. The data from a plug flow reactor or a column may be correlated as shown in Figure 14-7.

Sludge production for the completely mixed anaerobic systems with recycle may be determined identically to the methods described in Chapter 10, "Activated Sludge." For a flow-through reactor, the equilibrium solids in the reactor can be calculated as:

$$X_v = \frac{a(S_o - S_e)}{1 + bt} \qquad (14\text{-}2)$$

where:

X_v = equilibrium volatile suspended solids, mg/l

a = biological sludge production from synthesis of BOD, mg VSS produced/mg BOD removed

b = endogenous biological sludge destruction, mg VSS destroyed/mg VSS in system-day

Equation 14-2 may be rearranged as shown below:

$$\frac{S_o - S_e}{X_v} = \frac{1}{a} + \frac{b}{a} t \qquad (14\text{-}2a)$$

The data from a bench-scale or pilot system can be correlated as shown in Figure 14-8 to determine the coefficients, a and b. As can be seen in Figure 14-8, the methane fermentation stage generates substantially less sludge than the acid fermentation stage. In general, the anaerobic system will produce much less sludge than an aerobic system. Where an aerobic system may convert approximately 40 to 60 percent of the carbon removed into cellular material, an anaerobic system will only convert about 4 to 10 percent of the carbon to cells.

Biological Denitrification

Biological denitrification implies the reduction of nitrate to nitrogen gas plus small quantities of other nitrogen products, such as nitrogen oxides, in the absence of dissolved oxygen. A possible pathway for this process is shown in Table 14-4 [6]. The organisms which accomplish biological denitrification are facultative, that is, in the presence of oxygen they perform aerobically as in the activated sludge process. In the absence of dissolved oxygen, these organisms function anaerobically and utilize chemically-bound oxygen in the form of sulfates and nitrates for a final hydrogen acceptor. Fortunately, nitrates are more readily utilized than sulfates, thereby generating no odors during denitrification provided that the system is not grossly overdesigned. The facultative organisms are heterotopic and require an organic carbon source for growth.

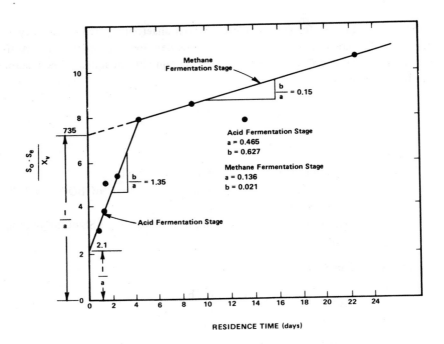

**FIG. 14-8. DETERMINATION OF SLUDGE PRODUCTION
COEFFICIENTS**

**TABLE 14-4. POSSIBLE PATHWAYS FOR
BIOLOGICAL DENITRIFICATION**

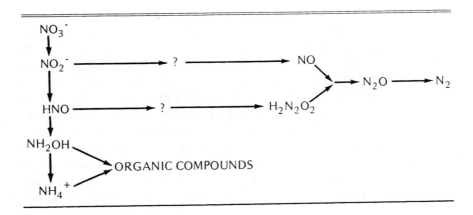

Methanol is the most referenced carbon source and the system requires approximately 2.9 lb methanol per lb of nitrate nitrogen removed. The rate of reaction is not controlled by the nitrate concentration but by the degradation rate of the organic carbon source. Therefore, the rate can vary with different wastewaters depending on the nature of the organic constituents. The pH of the reactor is significant with regard to the rate of denitrification under the influence of dissolved oxygen. Under acid conditions, active denitrification will occur in the presence of dissolved oxygen. However, strict anaerobic conditions are mandatory at pH levels greater than 7.0.

The kinetics and principles of anaerobic denitrification are the same as those described in the preceding section on organic wastewaters. The data may be correlated as previously described and as shown in Figures 14-9 and 14-10.

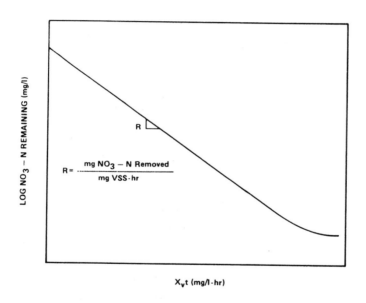

FIG. 14-9. DETERMINATION OF DENITRIFICATION RATE

EQUIPMENT REQUIRED

The equipment required for determining the design parameters for anaerobic degradation of organic wastewaters consists of various types of reactors which may be batch or continuously-fed systems. The reactors can be completely

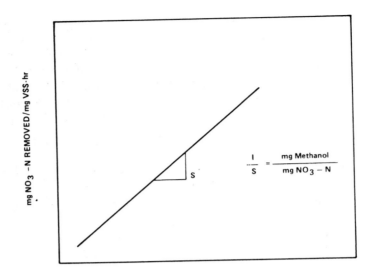

mg METHANOL REMOVED/mg VSS-hr

FIG. 14-10. DETERMINATION OF CARBON REQUIREMENTS

mixed or plug flow, for optimum kinetics, if the nature of the wastewater permits. The experimental systems must have the capability to contain the off-gases from the system. Several reactor types have been found suitable and are described below:

1. Completely mixed, batch fed reactor (Figure 14-11);

   a. Reactor with one liter minimum volume fitted with a 3-hole stopper plus arrangements for mixing.

   b. A mixer which may be either a magnetic stirrer or a mechanical mixer. If mechanical mixer is used, a gas type seal must be incorporated into the stopper.

   c. A gas collection tube which is approximately 500 to 1,000 ml in volume.

   d. An aspirator bottle to contain water and form a seal between the atmosphere and the collected gas.

2. Completely mixed, continuously-fed reactor (Figure 14-12)

   This system is more complex and requires several pumps and a gas recirculation apparatus as shown in Figure 14-12. The components are listed below:

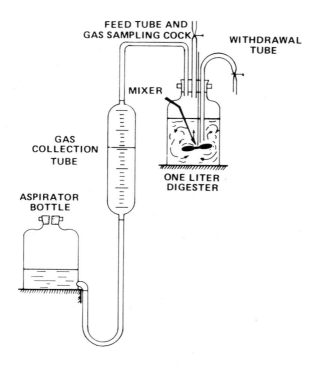

FIG. 14-11. BATCH-FED ANAEROBIC REACTOR

a. The reactor which ranges from 1 to 10 liters in volume. There should be a sample port and a three-way stopper for the reactor.

b. Condensate trap of approximately 500 ml volume to collect moisture prior to recirculation of the gas;

c. A wet test meter to measure gas volumes;

d. A positive displacement pump for gas recirculation to obtain mixing. The system shown in Figure 14-12 is a simple flow-through reactor and does not allow sludge recirculation or continuous liquid withdrawal. A system which allows for solids separation and return is shown in Figure 14-13.

3. Plug flow, horizontal fixed media reactor (Figure 14-14).

a. The reactor can be an acrylic plastic compartmentalized unit with three sections. Each section should be one to two liters in volume.

b. The media can be Raschig rings, gravel, coke or some synthetic plastic media.

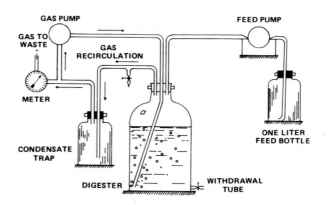

FIG. 14-12. CONTINUOUSLY-FED ANAEROBIC REACTOR

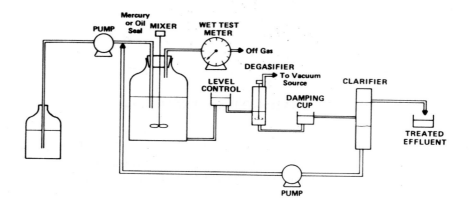

**FIG. 14-13. COMPLETELY MIXED ANAEROBIC REACTOR WITH
SOLIDS RECYCLE**

    c.   Wet test meter.

4. Plug flow, vertical upflow reactor (Figure 14-15)

    a.   The reactor should be a 6-in. diameter column of glass or acrylic plastic, approximately 4 ft in length.

    b.   A recycle pump for recirculating the treated effluent to the influent of the reactor.

    c.   A wet test meter for gas measurement.

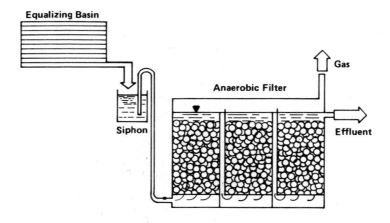

**FIG. 14-14. PLUG FLOW HORIZONTAL FIXED MEDIA
REACTOR**

    d.   Media: rashig rings

    e.   Insulation and heating tapes, if desired.

5. Synthetic substrate. A synthetic substrate can be effectively used to develop a healthy anaerobic seed prior to acclimation. A seed which has been used successfully by McCarty is shown in Table 14-5 [8].

EXPERIMENTAL PROCEDURES

The experimental procedures utilized for developing the required design criteria consist of developing an organic growth (on a fixed media in the case of plug flow reactors) and then acclimating this growth to the wastewater in question. After acclimation and stabilization, the various system parameters can be varied in order to develop the design criteria. It is desired to operate these systems at different organic loadings, detention times, or recycle ratios in order to examine the spectrum of design variables. An example of the treatability procedures and correlations will be illustrated herein using the continuous feed, flow-through, completely mixed reactor.

    1. Set up the apparatus as shown in Figure 14-12.

    2. Obtain an actively digesting seed from a municipal plant and immediately

271

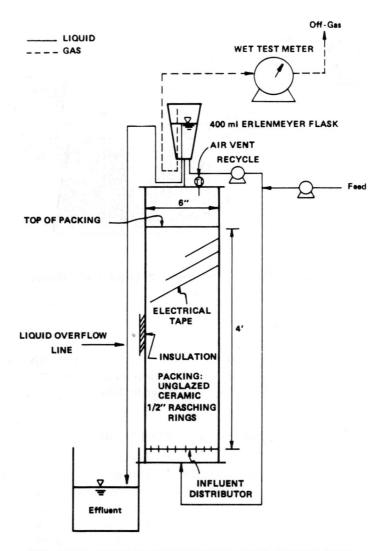

FIG. 14-15. PLUG FLOW VERTICAL UPFLOW REACTOR

place in the reactor. Initially maintain the contents at 35°C, if possible, during start up and acclimation.

3. If a significant quantity of air is entrapped in the digester, purge with an inert gas, preferably helium.

4. Adjust the suspended solids concentration to a level of approximately 6,000 to 10,000 mg/l.
5. Begin feeding the synthetic substrate (Table 14-5) to the reactor contents at a rate of a pre-established ml/liter of reactor volume.

TABLE 14-5. ANAEROBIC TREATMENT OF SYNTHETIC ORGANIC WASTES/MIXED CHEMICALS--DIGESTER FEED

Theoretical Oxygen Demand, mg/l	25,000
Measured COD, mg/l*	20,000
Measured BOD$_5$*	19,600
Substrate	
Acetic Acid	2,124
Benzoic Acid	1,165
Propionic Acid	1,505
Acetaldehyde	1,248
Phenol	955
Butanol	878
Ethanol	1,093
Vinyl Acetate	1,361
Butyl Acetate	1,033
Monoethanolamine	914
Diethylene Glycol	1,505
Buffer-Nutrient**	
$(NH_4)_2CO_3 \cdot H_2O$	4,292
$NaH_2PO_4 \cdot H_2O$	542
KH_2PO_4	542
Trace Elements	
$FeCl_3$	18.0
$MnSO_4 \cdot H_2O$	3.08
$CoCl_2 \cdot 6H_2O$	4.04
MoO_3	1.53
$ZnSO_4 \cdot H_2O$	5.32

Note: Concentrated mixtures were diluted with tap water as required.
  * Mean of several analyses of diluted feeds recalculated to original strength.
  ** Provided ratio COD:N:P ≅ 100:5:1.

273

6. Adjust the flow of the gas recirculation pump to completely mix the contents of the reactor. Alternatively, use a mechanical mixer or magnetic stirrer.

7. Check the entire system for gas leaks by putting small quantities of water or mineral oil around the joints and observing for bubbles.

8. After gas production is noticed and appears to be consistent (approximately 5 to 6 cu ft of gas per lb of COD removed or 0.35 ml of gas per mg COD removed at STP conditions), begin to introduce the wastewater materials diluted by the synthetic feed. It is recommended that the initial feed only contain a 10 percent dilution (by COD, not volume) of the wastewater. Cautiously, increase the dilution factor to 100 percent wastewater over a period of 5 to 20 days, depending on such factors as the relative degradability of the waste and the presence of inhibitors. During this acclimation period, it is desirable to maintain the organic loading to the system at less than 1.0 mg BOD/day-mg VSS. Another control parameter during acclimation is to feed the waste at a rate of less than 200 lb of BOD/day-1,000 cu ft of reactor volume.

9. Withdraw samples periodically for analysis of BOD or COD removals, pH, VSS level, alkalinity/acidity, and volatile acids. During start-up and acclimation, the pH should be carefully observed and controlled to ensure that it does not fall below 6.6. Sufficient alkalinity should be added to maintain the pH within the range of 6.6 to 7.6.

TABLE 14-6. EXPERIMENTAL DATA FROM COMPLETELY - MIXED ANAEROBIC SYSTEM

Characteristic	Residence Time, days							
	0.75	1.28	1.68	2.87	4.33	8.81	13.2	22.5
Influent COD, mg/l	9,820	10,410	10,410	10,500	10,500	10,430	10,370	10,070
Effluent COD mg/l	7,780	7,700	7,720	7,930	6,790	5,220	5,060	3,210
Mixture SS, mg/l	780	792	621	525	527	627	752	740
VSS, mg/l	683	747	528	477	467	597	680	648
Gas CH_4 (%)	25.4	26.1	27.1	24.6	41.6	52.7	56.7	68.7
Gas, cu ft STP/day	0.834	0.905	0.813	0.553	0.569	0.577	0.476	0.361
Liter/day feed	42.6	43.2	33.0	28.0	15.3	8.71	4.99	3.42

10. After stabilized conditions are obtained, the systems can be operated at the desired test conditions and samples withdrawn daily for analysis of BOD, COD, VSS, and pH. In addition, the gas production should be measured and recorded daily. The data which are collected can be tabulated as shown in Table 14-6.

CORRELATION OF RESULTS

The data collected from bench and pilot-scale-studies can be correlated to generate the parameters needed for design. Specifically, it is generally desired to determine optimum detention times, organic loadings, removal rates, and effects of temperature. Additionally, with denitrification it is desirable to determine the optimum carbon/nitrogen ratio. The data gathered in Table 14-6 may be correlated as follows:

1. From the data in Table 14-6, develop Tables 14-7 and 14-8.

TABLE 14-7. CALCULATION OF ORGANIC REMOVAL RATES

Time	S_o	S_o	$S_o - S_e$	X_v (VSS)	$\left(\dfrac{S_o - S_e}{X_v}\right)$	$\left(\dfrac{S_o - S_e}{X_v t}\right)$
0.75	9,820	7,780	2,040	683	2.99	4.00
1.28	10,410	7,500	2,910	747	3.90	3.05
1.68	10,410	7,720	2,690	528	5.10	3.04
2.87	10,500	7,930	2,570	477	5.38	1.88
4.33	10,500	6,790	3,710	467	7.93	1.83
8.81	10,430	5,220	5,210	597	8.70	0.988
13.2	10,370	5,060	5,310	680	7.80	0.59
22.5	10,070	3,210	6,860	642	10.58	0.47

2. Correlate the COD removal rate, $(S_o - S_e)/X_v t$, versus effluent COD, S_e, as shown in Figure 14-5.

3. Calculate the slope of the line as the reaction rate coefficient, k. In this case, the value of k is 0.0004 1/mg-day. The intercept on the x-axis represents the non-degradable COD and must be incorporated into Equation

275

14-1. Consequently, the design equation for COD removal is:

$$\frac{S_o - S_e}{X_v t} = 0.0004 \, (S_e - 2200)$$

4. Determine the sludge production coefficients in accordance with Equation 14-2a. In other words, plot $(S_o - S_e)/X_v$ versus t as shown in Figure 14-8. The coefficients, a and b, are found to be 0.136 and 0.021, respectively, for the methane fermentation stage which controls the design. Consequently, the design equation for sludge production is:

$$\frac{S_o - S_e}{X_v} = \frac{1}{0.136} + \frac{0.021}{0.136} \, t$$

or:

$$X_v = \frac{S_o - S_e}{7.35 + 0.154}$$

If denitrification is being examined, it will be necessary to correlate the data as shown in Figures 14-9 and 14-10.

TABLE 14-8. CALCULATION OF GAS PRODUCTION

COD Removed (mg/l)	Feed (liters/day)	COD Removed (lb/day)	Gas Production (cu ft/day)	CH_4 Content (%)	CH_4 Production (cu ft/day)	Calculated cu ft per lb COD removed
2,040	42.6	0.191	0.834	25.4	0.21	1.10
2,910	43.2	0.276	0.905	26.1	0.236	0.86
2,690	33.0	0.195	0.813	27.1	0.22	1.13
2,570	28.0	0.159	0.553	24.6	0.136	0.86
3,710	15.3	0.125	0.569	41.6	0.237	1.90
5,210	8.71	0.100	0.577	52.7	0.302	3.02
5,310	4.99	0.058	0.476	56.7	0.27	4.65
6,860	3.42	0.051	0.361	68.7	0.246	4.82

SCALE-UP AND LIMITATIONS

In extrapolating laboratory data to field conditions, the most important criteria is the influence of mixing. It is important to recognize the significance of mixing and the probability that greater power levels were utilized in the laboratory than will be practical in field conditions. Consequently, conservative mixing levels should be used in laboratory studies or a conservative safety factor employed in scale-up. Due to the high susceptibility of anaerobic processes to pH and temperature fluctuations, all expected situations should be examined in the laboratory and conscientiously controlled in the field. In addition, the laboratory and pilot studies should be subjected to all possible inhibitory constituents and conditions which might occur in the field.

REFERENCES

1. Eckenfelder, W. W., and Ford, D. L., *Water Pollution Control: Experimental Procedures for Process Design,* Pemberton Press, Austin, Texas (1970).
2. Eckenfelder, W. W., *Water Quality Engineering for Practicing Engineers,* Barnes and Noble, Inc., New York (1970).
3. Hemens, J. and Shurben, D. G., "Anaerobic Digestion of Waste Waters from Slaughter-houses," *Food Trade Review,* 29:7, 2-7 (1959).
4. Lawrence, A. W. and McCarty, P. L., Kinetics of Methane Fermentation in Anaerobic Waste Treatment, Tech. Rept. 75, Dept. of Civil Engineering, Stanford University, Stanford, California (February, 1967).
5. Speece, R. E., "Anaerobic Treatment," Process Design in Water Quality Engineering: *New Concepts and Developments,* E. L. Thackston and W. W. Eckenfelder, Eds., Jenkins Publishing Co., New York (1972).
6. McElroy, W. D. and Glass, B., *A Symposium on Inorganic Nitrogen Metabolism,* John Hopkins Press, Baltimore, Maryland (1956).
7. Andrews, J. F., Cole, R. D. and Pearson, E. A., *Kinetics and Characteristics of Multistage Methane Fermentations,* SERL Rept. 64-11, University of California, Berkeley, California (1964).
8. McCarty, P. L., "Anaerobic Treatment of Soluble Wastes," Advances in Water Quality Improvement, E. F. Gloyna and W. W. Eckenfelder, Eds., University of Texas, Austin, Texas (1968).

15

GRANULAR MEDIA FILTRATION

DISCUSSION OF PRINCIPLES

Granular media filtration is achieved by passing the wastewater through a bed of granular material at a controlled flow rate, with or without the addition of conditioning chemicals. The removal process is a complex one involving several different mechanisms such as straining, interception, impaction, sedimentation, and adsorption. The relative significance of each removal mechanism is dependent upon the physical and chemical properties of the granular media, the suspended particles, and the carrier liquid. The nature of the particulate matter in the influent and the size of the filter media are process variables of particular significance. Influent characteristics of importance are suspended solids concentration, particle size and distribution, and floc strength.

Granular media filtration is a cyclic operation involving two phases: filtration and backwashing. The end of the filtration phase is indicated either by reaching the limiting pressure drop across the bed, or by a breakthrough of suspended solids into the effluent. Ideally, these two events should occur simultaneously.

Although the theory of filtration has been the subject of numerous investigations in the past, reliable design can best be achieved on the basis of pilot plant studies augmented by theoretical considerations. Design should incorporate adequate flexibility so that optimization or process adjustments can be made by the plant operator to meet varying conditions.

Granular media filters may be classified as follows:

1. Type of Media -- single or multi-media — coarse to fine, fine to coarse

general gradation of media;
2. Flow direction — downflow or upflow;
3. Time variation of the flow rate — constant or declining;
4. Operating pressure — gravity or pressure.

In any granular media filtration system, maximum utilization of the filter bed is the ideal objective. This can be best achieved if the media is graded from coarse to fine in the direction of flow. Since media gradation from fine to coarse occurs during backwashing, a coarse-to-fine gradation çan best be achieved in one of the following systems (see Figure 15-1):

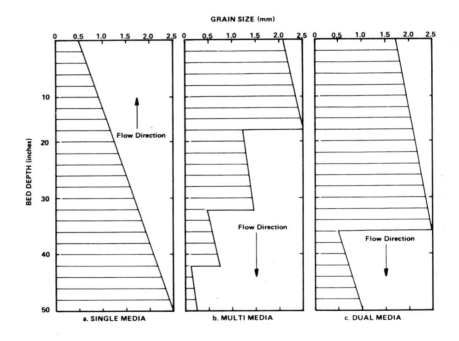

FIG. 15-1. COARSE-TO-FINE FILTRATION SYSTEMS

1. Upflow — single media;
2. Downflow — multi-media.

For upflow filtration, the maximum flow rate is limited by the buoyant weight of the filter media. If this flow rate is exceeded, fluidization will occur with a loss of filtration efficiency and media. A restraining grid is often placed on top of the media to control media expansion.

Downflow tri-media filters are generally more efficient than dual media filters. However, in many cases the improvement in effluent quality or length of filter run is insufficient to justify the extra cost of tri-media beds. A typical multi-media filter is shown in Figure 15-2.

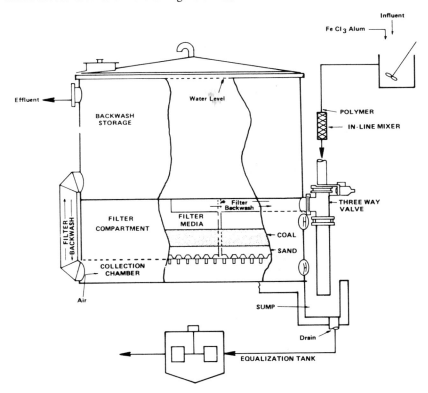

FIG. 15-2. TYPICAL GRANULAR MEDIA FILTER

Gravity-type filters may be designed for operation with either constant or variable flow. Declining rate filtration design involves a constant headloss during the filter run. The flow rate decreases gradually as the bed becomes progressively clogged. This design approach has some advantages over constant rate (variable headloss) filtration. Due to the reduced shearing forces exerted on the deposited matter, late in the filter run, the declining rate filter will produce a more uniform effluent. It should be noted that for either constant or variable flow design, rapid variations of filtration rate are undesirable as they may cause dislodging of deposited matter and subsequent deterioration of effluent quality.

Media used for filtration includes sand, coal (anthracite), and garnet. The specific gravities and the common size ranges of these media are listed in Table 15-1. Sand or anthracite are utilized in dual media filters, while garnet, sand and anthracite are used in tri-media filters.

TABLE 15-1. MEDIA COMMONLY USED FOR FILTRATION

Media	Specific Gravity	Size Range (mm)
Anthracite	1.5	0.8 - 3.0
Sand	2.6	0.4 - 1.5
Garnet	4.2	0.2 - 0.4

Gravity filters are generally backwashed at headloss values of 7 to 16 feet. This headloss usually occurs when the filter has reached its maximum solids holding capacity. The solids holding capacity for a downflow, dual-media filter ranges from 0.5 to 1.5 lb/sq ft of filter area.

EQUIPMENT REQUIRED

A schematic flowsheet of a pilot filter arrangement is shown in Figure 15-3.

1. A column, 8 ft high by a minimum of 4 in. in diameter. It is preferable to utilize a column of 6 to 8 in. diameter in order to minimize wall effects and allow for proper backwashing. Wall effects mitigate the applicability of small diamter units.

2. A backwash nozzle. In order to obtain the proper flow distribution during backwashing, it is beneficial to use an actual manufacturer's distribution nozzle. The nozzle should be installed in the bottom of the column according to the manufactuer's instructions. The diameter of the column should be coordinated with the particular nozzle. The 8 in. column, shown in Figure 15-2, is fitted with an EIMCO Flexkleen nozzle which requires an 8-in. diameter column.

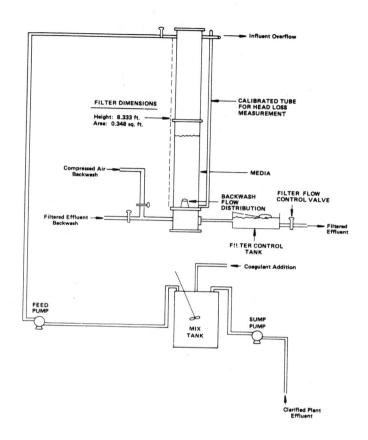

FIG. 15-3. SCHEMATIC OF PILOT SCALE FILTER

3. An overflow weir. The column should possess an overflow weir so that a constant liquid level can be maintained above the media.

4 Headloss tubes. The filter should be fitted with tubes, 1/4 to 3/8 in. in diameter located at different points in the filter. For routine design, the tubes can be located at the top and bottom of the filter media so that the total headloss in the filter can be determined, such as the top, middle or bottom of the filter media. This will allow a better analysis of the cause of headloss, such as excess coagulants, over-flocculation ahead of the filter, or poor media distribution.

5. Associated tanks, pumps, and tubing.

EXPERIMENTAL PROCEDURES

In order to design a granular media filter, several correlations must be developed experimentally. The major parameters which can be varied during testing include flow rate (hydraulic loading rate), type and concentration of chemical additions, location of chemical injection point, media configuration and type, and depth. The relative media sizes and specifications can be selected from Table 15-1. It is desired to test the suspended solids removal characteristics, and the bed expansion during backwash.

1. Set up the filter and put the media in place.

2. Various chemicals, optimum dosages and conditions for use can be examined by the use of common jar test methodology as explained in Chapter 5 entitled "Coagulation and Precipitation."

3. Initially, it is desirable to pump from a large container, which is capable of holding the entire flow for one run, so that the influent suspended solids concentration to the filter is constant. This is rarely possible with the larger diameter filters. If chemicals are added to the waste container, it is essential that flocculation not be allowed to occur unintentionally. Consequently, sufficient agitation must be provided to prevent flocculation. An alternate is to add the chemicals at the inlet to the filter so that flocculation occurs within the filter. After initial experimentation the filter can be operated on-line with the chemicals added directly ahead of the filter (or a flocculator if preflocculation is desired).

4. Set the pumping rate at the hydraulic flow to achieve the desired surface loading rate, such as 2, 4, or 6 gpm/sq ft. The flow rate can best be controlled by a control valve on the filter effluent.

5. Maintain a constant flow by periodically opening the effluent control valve. This is necessary because the flow tends to decrease as the filter becomes filled with solids. This mode of operation is the constant-flow method of operation. Alternatively, and often preferable, is the constant headloss mode, whereby the effluent valve is completely opened and a constant head is maintained on the filter. The run is continued until the headloss reaches the pre-selected level (6 to 8 ft) with the constant-flow mode or the flow is significantly reduced with the constant headloss mode.

6. Various media and hydraulic loadings are examined in order to determine the best conditions for suspended solids removals.

7. Monitor such effluent parameters as suspended solids, COD or BOD and turbidity with time and use a flow-weighted average (with flow)

to obtain the average effluent quality during the filter run. A more practical approach is to collect effluent samples in proportion to the flow, blend them, and perform one composite analysis. With the constant flow mode, headloss measurements should be made with time.

8. After determining the media arrangement, hydraulic loading and chemicals tests are conducted to correlate headloss with solids retention.

   a. Set the flow rate at the optimum level for the selected media and chemical dosage selected.

   b. Record the total headloss, influent and effluent suspended solids at fixed time intervals.

9. Establish the expansion characteristics of the selected media. This may be done experimentally by varying the backwash and measuring the expansion rate, or it can be calculated if all the media properties are known including the shape and porosity factor [1].

CORRELATION OF RESULTS

Two sets of tests have been conducted with different media arrangements. Initially, the filter media consisted of 18 in. of anthracite (effective size 0.55 mm), 6 in. of sand (effective size 0.42 mm) and a 4 in. of 3/8 in. support gravel. The function of the gravel is to aid in backwash flow distribution. Using this media, the filter was operated at hydraulic rates of 2, 4 and 8 gpm/sq ft without coagulant addition. Additionally, the filter was operated with coagulant additions of 13 and 25 mg/l alum at 4 gpm/sq ft.

When suspended solids removals appeared poor with the dual media, 4 in. of sand were added to the top layer and a 4-in. layer of garnet (effective size 0.30 mm) was added at the bottom. The filter was then operated with 12 mg/l of alum at 2 gpm/sq ft and 20 mg/l alum at 2, 4, 6, and 8 gpm/sq ft. Results of filtration studies were tabulated in Table 15-2.

Suspended Solids Removal Characteristics

1. Calculate the fraction of suspended solids remaining, C_e/C_o, for each run.
2. Plot the fraction of solids remaining versus the hydraulic loading as shown in Figure 15-4.

These data indicate that a 20 mg/l dosage of alum is necessary prior to filtration. Additionally, it is inferred that the tri-media filter is much superior to the dual media configuration.

TABLE 15-2. RESULTS OF FILTRATION STUDIES

Date	Run	Flow Rate (gpm/sq ft)	Al$_2$(SO$_4$)$_3$ (mg/l)	Media (in.)			pH		Average SS (mg/l)		Length of Run (hr)	Terminal Headloss (in.)	Waste-water Temp (°C)
				Anthracite	Sand	Garnet	Inf.	Eff.	Inf.	Eff.			
Dec. 11	I	2.16	0	18	6	..	..	..	57	40	23.0	58	..
Dec. 12	II	3.96	0	18	6	..	..	..	44	30	10.0	32	..
Dec. 13	III	7.84	0	18	6	..	..	..	67	53	9.0	69	..
Dec. 14	IV	3.80	13	18	6	..	6.8	6.7	38	14	10.0	96	..
Dec. 17	V	3,89	25	18	6	..	6.5	5.6	69	39	8.0	84	15.2
Dec. 30	VI	2.1	12	18	10	4	6.4	6.2	49	20	8.0*	29.5	17.3
Dec. 31	VII	2.07	20	18	10	4	6.3	6.0	52	7	23.0	82	19.5
Jan. 1	VIII	3.97	20	18	10	4	6.2	6.0	49	8	22.0	85	14.8
Jan. 4	IX	6.24	20	18	10	4	6.4	6.0	21	4	25.0	81	14.9
Jan. 9	X	8.13	20	18	10	4	6.6	6.3	80	20	5.5	86	17.2

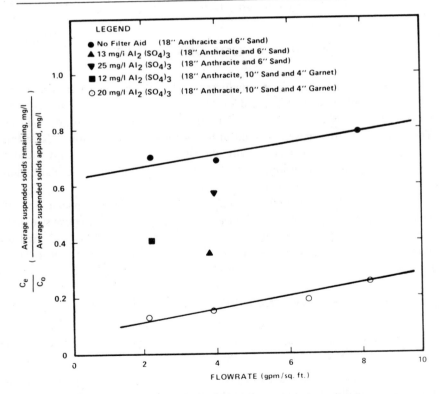

FIG. 15-4. CORRELATION OF SUSPENDED SOLIDS REMOVAL WITH FLOW RATE

Headloss and Solids Deposition Characteristics

1. For each run, plot the headloss versus time as shown in Figure 15-5. These results indicate that run times as long as 20 to 25 hours could be obtained with headlosses ranging from 7 to 10 ft.

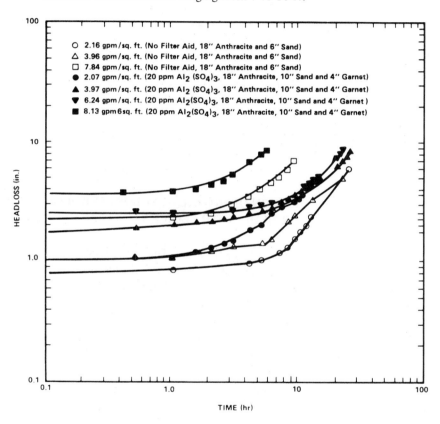

FIG. 15-5. **CORRELATION OF HEADLOSS THROUGH FILTER AND FILTER TIME**

2. Correlate the initial headloss as a function of hydraulic loading as shown in Figure 15-6. As expected, the tri-media filter with coagulant doses generated higher initial headlosses than the dual media with its shallower depth.

3. From the chronological variations of influent and effluent suspended

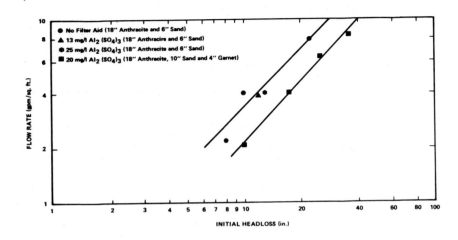

**FIG. 15-6. CORRELATION OF INITIAL HEADLOSS THROUGH
FILTER MEDIA WITH FLOW RATE**

solids, calculate the total solids deposited. The solids deposited are calculated at various times throughout the run. Each value is divided by the area of the filter to result in units of lb SS deposited/sq ft of filter at a given time.

4. Calculate the change in headloss at each time interval which corresponds to the time of the solids deposition calculated in Step 3 above.

5. Plot solids deposition versus change in headloss as shown in Figure 15-7. This figure is required for design in order to determine the length of filter run based on the solids applied and the solids which can be accumulated before the allowable head is exceeded.

Bed Expansion During Backwash

The bed expansion during backwash can be observed at backwash rates varying from 5 to 25 gpm/sq ft and correlated as shown in Figure 15-8.

LIMITATIONS AND SCALE-UP

In performing the experimental tests, it is essential that the backwashing

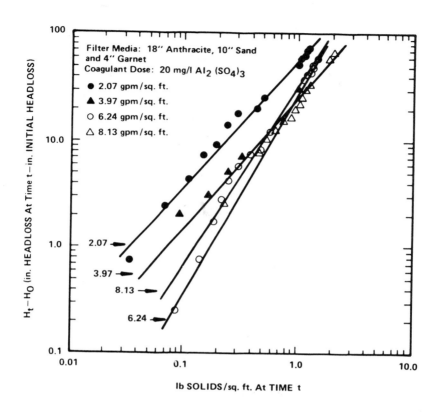

FIG. 15-7. CORRELATION OF DIFFERENTIAL HEADLOSS WITH SOLIDS ACCUMULATION ON FILTER MEDIA

between each run be efficient and complete. Otherwise, each successive run will indicate erroneous initial headlosses.

In design, certain parameters are selected from the experimental correlations, such as:

1. Media type and gradation specification.
2. Coagulants, coagulant aids, and dosage requirements.
3. Method and location of coagulant addition.
4. Hydraulic loading rate.
5. Terminal headloss.
6. Required expansion during backwash.

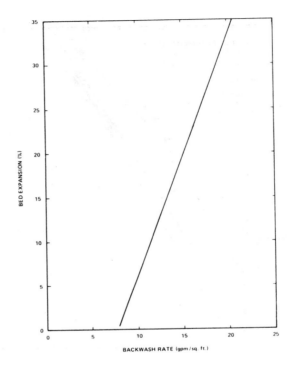

FIG. 15-8. BED EXPANSION VS BACKWASH RATE

The area is determined and then the maximum headloss increment, $H_t - H_o$, is calculated from the selected terminal headloss, H_t, and the experimentally-determined initial headloss, H_o (Figure 15-6). The solids deposition which relates to this headloss is determined from Figure 15-7. Knowing this quantity of solids and calculating the rate of deposition, the length of run can be calculated [1].

Finally, backwash requirements are determined. If the backwash quantity exceeds 5 percent of the influent flow, the filter area should be increased proportionately to accommodate the extra flow.

REFERENCE

. Adams, C.E., Jr., and Eckenfelder, W.W., Jr., Eds., *Process Design Techniques for Industrial Wastewaters*, Enviro Press, Nashville, Tn. (1974).

16

ACTIVATED
CARBON ADSORPTION

DISCUSSION OF PRINCIPLES

Activated carbon adsorption is most often employed for the removal of organic constituents from wastewater. Although carbon is sometimes used as a catalyst for dechlorination or oxidation of cyanide and for the removal of certain heavy metals, these special cases have limited applications to wastewater treatment and are not included in this discussion.

The principal applications of carbon adsorption for the treatment of organic wastewaters include the removal of non-degradable substances, such as color-producing compounds and pesticides, and the reduction of specific organic constituents, such as phenols, in wastestreams which contain relatively small concentrations of specific organic species. This process may be performed in combination with biological treatment for the removal of either degradable or refractory organic constituents. It should be noted that the powdered activated carbon-activated sludge system is not discussed in this chapter.

The efficacy of utilizing carbon adsorption for the treatment of organic wastewaters at any point in a process sequence can be determined only after a thorough investigation using continuous-flow pilot systems. There is a tendency for investigators and equipment developers to oversimplify the process adaptability for industrial wastewater applications. Specifically, the translation of data from carbon systems receiving domestic wastes into design criteria for industrial utilization has limited validity, and the use of batch isotherm information under any testing condition as a basis for process selection is not precise. The technical and economic justification for including carbon adsorption as a treatment process in an industrial application therefore must be predicated on pilot plant simulation, particularly in the absence of case histories and full-scale operational experience. A proper interpretation of the results is then necessary to consummate the process evaluation, determine the economics, and select the most appropriate treatment sequence.

In most cases, granular activated carbon is employed for wastewater treatment applications in either fixed or fluidized-bed processes. By using several carbon columns in series, maximum utilization of the carbon capacity may be achieved prior to removing the carbon for regeneration or disposal. The adsorption of organics from the liquid to a solid phase is generally assumed to occur in three stages; namely, the movement of the contaminant (adsorbate or solute) through a film surface surrounding the solid phase (adsorbant); the diffusion of the adsorbate within the pores of the activated carbon; and, finally, the sorption of the material onto the surface of the sorbing medium. Of these three phases, the first two resistances are usually the rate limiting factors and can be combined in an overall mass transfer term [1]. Using this rationale, an expression for adsorption kinetics in column systems can be developed:

$$q \frac{dC}{dD} = K(C_s - C) \tag{16-1}$$

where:

q = mass flow rate per unit of surface area of adsorbant
C_s = concentration of adsorbate in solution
D = adsorbant bed bath
C = equilibrium adsorbate concentration
K = overall mass transfer coefficient

A more convenient expression of Equation 16-1 is in terms of the adsorbate removal rate with respect to the weight of adsorbant in the columns:

$$Q \frac{dC}{dM} = \frac{k}{\rho_s} (C_s - C) \tag{16-2}$$

where:

Q = volumetric flow rate
ρ_s = packed density of carbon in the column
M = weight of carbon in the column
k = adsorption rate constant

Unfortunately, adsorption theory as described by these rate equations applies only to binary solutions and ignores process variables such as temperature, pH, linear flow velocity, modes of wastewater-carbon contact, and characteristics of the carbon.

The complexity of industrial wastewaters and the extremes in adsorbability of various types of chemical compounds limit the applicability of general rate

TABLE 16-1. INFLUENCE OF MOLECULAR STRUCTURE AND OTHER FACTORS ON ADSORBABILITY

1. An increasing solubility of the solute in the liquid phase decreases its adsorbability.

2. Branched chains are usually more adsorbable than straight chains. An increasing length of the chain decreases solubility.

3. Substitute groups affect adsorbability:

Substitute Group	Nature of Influence
Hydroxyl	Generally reduces adsorbability; extent of decrease depends on structure of host molecule.
Amino	Effect similar to that of hydroxyl but somewhat greater. Many amino acids are not adsorbed to any appreciable extent.
Carbonyl	Effect varies according to host molecule: glyoxylic is more adsorbable than acetic, but similar increase does not occur when introduced into higher fatty acids.
Double bonds	Variable effect as with carbonyl.
Halogens	Variable effect.
Sulfonic	Usually decreases adsorbability.
Nitro	Often increases adsorbability.

4. Generally, higher ionized solutions are not as adsorbable as weakly ionized ones; i.e., undissociated molecules are in general preferentially adsorbed.

5. The amount of hydrolytic adsorption depends on the ability of the substance to hydrolyze and form an adsorbable acid or base.

6. Unless the screening action of the carbon pores intervene, large molecules are more sorbable than small molecules of similar chemical nature. This is attributed to more solute carbon chemical bonds being formed, making desorption more difficult.

7. Molecules with low polarity are more sorbable than highly polar ones.

equations. The influence of molecular structure and other factors on adsorbability, for example, is presented in Table 16-1 [2]. This relative adsorbability, combined with unpredictable effects of process variables, forces an empirical approach for investigating carbon process applicability. Breakthrough curves defining contaminant removal (in terms of BOD, COD, TOC, color, or specific organic constituents), carbon capacities, and the influence of process variables on performance, can therefore be developed using continuous-flow columns in pilot-scale testing. Recently published data citing the sorbability of many organic compounds are presented in Table 16-2 [3].

The effectiveness of a carbon in removing selected contaminants can be predicted using equilibrium adsorption isotherms developed from batch tests. The Freundlich isotherm is usually used to describe adsorption phenomena involving industrial wastewater applications:

$$X/M = KC^{1/n} \qquad (16\text{-}3)$$

where:

X	=	amount of impurity adsorbed
M	=	weight of carbon
C	=	equilibrium concentration of impurity in solution
K,n	=	constants

This relationship may be graphically linearized by plotting the logarithm of the quantity of contaminant adsorbed (X/M) as a function of the logarithm of the equilibrium contaminant concentration, such as BOD, COD, TOC, or color. The presentation of data obtained from the Freundlich isotherm is shown in Figure 16-1. The use of this relationship may be limited where concentrated and complex wastewaters are involved, with a significant portion of the organic impurities not amenable to adsorption. This results in a constant residual regardless of the carbon dosage.

If Equation 16-3 does express the equilibrium relationship which is established between a wastewater and carbon, the constants, K and n, are indicative of the adsorbability of the wastewater constituents. Generally, n and K decrease with increasing wastewater complexity. High K and high n values indicate high adsorption throughout the concentration range studied. A low K and high n indicates a low adsorption throughout the concentration range studied. A low n value, or steep slope, indicates high adsorption at strong solute concentrations and low adsorption at dilute solute concentrations. It should be emphasized, however, that isotherm development for a particular wastewater has a limited application. This is underscored by the variations of isotherm constants devel-

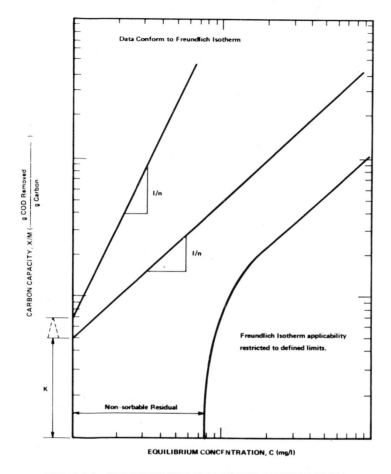

FIG. 16-1. FREUNDLICH ISOTHERM APPLICATION

oped in investigations and reported in the literature for refinery wastewaters following primary and secondary treatment. These values are listed in Table 16-3. (See references 2 to 6, inclusive.) Moreover, the carbon capacity, which increases with the COD gradient in accordance with Equation 16-2, was higher when determined from continuous-flow carbon studies than that indicated from batch isotherms as shown in Figure 16-2 using the same conditions. This discrepancy has been reported previously. although the higher capacity demonstrated in columnar operations has been attributed solely to biological removal in columns [7]. It is proposed, however, that a portion of this higher capacity is attributed to inherent differences in the continuous and batch tests. The capacity of the columnar operation is established by the continuously high

TABLE 16-2. AMENABILITY OF TYPICAL ORGANIC COMPOUNDS TO ACTIVATED CARBON ADSORPTION

Compound	Molecular Weight	Aqueous Solubility (%)	Concentration (mg/l)		Adsorbability*	
			Initial (C_0)	Final (C_f)	g compound / g carbon	Percent Reduction
Alcohols						
Methanol	32.0	∞	1.000	964	0.007	3.6
Ethanol	46.1	∞	1.000	901	0.020	10.0
Propanol	60.1	∞	1.000	811	0.038	18.9
Butanol	74.1	7.7	1.000	466	0.107	53.4
n-Amyl alcohol	88.2	1.7	1.000	282	0.155	71.8
n-Hexanol	102.2	0.58	1.000	45	0.191	95.5
Isopropanol	60.1	∞	1.000	874	0.025	12.6
Allyl alcohol	58.1	∞	1.010	789	0.024	21.9
Isobutanol	74.1	8.5	1.000	581	0.084	41.9
t-Butanol	74.1	∞	1.000	705	0.059	29.5
2-Ethyl butanol	102.2	0.43	1.000	145	0.170	85.5
2-Ethyl hexanol	130.2	0.07	700	10	0.138	98.5
Aldehydes						
Formaldehyde	30.0	∞	1.000	908	0.018	9.2
Acetaldehyde	44.1	∞	1.000	881	0.022	11.9
Propionaldehyde	58.1	22	1.000	723	0.057	27.7
Butyraldehyde	72.1	7.1	1.000	472	0.106	52.8
Acrolein	56.1	20.6	1.000	694	0.061	30.6
Crotonaldehyde	70.1	15.5	1.000	544	0.092	45.6
Benzaldehyde	106.1	0.33	1.000	60	0.188	94.0
Paraldehyde	132.2	10.5	1.000	261	0.148	73.9
Amines						
Di-N-Propylamine	101.2	∞	1.000	198	0.174	80.2
Butylamine	73.1	∞	1.000	480	0.103	52.0
Di-N-Butylamine	129.3	∞	1.000	130	0.174	87.0
Allylamine	57.1	∞	1.000	686	0.063	31.4
Ethylenediamine	60.1	∞	1.000	893	0.021	10.7
Diethylenetriamine	103.2	∞	1.000	706	0.062	29.4
Monethanolamine	61.1	∞	1.012	939	0.015	7.2
Diethanolamine	105.1	95.4	996	722	0.057	27.5
Triethanolamine	149.1	∞	1.000	670	0.067	33.0
Monoisopropanolamine	75.1	∞	1.000	800	0.040	20.0
Diisopropanolamine	133.2	87	1.000	543	0.091	45.7
Pyridines & Morpholines						
Pyridine	79.1	∞	1.000	527	0.095	47.3
2-Methyl 5-Ethyl pyridine	121.2	sl.sol.	1.000	107	0.179	89.3
N-Methyl morpholine	101.2	∞	1.000	575	0.085	42.5
N-Ethyl morpholine	115.2	∞	1.000	467	0.107	53.3
Aromatics						
Benzene	78.1	0.07	416	21	0.080	95.0
Toluene	92.1	0.047	317	66	0.050	79.2
Ethyl benzene	106.2	0.02	115	18	0.019	84.3
Phenol	94	6.7	1.000	194	0.161	80.6
Hydroquinone	110.1	6.0	1.000	167	0.167	83.3
Aniline	93.1	3.4	1.000	251	0.150	74.9
Styrene	104.2	0.03	180	18	0.028	88.8
Nitrobenzene	123.1	0.19	1.023	44	0.196	95.6
Esters						
Methyl acetate	74.1	31.9	1.030	760	0.054	26.2
Ethyl acetate	88.1	8.7	1.000	495	0.100	50.5
Propyl acetate	102.1	2	1.000	248	0.149	75.2
Butyl acetate	116.2	0.68	1.000	154	0.169	84.6
Primary amyl acetate	130.2	0.2	985	119	0.175	88.0

TABLE 16-2. AMENABILITY OF TYPICAL ORGANIC COMPOUNDS TO ACTIVATED CARBON ADSORPTION, (continued)

Compound	Molecular Weight	Aqueous Solubility (%)	Concentration (mg/l) Initial (C_0)	Concentration (mg/l) Final (C_f)	Adsorbability* g compound/ g carbon	Adsorbability* Percent Reduction
Esters						
Isopropyl acetate	102 1	2 9	1.000	319	0 137	68 1
Isobutyl acetate	116 2	0 63	1.000	180	0 164	82.0
Vinyl acetate	86 1	2 8	1.000	357	0 129	64 3
Ethylene glycol monoethyl ether acetate	132 2	22 9	1.000	342	0 132	65 8
Ethyl acrylate	100 1	2 0	1.015	226	0 157	77 7
Butyl acrylate	128 2	0 2	1.000	43	0 193	95 9
Ethers						
Isopropyl ether	102 2	1 2	1.023	203	0 162	80.0
Butyl ether	130 2	0 03	197	nil	0 039	100 0
Dichloroisopropyl ether	171 1	0 17	1.008	nil	0 200	100 0
Glycols & Glycol Ethers						
Ethylene glycol	62 1	∞	1.000	932	0 0136	6 8
Diethylene glycol	106 1	∞	1.000	738	0 053	26 2
Triethylene glycol	150 2	∞	1.000	477	0 105	52 3
Tetraethylene glycol	194 2	∞	1.000	419	0 116	58 1
Propylene glycol	76 1	∞	1.000	884	0 024	11 6
Dipropylene glycol	134 2	∞	1.000	835	0 033	16 5
Hexylene glycol	118 2	∞	1.000	386	0 122	61 4
Ethylene glycol monomethyl ether	76 1	∞	1.024	886	0 028	13 5
Ethylene glycol monoethyl ether	90 1	∞	1.022	705	0 063	31 0
Ethylene glycol monobutyl ether	118 2	∞	1.000	441	0 112	55 9
Ethylene glycol monohexyl ether	146 2	0 99	975	126	0 170	87 1
Diethylene glycol monoethyl ether	134 2	∞	1.010	570	0 087	43 6
Diethylene glycol monobutyl ether	162 2	∞	1.000	173	0 166	82 7
Ethoxytriglycol	178 2	∞	1.000	303	0 139	69 7
Halogenated						
Ethylene dichloride	99 0	0 81	1.000	189	0 163	81 1
Propylene dichloride	113 0	0 30	1.000	71	0 183	92.9
Ketones						
Acetone	58 1	∞	1.000	782	0 043	21 8
Methylethyl ketone	72 1	26 8	1.000	532	0 094	46 8
Methyl propyl ketone	86 1	4 3	1.000	305	0 139	69 5
Methyl butyl ketone	100 2	v sl sol	988	191	0 159	80.7
Methyl isobutyl ketone	100 2	1 9	1.000	152	0 169	84.8
Methyl isoamyl ketone	114 2	0 54	986	146	0 169	85 2
Diisobutyl ketone	142 2	0 05	300	nil	0 060	100.0
Cyclohexanone	98 2	2 5	1.000	332	0 134	66 8
Acetophenone	120 1	0.55	1.000	28	0 194	97 2
Isophorone	138.2	1 2	1.000	34	0 193	96 6
Organic Acids						
Formic acid	46 0	∞	1.000	765	0 047	23 5
Acetic acid	60.1	∞	1.000	760	0 048	24 0
Propionic acid	74 1	∞	1.000	674·	0.065	32 6
Butyric acid	88 1	∞	1.000	405	0 119	59 5
Valeric acid	102.1	2 4	1.000	203	0 159	79 7
Caproic acid	116.2	1.1	1.000	30	0 194	97 0
Acrylic acid	72 1	∞	1.000	355	0 129	64 5
Benzoic acid	122 1	0.29	1.000	89	0.183	91 1
Oxides						
Propylene oxide	58 1	40 5	1.000	739	0 052	26 1
Styrene oxide	120.2	0 3	1.000	47	0 190	95 3

* Dosage: 5 g Carbon C/l solution

TABLE 16-3. COMPARATIVE ANALYSIS OF ISOTHERM DATA
REFINERY AND PETROCHEMICAL WASTEWATERS

Wastewater Source	K	1/n
OIL SEPARATOR (PRIMARY) EFFLUENT		
Refinery — Petrochemical Complex No. 1	0.0290	0.77
Refinery — Petrochemical Complex No. 2	0.0036	0.80
Refinery No. 3	0.0140	0.36
SECONDARY (ACTIVATED SLUDGE) EFFLUENT		
Refinery — Petrochemical Complex No. 1	0.0062	0.60
Refinery No. 3	0.0043	1.00
Refinery Secondary Effluent	0.0051	0.96
Refinery Secondary Effluent	0.0038	1.08
Refinery Secondary Effluent	0.0020	0.69
SINGLE ADSORBATES		
Phenol	0.11	5.80
Formic Acid	2.47	2.31
Acetic Acid	2.46	2.85
Succinic Acid	2.83	3.30
Adipic Acid	1.79	6.20
Citric Acid	0.73	4.93

concentration gradient at the interface of the adsorption zone with the virgin carbon as it passes through the column, while the concentration gradient decreases with time in the batch isotherm test.

The limitations of theoretical adsorption concepts relative to the practicalities of treatment requirements for industrial wastewaters necessitate that comprehensive process simulation studies precede the final design decisions. Because of these limitations and discrepancies between predicted carbon capacities in batch and column systems, unpredictable breakthrough geometry, and leakage of certain organics through carbon beds, not discussed in this chapter, a more detailed discussion of these aspects is merited.

Consideration for placement of the fixed-bed carbon adsorption process includes biological-carbon series treatment, carbon-biological series treatment, and carbon adsorption as a total process. Each of these applications may require primary treatment for the removal of oily substances and suspended matter. For

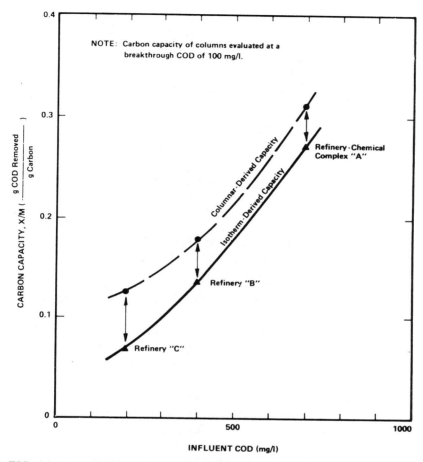

FIG. 16-2. CARBON CAPACITY FROM BATCH AND COLUMN SYSTEMS

example, refinery wastewater may require pretreatment by gravity separators and, in many cases, secondary oil removal such as dissolved air flotation or filter coalescers. A conceptual flow diagram for each of these candidate systems is shown in Figure 16-3 for application to refinery wastewaters.

Of the applications indicated above, the series biological-carbon treatment scheme will probably be most prevalent in the immediate future for the treatment of selected organic wastewaters. This is true for many systems as a capital investment in biological plants has already been expended to meet the 1977 provision of Public Law 92-500 (Water Pollution Control Amendments) and additional treatment will be required to meet the probable new water quality criteria. In the case of a new facility, this approach lends itself to phase con-

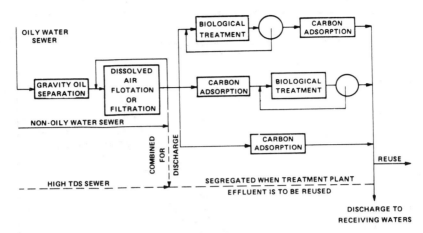

**FIG. 16-3. CANDIDATE SYSTEM APPLICATION FOR CARBON
ADSORPTION WITHIN A REFINERY TREATMENT COMPLEX**

struction by installing biological facilities to meet interim effluent requirements
and to provide effluent polishing if required. For other applications, including
the removal of non-degradable organic constituents and for the treatment of
low-strength wastes where stringent discharge requirements must be met, selection of a final process design will involve a choice between carbon adsorption
and other physical-chemical treatment methods of effluent polishing such as
chemical oxidation.

The series carbon-biological system is being considered by some refineries and
chemical plants. The apparent, although unproven, advantages include a more
effective use of carbon, less chance of biological upset because biologically toxic
substances are often adsorbed prior to biological exposure, and a reduction of
excess biological sludge inherent with the reduced organic loading. Although
these stated advantages merit consideration, one must also recognize the disadvantages; namely, potential effluent suspended solids and color problems
often associated with biological systems, less efficient biological removal of
organics, and the dependence upon a sometimes sensitive biological population
to consistently produce an effluent which will meet stringent quality requirements.

The results of recently conducted pilot studies applying granular carbon as a
total process for refinery and petrochemical wastewater treatment were somewhat
discouraging. Although there are obvious advantages to eliminating biological
treatment altogether in favor of carbon adsorption, these studies consistently
indicated a "leakage" of organics (BOD and COD) regardless of the applied
contact time, type of carbon, or linear flow velocity. This leakage and organic

residual as illustrated by the two-phase breakthrough curve shown in Figure 16-4 was actually higher than that observed in activated carbon sludge reactors which were operated in parallel. Because of these results, carbon adsorption was not recommended as a total treatment system for the refineries where these results were observed.

The aforementioned column studies have demonstrated some interesting features when evaluating performance using primary effluent (from an API separator) for the column feed as compared to using biologically treated effluent. For example, the carbon appeared to be non-selective with respect to its affinity for adsorbing compounds responsible for BOD and COD, respectively. This is evidenced by the fact that the BOD/COD ratio remained relatively constant throughout the carbon test series, regardless of the throughput volume. This was true when both the API separator effluent and the activated sludge effluent were applied to the columns. These results are plotted in Figure 16-5a and illustrate the magnitude of this ratio for both sequences of the biological-carbon series treatment. The reduction of the BOD/COD ratio through an activated sludge system is well documented and has been reported previously [8]. Unfortunately, this results in unacceptable effluent BOD levels in many instances when applying the carbon system as a total process. The advantage of

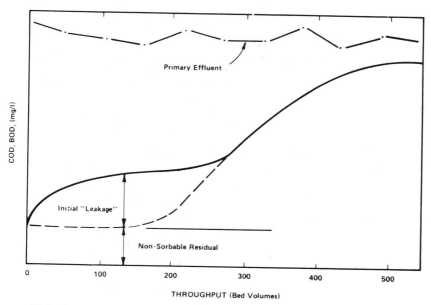

FIG. 16-4. TWO-PHASE BREAKTHROUGH CURVE-UNTREATED
REFINERY WASTEWATER (PRIMARY EFFLUENT)

apparent when considering stringent effluent BOD criteria.

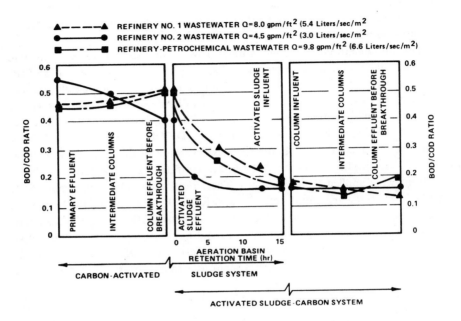

FIG. 16-5a. ORGANIC SELECTIVITY THROUGH COMBINED SYSTEMS

using carbon as a tertiary process following biological treatment is therefore

For design purposes it is convenient to present the data of Figure 16-5b in a bed-depth/service-time (BDST) diagram [9, 10]. This type of diagram correlates the bed-depth with the service-time for given values of effluent concentration. As shown in Figure 16-5b, to obtain data points for a BDST curve based on a reduction of 90 percent of the feed concentration, a horizontal line is drawn in Figure 16-5b through $C_B/C_o = 0.1$. This line intersects the breakthrough curves of the three columns at different times which are interpreted as the service time corresponding to the respective bed depth. A similar procedure can be employed for deriving BDST curves for any desired effluent concentration. Three such curves are shown in Figure 16-5c for effluent concentrations of 10, 20 and 90 percent of feed concentration. According to Bohart-Adams, the BDST curves are described by the following linear relationship:

$$t = \frac{N_o D}{C_o v} - \frac{1}{K C_o} \ln \left(\frac{C_o}{C_B} - 1 \right) \qquad (16\text{-}4)$$

302

where:

t	=	service time, hr
D	=	bed depth, ft
v	=	hydraulic loading or linear velocity, ft/hr
C_o	=	concentration of impurity in influent, mg/l
C_B	=	concentration of impurity in effluent, mg/l
N_o	=	adsorption efficiency, mg/l
K	=	adsorption rate constant, l/mg-hr

The values of N_o and K can be determined from the slope and intercept of the straight lines of Figure 16-5c. However, these parameters vary with hydraulic loading, v, and feed concentration, C_o. Thus in order to employ the BDST method for carbon column design, the laboratory columns should be operated at a loading rate and feed concentration similar to those expected in the prototype. Successful attempts to predict column performance at different loading rates and feed concentration by extrapolation of BDST data have been reported in the past. However, at the present time, there is not sufficient evidence for general validity of such a procedure.

The carbon capacity as established by continuous column studies is particularly significant in that the design carbon capacity dictates the size of the columns and regeneration furnace as well as the carbon inventory requirements.

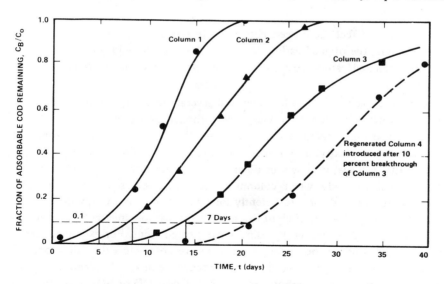

**FIG. 16-5b. BREAKTHROUGH CURVES FOR THREE COLUMNS
IN SERIES**

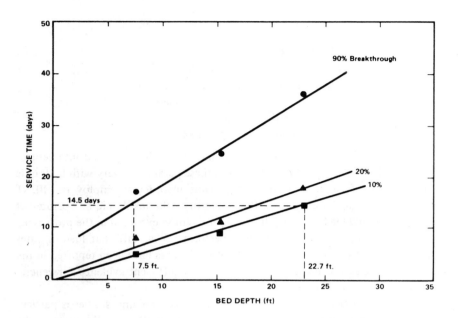

FIG. 16-5c. BDST CURVES FOR EFFLUENT CONCENTRATION

These in turn affect the process economics in terms of capital and annual costs. For example, the original carbon inventory alone accounted for over 15 percent of the estimated capital cost for a carbon system designed to treat a flow of 2 mgd.

Carbon capacity can also be calculated several other ways from column data. This is shown in Figure 16-6 where the carbon capacity at breakthrough and exhaustion is illustrated as a function of the depth of the adsorption zone and wastewater complexity. The influence of breakthrough curve geometry, particularly initial leakage, is shown in Figure 16-7. A true carbon capacity therefore can be assigned only when column studies using representative wastewater samples are operated for a sufficiently long period of time to fully develop the breakthrough geometry. Full utilization of the carbon in a column prior to regeneration can be realized by using a series of columns. For example, a series of three columns can be operated using one to complete exhaustion, one for polishing, and regenerating the third, with a sequence mode of operation.

It is recognized that carbon capacity based on COD or BOD breakthrough geometry may exclude consideration of selected critical contaminants such as phenols or surfactants. If the breakthrough carbon capacity in the polishing column is less than that for COD or BOD, then effluent quality requirements for these constituents may necessitate selection of a lower carbon capacity or design of a deeper system.

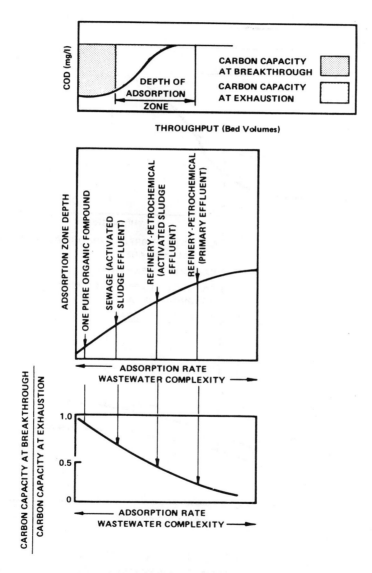

FIG. 16-6. INFLUENCE OF WASTEWATER COMPLEXITY
ON CARBON CAPACITY

Based on pilot studies, the anticipated removal of refinery wastewater constituents by activated sludge, total carbon, and combined treatment systems is tabulated in Table 16-4 [11]. These levels of removal may not apply in all cases, but are indicative of general treatment effectiveness.

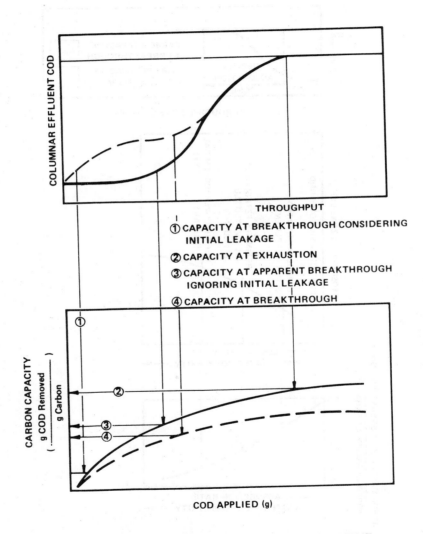

FIG. 16-7. INFLUENCE OF BREAKTHROUGH CURVE GEOMETRY ON CARBON CAPACITY

TABLE 16-4. ESTIMATED EFFLUENT QUALITY FOR THE ACTIVATED SLUDGE, CARBON, AND COMBINED TREATMENT OF REFINERY WASTEWATERS*

CONSTITUENT	Mean Value Range Primary Effluent	Activated Sludge Effluent	Total Carbon Effluent	Combined Activated Sludge-Carbon Effluent	REMARKS
COD	500-700 mg/l	100-200 mg/l	100-200 mg/l	30-100 mg/l	Exact COD residuals vary with complexity of refinery & design contact times in the Activated Sludge and Carbon Treatment Plants
BOD_5	250-350 mg/l	20-50 mg/l	40-100 mg/l	5-30 mg/l	BOD residual depends on BOD/COD ratio which characterizes relative biodegradability of wastewater.
Phenols	10-100 mg/l	<1 mg/l	<1 mg/l	<1 mg/l	Phenols(ics) are generally amenable to biological and sorption removal.
pH	8.5-9.5	7-8.5	7-8.5	7-8.5	pH drop in activated sludge systems attributed to biological production of CO_2 and intermediate acids. pH change in carbon columns depends on preferential adsorption of acidic and basic organics.
SS	50-200 mg/l	20-50 mg/l	<20 mg/l	<20 mg/l	Primary effluent solids depend on design and operation of oil removal units. Activated sludge effluent solids depend on effectiveness of secondary clarifier. Low effluent solids characterize carbon column effluent.
TDS	1500-3000 mg/l	1500-3000 mg/l	1500-3000 mg/l	1500-3000 mg/l	TDS is essentially unchanged through all three treatment systems.
NH_3 N	15-150 mg/l	5-100 mg/l	10-140 mg/l	2-100 mg/l	Exact concentration depends on pre-stripping facilities, nitrogen content of crude charge, corrosion additive practice and biological nitrification.
P	1-10 mg/l	<1-7 mg/l	1-10 mg/l	<1-7 mg/l	Only removal attributed to biological synthesis.

*Based on wastewater characterization data and treatability studies conducted by the author at eight refineries and petrochemical installations.

EQUIPMENT REQUIRED

Lab-Scale Isotherm Evaluation

1. Shaker assembly or jar test apparatus (see Figure 16-8).
2. Selected powdered or crushed granular carbon.
3. Beakers, pipettes, and other glassware.

Pilot-Scale Carbon Columns

1. Three to six acrylic plastic carbon columns, 3 to 6 in. diameter by approximately 6 ft in depth. Connector piping, valves, pressure gauges, and pumps designed for series column operation with backwash capability. Pressure gauges should be attached to each column (see Figure 16-9).
2. Selected granular carbon.
3. Filtration column (if required) using graded sand.
4. Sample collection capability from each column.
5. Flow measuring equipment.

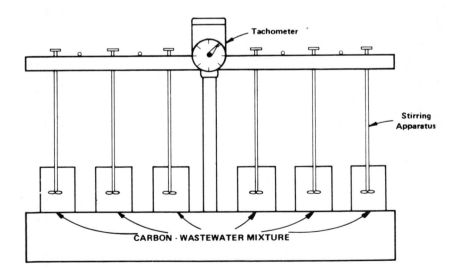

FIG. 16-8. LABORATORY SCALE JAR TEST ASSEMBLY FOR CARBON ISOTHERM DETERMINATION

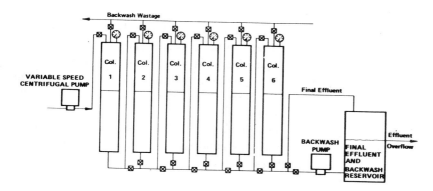

FIG. 16-9. PILOT SCALE CARBON COLUMN ASSEMBLY

EXPERIMENTAL PROCEDURES

Lab-Scale Isotherm Evaluation

1. Fill six to eight flasks (for shaker assembly) or beakers (for jar test assembly) with a fixed volume of wastewater. The initial organic concentration in terms of BOD, COD, TOC, or TOD should be accurately determined. Other parameters of interest, such as color or MBAS (methylene blue active substances) can be determined as required.

2. Put varying weights of prewashed test carbon into each container, corresponding to desired initial X/M ratios. This value might range from 0.05 to 5.0 lb COD/lb carbon. If any volatile compounds are present in the wastewater which might be air stripped during agitation, then a "blank" should be included to correct this organic removal (one container with the wastewater but no activated carbon).

3. Begin the agitation of the flasks (or mixing of the beakers) and monitor the organic concentration with time. The total sample withdrawal during the test should not exceed more than 5 percent of the total liquid contents. The best approach is to use micro-samples for TOC or TOD determination. All samples withdrawn for organic analysis should first be filtered.

4. Once contaminant level in the flask or beaker has stabilized, record the time to reach this level and note the equilibrium concentration.

5. The equilibrium value, C, as a function of the given initial X/M value is plotted on log-log paper, with X/M as the ordinate and C as the abscissa. Each flask or beaker will represent one point on the plot. Typical results are shown in Figure 16-1.

Pilot-Scale Carbon Columns

1. Set up the acrylic plastic carbon columns in a manner similar to that shown in Figure 16-9. They should be located close to the source of feed water to minimize pumping losses. A variable speed centrifugal pump is desirable for flexibility of operation. If the suspended solids or oil is high in the feed wastewater (>50 mg/l), then using one column as the prefilter will minimize backwashing.

2. The units should be piped and valved so that samples can be taken from each column and each column can be backwashed individually. Down flow operations are normally used, although the upflow mode of operation can be investigated if desired.

3. Load the columns with the required amount of test carbon. Each column should have an equal amount. It may be helpful to paint the columns black or to cover them to prevent sunlight penetration during the test run. This will minimize algal growth in the columns and reduce backwash frequency.

4. Begin the run at the prescribed linear flow velocity and initial conditions. Monitor the effluent quality of each column by withdrawing samples at least once daily. If composite samples are required, electrically operated solenoid valves can be used to deliver the samples to compositing containers.

   The collected samples can be analyzed for any or all of the following parameters:
   a. BOD_5
   b. COD
   c. TOD
   d. TOC
   e. Phenolic materials
   f. Color
   g. MBAS
   h. Total Kjeldahl nitrogen (TKN)
   i. Specific organic or inorganic constituents

5. The effluent from the last column should be collected in a 55-gal drum which can serve as a reservoir for backwash water. Each column can be backwashed on a routine basis or at a specified pressure drop through the column.

6. The test should be continued until the breakthrough curves are fully developed; for example, the final column effluent concentration of the

most slowly removed constituent approaches that of the first column influent concentration.

Powdered Activated Carbon

Powdered activated carbon (PAC) added to activated sludge is becoming popular as a treatment process and is covered in detail elsewhere [12]. The basic procedure, however, is adding powdered activated carbon to biological reactors as shown in Chapter 10, varying the PAC addition and monitoring the effluent constituent response.

CORRELATION OF RESULTS

The results from the batch isotherm tests can be plotted as shown in Figure 16-1. The resulting K and n values are then determined as well as the non-sorbable residual. The information is then used in the context as described in the first part of this chapter.

The continuous column test results used to plot a breakthrough curve, as shown in Figure 16-5b, uses the parameter of concern as the ordinate. A family of curves can be developed as required, one for each column when the series mode is used. These data can then be correlated using the Bed-Depth/Service-Time (BDST) analysis outlined previously in this chapter. The carbon capacity and observed residual can then be compared to the isotherm values; however, the column study results should govern when establishing design and effluent criteria.

LIMITATIONS AND SCALE-UP

Providing the wastewater charge to the pilot-scale columns is representative, and the process calculations are properly made, the scaled-up carbon capacity and organic residual to a full scale operation should not change significantly. The phenomenon that is difficult to translate from the pilot-scale to the full-scale system, however, is the degree of biological activity in the columns. Excessive biological synthesis in a column tends to cause fouling, plugging, and odor problems which may not prevail in the pilot tests. Provisions to control excessive biological growth should therefore be made when considering the full-scale system design. Use of regenerated carbon should be attempted in all columnar tests as virgin and regenerated activated carbons give slightly different results.

311

REFERENCES

1. Weber, W.J., "Adsorption in Direct Physicochemical Treatment," *Process Design in Water Quality Engineering: New Concepts and Developments*, E.L. Thackson and W.W. Eckenfelder, eds., Jenkins Publishing Co., Austin, Texas (1972).

2. Hassler, J.W., *Activated Carbon*, Chemical Publishing Co., New York (1974).

3. Confidential Report submitted to the Suntide Refining Company, Corpus Christi, Texas, by Engineering-Science of Texas (February 1971).

4. Guisti, D.M., Conway, R.A., and Lawson, L.T., "Activated Carbon Adsorption of Petrochemicals." *Journal, Water Pollution Control Federation* (May, 1974).

5. "Adsorption as a Treatment of Refinery Effluents," Report for the CDP Subcommittee on Chemical Wastes, American Petroleum Institute, Washington, D.C. (1969).

6. Snoeyink, V.L., Weber, W.J., and Mark, H.B., "Sorption of Phenol and Nitrophenol by Active Carbon," *Environmental Science & Technology*, 10, 918-926 (1969).

7. "Appraisal of Granular Contacting, Phase I, Evaluation of the Literature on the Use of Granular Carbon for Tertiary Wastewater Treatment. Phase II, Economic Effect of Design Variables," Report No. TWRC-11, Robert A. Taft Water Research Center, Cincinnati, Ohio.

8. Eckenfelder, W.W., and Ford, D.L., *Water Pollution Control: Experimental Procedures for Process Design*, Pemberton Press, Austin, Texas (1970).

9. Hutchins, R.A., "New Method Simplifies Design of Activated-Carbon Systems," *Chemical Engineering*, 80:19, 133-138 (1973).

10. Argaman, Y., and Eckenfelder, W.W., "Factors Affecting the Design of Multistage Carbon Columns for Industrial Wastewater Treatment," Water-1976, AIChE Symp. Series, 73: 166, 36-42 (1977).

11. Confidential Report submitted to the Exxon Corp., Baytown, Texas, by Engineering-Science of Texas (October 1968).

12. Cheremisinoff, P.N., and Ellerbusch, F., *Carbon Adsorption Handbook*, Ann Arbor Science (1978).

17

ION EXCHANGE

DISCUSSION OF PRINCIPLES

Ion Exchange is a process in which ions, held by electrostatic forces to functional groups on the surface of a solid, are exchanged for ions of a similar charge in solution. Ion exchange is more often applied for the removal or exchange of dissolved inorganic salts in waters or wastewaters, such as hardness (calcium and magnesium) or heavy metals (chromium and zinc).

Resin Description

Although natural zeolites, such as aluminosilicates, have been used in the past, their low capacity and high attrition rates have generally rendered them inefficient in wastewater treatment. Most ion exchange resins in use today are synthetic materials consisting of a network of hydrocarbon radicals with soluble ionic functional groups attached. The nature of the group determines the resin behavior, and the number of groups per unit weight of resin determines the exchange capacity. The group type affects the selectivity and the exchange equilibrium of the resin. Synthetic resins may be classified as follows:

Cation exchangers (carry exchangeable cations) contain functional acid groups, such as sulfonic ($R - SO_3H$), phenolic ($R - OH$), carboxylic ($R - COOH$), and phosphoric ($R - PO_3H_2$), may be classified as strongly or weakly acidic.

1. Strongly acidic cation exchanger (SACE) — the functional groups are derived from a strong acid such as H_2SO_4.

2. Weakly acidic cation exchanger (WACE) — the functional groups are derived from a weak acid such as H_2CO_3.

Anion exchangers (carry exchangeable anions) contain functional amine groups such as the primary amine $(R - NH_2)$, the secondary amine $(R - R'NH)$, the tertiary amine, $(R - R'_2N)$, and the quaternary ammonium group $(R - R'_3NOH)$. The R' represents organic radicals such as CH_3.

1. Strongly basic anion exchanger (SBAE) — the functional groups are derived from quaternary ammonium group.
2. Weakly basic anion exchanger (WBAE) — the functional groups are derived from the primary, secondary and tertiary amine groups.

The exchangeable counter-ion of an acidic cation resin may be either hydrogen or some monovalent cation such as sodium. For a basic anion resin the exchangeable counter-ion may be the hydroxide ion or some other monovalent anion. The regenerant for the resin will be a corresponding acid, base, or simple salt. Example reactions for the different types of resins are shown in Table 17-1 [1].

TABLE 17-1. TYPICAL REACTIONS FOR EXCHANGE RESINS (1)

1. Strongly acidic cation exchangers. (SACE)
   a. Hydrogen form, regenerate with HCl or H_2SO_4.
   $$2R - SO_3H + Ca^{2+} \rightleftharpoons (R - SO_3)_2Ca + 2H^+$$
   b. Sodium form, regenerate with NaCl.
   $$2R - SO_3NA + Ca^{2+} \rightleftharpoons (R - O_3)_2Ca + 2Na^+$$

2. Weakly acidic cation exchanger. (WACE)
   a. Hydrogen form, regenerate with HCl or H_2SO_4.
   $$2R - COOH + Ca^{2+} \rightleftharpoons (R - COO)_2Ca + 2H^+$$
   b. Sodium form, regenerate with NaOH.
   $$2R - COONa + Ca^{2+} \rightleftharpoons (R - COO)_2Ca + 2Na^+$$

3. Strongly basic anion exchanger. (SBAE)
   a. Hydroxide form, regenerate with NaOH.
   $$2R - R'_3NOH + SO_4^{2-} \rightleftharpoons (R - R'_3N)_2SO_4 + 2OH^-$$
   b. Chloride form, regenerate with NaCl or HCl.
   $$2R - R'_3NCl + SO_4^{2-} \rightleftharpoons (R - R'_3N)_2SO_4 + 2Cl^-$$

4. Weakly basic anion exchanger. (WBAE)
   a. Free base or hydroxide form, regenerate with NaOH, NH_4OH, or Na_2CO_3.
   $$2R - NH_3OH + SO_4^{2-} \rightleftharpoons (R - NH_3)_2SO_4 + 2OH^-$$
   b. Chloride form, regenerate with HCl.
   $$2R - NH_3Cl + SO_4^{2-} \rightleftharpoons (R - NH_3)_2SO_4 + 2Cl^-$$

Ion exchangers may be operated as batch or continuous operations. The most common system is continuous column operation in which the liquid is applied to a downflow, packed bed. In order to minimize headloss through the ion exchange bed, prefiltration of the water or waste is usually employed. The wastewater is passed through the column until breakthrough occurs or the concentration of ions in the effluent from the column exceeds the desired level. The exchanger is then removed from service, backwashed to remove accumulated dirt and solids, and regenerated by passing a concentrated solution containing the exchangeable cation or anion through the bed. The bed is rinsed to remove residual regenerant and subsequently placed back in service. Some suggested regeneration levels are given in Table 17-2.

TABLE 17-2. SUGGESTED REGENERATION LEVELS

Ion Exchange Resin	Ionic Form	Regenerant	Requirement $\frac{\text{Meq Regen.}}{\text{Meq Resin}}$
Strong Acid Cation	H+	HCl	3-5
	Na+	H_2SO_4	3-5
		NaCl	3-5
Weak Acid Cation	H+	HCl	1.5-2
	Na+	H_2SO_4	1.5-2
		NaOH	
Strong Base Anion I	OH⁻	NaOH	4-5
	Cl⁻	NaCl	4-5
		HCl	
	$SO_4^=$	Na_2SO_4	4-5
		H_2SO_4	
Strong Base Anion II	OH⁻	NaOH	3-4
Weak Base Anion		NaOH	
	Free Base	NH_4OH	1.5-2
		Na_2CO_3	
	Cl⁻	HCl	1.5-2
	$SO_4^=$	H_2SO_4	1.5-2

Typical Systems

Several systems have been used for the treatment of water and wastewaters and are briefly presented below and illustrated in Figures 17-1 through 17-3.

Two-Stage Cation-Anion Exchange System. For complete demineralization, generally a cation 'exchanger followed by a weakly basic anion exchanger is employed as shown in Figure 17-1.

By employing the cation resin on the hydrogen cycle and the anion resin on the hydroxide cycle, the exchangers will successfully convert salts into acids

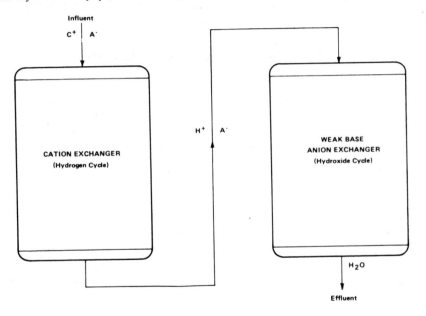

FIG. 17-1. TWO-STAGE ION EXCHANGE SYSTEM

and subsequently into water thereby removing all ionic materials except carbon dioxide and silica. If carbon dioxide and silica removal are desired, a degasifier for carbon dioxide removal can be placed between the two exchangers and a strongly basic anion exchanger used for the second stage. The two-stage system can accomplish essentially 90 to 99 percent dissolved solids reduction.

Mixed-Resin Exchange Operation. The mixed bed exchanger, shown in Figure 17-2, can remove 99 plus percentage of the dissolved solids. The mixed bed exchangers must be separated for regeneration. This is accomplished by using resins of different specific densities so that they may be separated during backwashing.

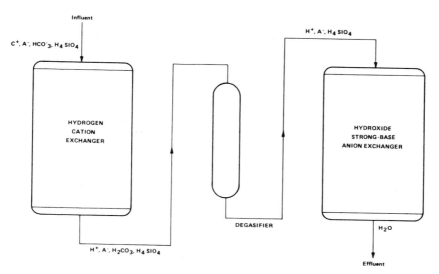

FIG. 17-2. TWO-STAGE, ION EXCHANGE SYSTEM WITH PROVISION FOR CARBON DIOXIDE AND SILICA REMOVAL

The DESAL Process. The DESAL process is a patented process involving a three-step series operation:

1. A weakly basic anion resin is in the bicarbonate form, R-NH (HCO_3).
2. A weakly acidic cation exchanger is in the hydrogen form, R-COOH.
3. A weakly basic anion resin is in the free base form, R-N.

The first resin is regenerated with ammonia, the second with sulfuric acid and the third resin is self-regenerating. An example of the system is shown in Figure 17-3. The water passes through the first anion exchanger and exchanges bicarbonate ions for chloride ions. This step is called alkalization and the reaction is:

$$(R - NH)HCO_3 + Cl^- \rightleftharpoons (R - NH)Cl + HCO_3^- \qquad (17\text{-}1)$$

The water then passes through the WACE and exchanges hydrogen ions for sodium ions, thereby reducing the pH and converting the bicarbonate to carbonic acid and carbon dioxide. This step is called dealkalization:

$$R - COOH + Na^+ + H_2O \rightleftharpoons R - COONa + H_3O^+$$
$$H_3O^+ + HCO_3^- \rightleftharpoons H_2CO_3 + H_2O \tag{17-2}$$

Finally, the carbonic acid from the second exchanger reacts with the WBAE resin to generate (R-NH)HCO$_3$ which is the original form of the resin in the first stage. This is the carbonation step:

$$R - N + H_2CO_3 \rightleftharpoons (R - NH)HCO_3 \tag{17-3}$$

After regenerating the first stage resin with ammonia to convert it to the free base form as shown below:

$$(R - NH)Cl + NH_3 \rightleftharpoons R - N + NH_4Cl \tag{17-4}$$

and regenerating the second stage resin with sulfuric acid, the flow through the beds is reversed for the next cycle of operation.

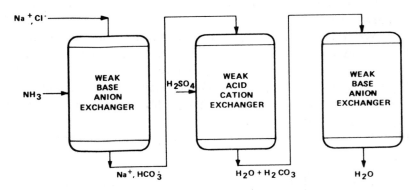

FIG. 17-3. DESAL PROCESS

In the design and selection of an ion exchange resin, the capacity of the resin and the efficiency of the process must be established. The theoretical capacity of the resin is the equivalent number of exchangeable ions per unit weight or unit volume of resin and is expressed as equivalents per gram of resin or lb calcium carbonate/cu ft of resin. The degree of theoretical capacity achieved depends on the quantity of regenerant used, and an economic balance must be derived between the degree of theoretical capacity attained (degree of column utilization and the quantity of regenerant employed) and the regeneration efficiency. Typical data for a system are shown in Figure 17-4.

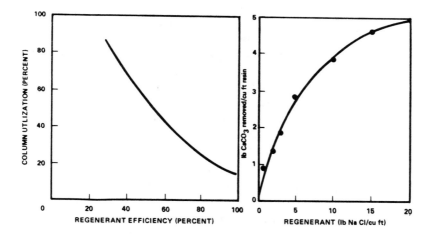

FIG. 17-4. TYPICAL COLUMN EXCHANGE DATA

The properties and performance specifications for ion exchange resins are usually given by a resin manufacturer. However, there are many instances in which it is necessary to determine or evaluate resin performance prior to selection for specific applications. This is of particular significance with resins which have been in service and may have experienced changes in capacity due to loss of exchange sites or the reduction of cross linkage. The properties of the resin generally evaluated include:

1. Dry weight capacity;
2. Wet weight capacity;
3. Wet volume capacity; and
4. Percent moisture content.

By evaluating the changes in these properties, one can determine such factors as the loss of active exchange sites (decrease in both wet volume capacity and dry weight capacity), and the stability or decreased cross linkage (increase in moisture content plus decrease in wet volume capacity) [1].

319

EXPERIMENTAL PROCEDURES

In developing a design for an ion exchange system many factors must be considered, such as exchange capacity, effects of certain parameters such as pH and temperature on removal characteristics of the resin, type and concentration of regenerant, and the attrition characteristics of the resin. The procedures and data correlations presented herein are based on actual data developed with clinoptilolite for removal of ammonia. Although clinoptilolite is a zeolite and not a resin, all of the. exchanging material, whether resin or zeolite, will be referred to in this context as "resin". The procedural methodology discussed below can be applied to both synthetic and natural resins. For illustrative purposes, an experimental program on ammonia removal by clinoptilolite will be used as an example of both Experimental Procedures and Correlation of Results. Five evaluations are described below:

1. Determination of the Resin Exchange Capacity;
2. Evaluation of pH Effects on Exchange;
3. Evaluation of Two Types of Regenerant;
4. Optimization of Regenerant Use; and
5. Determination of Attrition Characteristics of Resin.

Determination of Resin Exchange Capacity

In order to measure the exchange capacity of a resin, the resin must be cleaned, dried, saturated with the wastewater or the constituent under examination, and eluted with a regenerant:

1. Obtain samples of fresh clinoptilolite resin and wash in an Erlenmeyer flask to remove fines.
2. Equilibrate with a solution of 1.0 M NaCl for 2 days. (With other resins, other regenerants can be employed.)
3. Wash the resin with distilled water to remove all traces of the regenerant. Check for chlorides with $AgNO_3$ or conductivity.
4. Air dry the resin and then dry over night in a $105^\circ C$ oven.
5. Place samples of 10 to 20 g in a 50-ml burette and saturate with 1 M NH_4Cl at a flow of about 50 ml/hr for 2 days.
6. After saturation, wash the resin (in place) with distilled water for 2 days. Due to the nature of ion exchange resins, the ammonia (or other constituents) will not significantly elute into the distilled water.
7. Determine the ammonia content of the resin by one of three methods:
   a. Direct distillation of ammonia by placing the resin in a Kjeldahl flask.
   b. Elute the ammonia from the resin with 0.5 M NaCl (50 ml/hr for 2

days) and determine the ammonia content of the elutant.

c. Elute the ammonia as in Step b, but use 0.25 M $CaCl_2$.

Evaluation of pH Effects on Exchange

Many constituents, particularly ammonia, are significantly affected by pH when subjected to an exchange resin. Optimum conditions (pH or effects of certain salts) can be evaluated by combination of batch and continuous experiments.

1. Prepare the resin as explained above (Steps 1 through 4).
2. Place 100 ml of waste and 0.5 g of resin into 125-ml Erlenmeyer flasks and cap with a rubber stopper. A control with no resin should be set up to check air stripping of ammonia.
3. Adjust the pH to various levels.
4. Shake the flasks two hours and determine residual ammonia or other constituents of interest.
5. From the results of the batch tests, columns can be run to confirm the optimum pH ranges.
   a. Set up a 3-ft bed of resin (see Figure 17-5).
   b. Feed waste solution at 18 BV (Bed Volumes)/hr.
   c. Monitor ammonia concentration in effluent.
   d. Regenerate column with 30 BV of 0.35 M NaCl (0.17 lb NaCl/gal waste). Rinse with distilled water.
   e. Repeat at different pH levels of influent.

These breakthrough and exhaustion studies can be run until the resin is exhausted and the effluent ammonia concentration equals the influent. Alternatively, the columns could be run to breakthrough at a specified effluent concentration such as 1 mg/l NH_3-N.

Evaluation of Regenerants

Column studies can be effectively utilized to evaluate the effectiveness of the counter ion which is initially on the resin or to examine exhaustion performance. For example, with clinoptilolite both sodium and calcium are effective counter ions. Therefore, the resin could be evaluated to determine the most effective forms, i.e., Na or Ca, for ammonia removal.

1. Prepare sufficient clinoptilolite for a 3-ft column.
2. Place the resin in the Na form by regneration with 40 BV of 0.35 M NaCl at a pH of 12.0.
3. Perform column runs to exhaustion using a waste with 20 mg/l of ammonia.

321

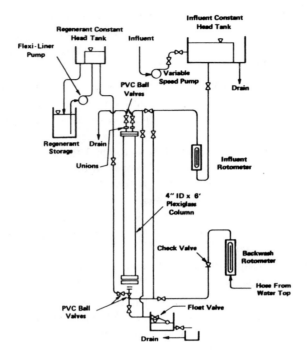

FIG. 17-5. SCHEMATIC DIAGRAM OF LABORATORY ION EXCHANGE SYSTEM

4. Place the resin in the Ca form by regeneration with 0.17 M $CaCl_2$ in a saturated lime solution with a pH of 12.2. This will require about 50 BV of regenerant.

5. Repeat Step 3.

Optimization of Regenerant Use

After determining the proper operating range of the resin for removal and selecting the most effective regenerant, it is then necessary to optimize the regeneration process. It is desired to examine regenerant flow rate, strength, pH and quantity.

Previous testing or preliminary evaluations should determine the approximate run time on a column to exhaustion or to a specified breakthrough. For example, with clinoptilolite and ammonia levels of 20 mg/l, approximately 180 BV can be treated prior to breakthrough. Therefore, the column runs can be set up to be fed at a rate of 15 BV/hr for 12 hr, after which they are immediately regenerated. In this manner, the laboratory procedures are simplified and columns are loaded with about the same amount of ammonia prior to each regeneration.

1. Examine the effects of the regenerant flow rate by varying the flow from 4 to 30 BV/hr. Use 0.1 M NaCl and monitor the ammonia concentration in the regenerant with time.

2. At the optimum flow rate, evaluate the effects of regenerant strength and pH:

    a. At a regenerant concentration of 0.1 M NaCl, vary the pH at 11.5, 12.0 and 12.5 using NaOH;

    b. At the optimum feed rate, namely, 15 BV/hr, regenerate the column and the measure the eluted ammonia with time;

    c. Repeat, varying the salt to 0.2, 0.35, 0.5 and 1.5 M NaCl; and

    d. Make one run using only pH adjustment with NaCl.

Determination of Attrition Characteristics of Resin

In optimizing the methods of regeneration, it is essential to consider potential attrition characteristics of resins. The use of a concentrated regenerant may cause shrinkage of resin whereas subjection to the dilute feed causes swelling. This continued shrinking and swelling can result in significant attrition rates. Consequently, there is an optimum cost between regeneration efficiency with more concentrated regenerant and attrition rate. In addition, the effects of pH can be detrimental to some resins, particularly clinoptilolite (higher pH levels cause higher rates of attrition). To test for attrition, samples of resin are alternately subjected to concentrated or high pH regenerant and then distilled water. The studies can be conducted on a batch and continuous basis.

1. Add 1-gram samples of clinoptilolite (20 x 50 mesh) to 12 flasks, each 125 ml in volume.

2. Add 100 ml of 2% NaOH (pH about 13.3) to 8 of the 12 flasks. These are the experimental samples. Operate 4 of the flasks as controls to measure the rate of mechanical attrition. Add 100 ml of distilled water to the controls.

3. Shake the samples for 2 hr in a wrist-action shaker and then drain the NaOH from the 8 experimental flasks. Add 100 ml of distilled water to the flasks and rinse for 2 hr. Change the distilled water in the controls so that the decanting error is the same in all flasks.

4. Repeat Steps 2 and 3. After 5, 7, 25 and 50 cycles, remove one control and two test flasks.

5. Dry the samples overnight at 105°C and sieve through 20 x 50 mesh. The weight of material lost is that resin quantity lost to attrition.

CORRELATION OF RESULTS

The data correlations presented in this section are derived from the "EXPERIMENTAL PROCEDURES" section of this chapter and are concerned with ammonia removal by the natural zeolite, clinoptilolite.

Determination of Resin Exchange Capacity

1. The quantity of ammonia remaining in solution after shaking is determined. The difference between this value and the original value (1 M NH_4Cl) represents the quantity of ammonia exchanged into the resin.
2. Convert the quantity of ammonia exchanged into meq and divide by the dry weight of the resin to get meq/g. These results are given in Table 17-3.

TABLE 17-3. CLINOPTILOLITE EXCHANGE CAPACITY

Method Used for Ammonia Recovery	Exchange Capacity[a] (meq/g)
Distillation of clinoptilolite particles	1.95 (1.93-1.98)
Elution using NaCl	1.88 (1.86-1.91)
Elution using $CaCl_2$	1.77 (1.75-1.79)

[a]Range of experimental values indicated in parentheses

These data show that the value for exchange is influenced by the method of ammonia recovery. The smaller value for NaCl elution may have been due to insufficient elution volume of NaCl. It appears that sodium and ammonia ions have access to all sites in the resin. The calcium elution inferred a smaller exchange capacity than elution with sodium. This lower capacity for calcium may be due to a slower exchange rate of calcium for ammonia or to the inaccessibility of calcium to some of the exchange sites [2].

Evaluation of pH Effects on Exchange

1. The liquid from the batch tests is analyzed for ammonia. The difference between this concentration and the initial level (20 mg/l) represents the quantity exchanged into the resin.

2. Express the quantity exchanged in meq and divide by the weight of resin (0.5 g).

3. These results can be correlated to the pH of the solution as shown in Figure 17-6. Observation of Figure 17-6 indicates that the optimum pH for exchange is in the range of 6 to 8.

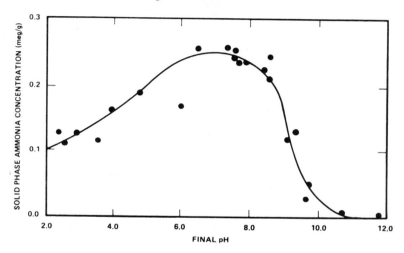

FIG. 17-6. EFFECTS OF pH ON AMMONIA EXCHANGE: BATCH RESULTS

4. The breakthrough results of the column tests are shown in Figure 17-7. Observation of these data concludes that the greatest ammonia capacity occurred at a pH of 6.

5. The quantity of ammonia in the resin is obtained by graphically integrating the area above the breakthrough curves. These quanitities can be divided by the quantity of resin in the column shown in Table 17-4, to obtain specific capacities.

The results in Table 17-4 were calculated for both saturation and breakthrough to 1 mg/l of NH_3-N. Optimum conditions for exhaustion occur between pH 4 and 8. Operation outside this range results in a rapid decrease of ammonia exchange capacity and increased ammonia leakage prior to beginning of breakthrough. However, the poor ammonia exchange at high pH can be used advantageously during regeneration.

Evaluation of Regenerants

1. Plot the breakthrough curves for the sodium and calcium forms of regenerant as shown in Figure 17-8.

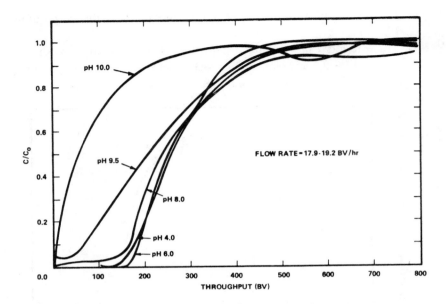

**FIG. 17-7. EFFECTS OF pH ON AMMONIA EXCHANGE:
COLUMN RESULTS**

**TABLE 17-4. RESIN AMMONIA CAPACITIES FOR pH RUNS:
COLUMN STUDIES**

Influent pH	Capacity to Saturation (meq/g)	Capacity to 1 mg/ℓ NH$_3$-N breakthrough (meq/g)
4.0	0.48	0.27
6.0	0.51	0.33
8.0	0.48	0.24
9.5	0.37	0.06
10.0	0.14	0.01

Since the resin (clinoptilolite) is more selective for sodium than calcium (Table 17-3), it appears reasonable that regeneration will be more effective with sodium salts. Using the same reasoning, it seems that the ammonia-calcium

exchange would occur more readily than the ammonia-sodium exchange. However, evaluation of Figure 17-8 infers that the sodium form is superior to the calcium form for retardation of the breakthrough. Apparently, calcium mobility in
the resin is more restricted than that of sodium [2].

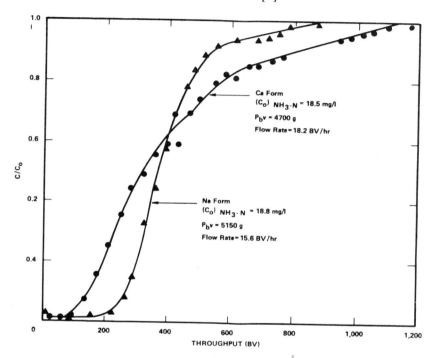

FIG. 17-8. EXHAUSTION CURVES FOR SODIUM AND CALCIUM
FORMS OF REGENERANT

Optimization of Regenerant Use

Optimization of regenerant use involves evaluation of the regenerant flow
rate, strength, pH, and quantity. These results are shown in Table 17-5.

    1. The elution curves at various flow rates are plotted in Figure 17-9. These
results indicate little difference in rates from 4 to 20 BV/hr. The 15 BV/hr
run was inadvertently conducted at a lower influent ammonia concentration so that the elution curve appears lower. Actually, it seems that there
are no adverse effects of flow rate up to 20 BV/hr. Performance of the
30 BV/hr was decidedly poorer than the lower flow rates, resulting in
decreased regenerant utilization.

TABLE 17-5. REGENERATION DATA SUMMARY

Exhaustion			Regenerant[a]					Regeneration Efficiency		
Inf. NH₃-N (mg/l)	Eff. NH₃-N (mg/l)	NH₃-N Removed During Run (equivalents)	Flow, Upflow (BV/hr)	NaCl Conc. (lb/gal)	pH	NH₃-N Eluted (equivalents)	Ammonia Recovery (%)	Regen. to 95% Elution (BV)	Na Used (equivalents)[b]	Efficiency[c] (%)
15.7	0.56	1.44	4	0.049	11.5	1.65	114	27.0	20.9	6.9
16.2	0.72	1.30	7	0.049	11.5	1.36	38.0	23.5	18.3	7.6
18.8	1.10	1.34	10	0.049	11.3	1.48	108	27.0	20.9	6.4
18.6	1.09	1.67	20	0.049	11.6	1.63	97.5	25.4	19.7	8.5
29.0	2.85	1.68	30	0.049	11.6	1.02	62.8	...	...	...
17.5	0.20	1.65	10	0.24	11.5	1.50	91.0	14.7	55.0	3.0
19.3	1.97	1.65	25	0.10	12.5	1.49	90.4	11.0	18.9	8.8
22.9	0.53	2.06	15	none	11.5	1.26	61.5	...	...	...
13.0	0.02	1.24	15	0.049	11.5	1.04	84.5	26.6	20.7	6.0
18.0	0.29	1.78	15	0.10	11.5	1.50	84.3	26.0	39.5	4.5
16.9	0.27	1.69	16	0.17	11.5	1.56	88.0	18.2	47.5	3.3
21.0	0.43	1.97	15	0.24	11.5	1.69	87.7	17.0	63.2	3.1
10.2	0.98	1.84	15	0.73	11.5	1.82	99.1	16.0	178	1.0
32.0	4.06	1.71	15	none	12.0	1.62	94.1	28.0	3.1	55.0
20.0	3.39	1.60	15	0.049	18.0	1.84	115	21.0	17.9	8.9
16.6	0.28	1.56	15	0.10	12.0	1.26	79.0	16.6	26.5	5.9
19.0	0.47	1.77	15	0.10	12.0	1.86	105	16.8	26.7	6.6
20.0	0.60	1.98	15	0.17	12.0	1.54	81.5	16.0	43.4	4.4
16.3	0.47	1.51	15	0.24	12.0	1.57	104	17.0	64.9	2.3
22.3	2.08	1.94	15	none	12.5	2.05	105	15.3	3.7	52.0
29.8	0.49	1.85	15	0.049	12.4	1.72	92.4	15.0	14.8	12.6
17.9	0.11	1.70	15	0.10	12.4	1.37	89.5	10.0	17.3	9.3
18.8	0.25	1.77	15	0.17	12.3	1.35	76.2	9.2	26.2	6.8
18.1	0.68	1.71	15	0.17	12.5	1.64	95.8	9.0	25.6	6.7
19.5	0.31	1.68	15	0.84	12.4	1.46	89.1	9.4	37.3	4.9
18.4	1.31	1.63	15	0.73	12.5	1.61	99.4	9.0	101	1.6
20.8	1.07	1.89	15	0.73	12.5	1.80	96.5	10.0	112	1.7
19.9	1.82	1.73	15	0.10	8.2	0.96	55.2	51.6[d]	76.6[d]	2.3[d]
22.0	1.45	1.95	15	0.10[e]	12.2	1.84	105	14.5	22.6	8.6
22.9	4.62	1.76	15	0.10	11.8	1.69	96.8	20.0	31.2	5.6

[a] Volume of regenerant used was 30 BV.

[b] Includes total Na in regenerant.

[c] Efficiency = $\dfrac{\text{Eq. NH}_3\text{-N removed during previous exhaustion}}{\text{Eq ... used for regeneration}} \times 100$.

[d] Values obtained by extrapolating available data

[e] Regenerant also contained 0.046 lb CaCl₂/gal.

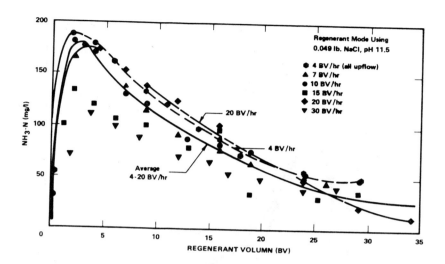

FIG. 17-9. EFFECT OF FLOW RATE ON REGENERATION

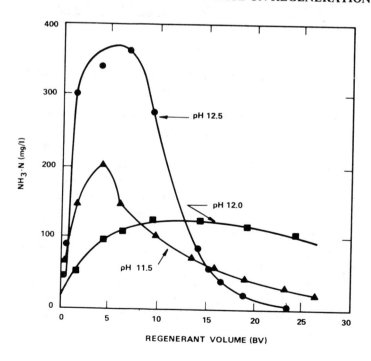

FIG. 17-10 AMMONIA ELUTION DURING REGENERATION: No NaCl

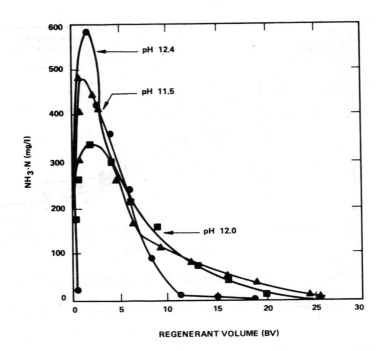

FIG. 17-11 AMMONIA ELUTION DURING REGENERATION:
0.24 lb NaCl/gal

2. To evaluate salt strength and pH, plot the elution curves as illustrated in
Figures 17-10 through 17-12. From these results, it is evident that progressively less regenerant volume is required to elute a given quantity of
ammonia as the pH is increased. As the pH of the regenerant was increased, elution curves became sharper, resulting in the removal of ammonia in much less regenerant volume. The difference in salt concentration
is evidenced by comparing the various runs in Table 17-5. Increasing the
salt concentration beyond 0.17 lb NaCl/gal has little effect on elution at
a pH of 11.5. Likewise, increasing the salt concentration beyond 0.10 lb
NaCl/gal at pH 12.0 and 12.5 had no effect on regeneration performance.

3. The volume of regenerant required for 95 percent elution of ammonia per
equivalent of ammonia in the resin bed was calculated for different salt
strengths in Table 17-5. The results are correlated in Figure 17-13. These
data can be used to optimize regeneration.

The steps above will define the percent ammonia eluted with a particular
quantity of regenerant. These data are useful for predicting the volume of regenerant and the time required for regeneration. However, the relationships shown

330

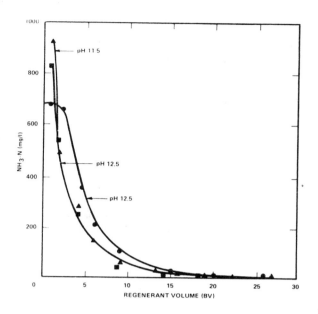

FIG. 17-12. AMMONIA ELUTION DURING REGENERATION:
0.73 lb NaCl/gal

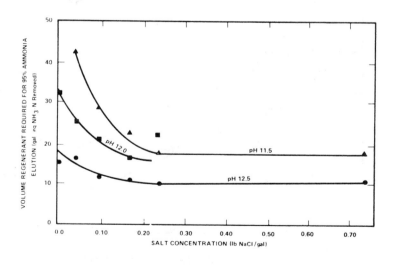

FIG. 17-13. SALT CONCENTRATION EFFECTS ON VOLUME OF
REGENERANT REQUIRED: 95% AMMONIA ELUTION

in Figures 17-8 through 17-13 do not directly indicate the efficiency of regeneration. The efficiency may be defined as follows [3]:

$$\% \text{ Efficiency} = \frac{\text{NH}_3\text{-N Removed During Previous Exhaustion, equivalents}}{\text{Na Used for Regeneration, equivalents}} \times 100$$

The data in Table 17-5 can be used to calculate the percent efficiency and the results correlated as in Figure 17-14. As can be seen, the efficiencies for pH 12.5 were about twice those for pH 11.5.

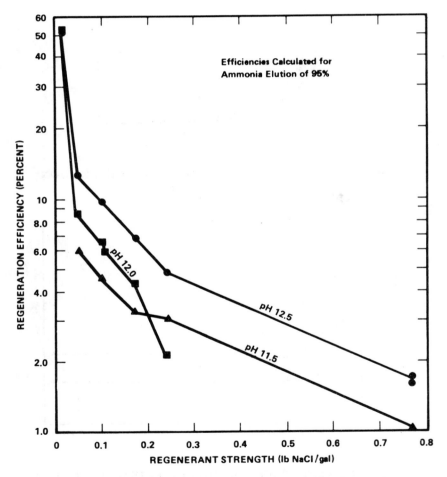

FIG. 17-14. REGENERANT CONCENTRATION EFFECTS ON REGENERATION EFFICIENCY

The efficiencies can be calculated for any percent ammonia elution from the resin although 95 percent is typically used. The efficiencies observed in Figure 17-14 are considerably lower than those observed in water softening operations. However, the efficiencies in Figure 17-14 are based only on the elution of one ion (NH_3-N) and do not reflect the elution of other ions which would increase the overall elution of regeneration efficiency.

Attrition Characteristics of Resin

1. From the batch studies the calculated loss of weight can be presented as shown in Table 17-6. These results demonstrate that the clinoptilolite

TABLE 17-6. RESIN ATTRITION RESULTS: BATCH TESTS

Cycles	Caustic Wt. Loss[a,b] 20x50 Mesh Material (g)	Control Wt. Loss 20x50 Mesh Material (%)	Wt. Loss[a] 20x50 Mesh Material (g)	Wt. Loss 20x20 Mesh Material (%)	Weight Loss (%/Cycle) Caustic-Control	Caustic
5	0.304	30.4	0.305	30.5	0	6.1
7	0.327	32.7	0.312	31.2	0.21	4.7
25	0.506	50.6	0.350	35.0	0.62	2.0
50	0.789	78.9	0.370	37.0	0.84	1.6

[a]Initial weight for all samples was 1,000 grams.

[b]Weights reported are average of two samples; maximum variation between two samples of any set was 5%.

was severely attacked by the caustic solution. After exposure to 50 simulated cycles, the attrition rate was 1.6 percent per cycle. This rate corrects to 0.8 percent per cycle for the caustic effects when corrected for the mechanical attrition observed in the control. The total rate is more representative of actual column operation.

2. The results of the column studies are summarized in Table 17-7. The effects of pH were significant from 11.5 to 12.5. Over 100 cycles the total attrition rate was 0.57 per cycle at 12.5 as compared to 0.34 and 0.24 percent per cycle at pH 12.0 and 11.5, respectively. These values are significantly less than the batch results in Table 17-6 (1.6 percent per cycle). However, the mechanical attrition rate was also much lower in the column tests than the batch tests.

The variation in attrition rate with increasing exposure to caustic is also evident from Table 17-7. The total attrition rates for 50, 100 and 150 .

TABLE 17-7. RESIN ATTRITION RESULTS: COLUMN TESTS

| pH | Cycles | Caustic | | Control | | Weight Loss (%/Cycle) | |
		Wt. Loss[a] 20x50 Mesh Material (g)	Wt. Loss 20x50 Mesh Material (%)	Wt. Loss[a] 20x50 Mesh Material (g)	Wt. Loss 20x50 Mesh Material (%)	Caustic-Control	Caustic
11.5	100	2.436[b]	24.4	0.904[b]	9.0	0.15	0.24
12.0	100	2.698[c]	33.8	0.904[b]	9.0	0.25	0.34
12.5	50	2.261[c]	28.3	0.398[c]	11.7	0.34	0.56
12.5	100	5.738[b]	57.4	0.904[b]	9.0	0.43	0.57
12.5	150	6.071[c,d]	76.0	0.716[c]	9.0	0.45	0.51

[a]Weights reported are average of three samples; maximum variation among samples of any set was 11%, except where noted.

[b]Initial sample weight was 10,000 grams.

[c]Initial sample weight was 8,000 grams.

[d]Weight of samples in this set varied by 26%.

cycles were 0.56, 0.57 and 0.51 percent per cycle, respectively, inferring that the rates may become lss after 100 cycles. Further evidence of this premise is the weight loss of 28.3 percent from 0-50 cycles, 29.1 percent from 50-100 cycles but only 18.6 percent from 100-150 cycles.

LIMITATIONS AND SCALE-UP

In conducting laboratory and pilot ion exchange studies on industrial wastewaters, it is essential to be cognizant of the potential fouling by organics. Severe decreases in exchange capacity over many cycles could very well be due to fouling. Additionally, calculated attrition rates from laboratory data may be significantly low due to high rates of mechanical attrition from closing valves and transport of resin in large systems. The designer should thoroughly discuss mechanical attrition with the manufacturer before developing final operating costs.

REFERENCES

1. Weber, W. J., "Physiocochemical Processes for Water Quality Control," Wiley-Interscience, New York (1972).
2. Koon, J. H. and Kaufman, W. J., "Optimization of Ammonia Removal by Ion Exchange Using Clinoptilolite," SERL Report No. 71-5, University of California, Berkeley, California (1971).
3. Klein, G., Private Communication (1971).

18

CHEMICAL OXIDATION

DISCUSSION OF PRINCIPLES

The vocabulary of Federal and State regulatory authorities is rapidly evolving to include such terms as "resistant," "refractory," "incompatible," and "perdurable" to describe those constituents which are not removed by conventional wastewater treatment methods. Chemical oxidation, although considered novel by many practicing engineers, possesses the potential of treating selected organics and inorganics which are resistant to other treatment methods.

The objective of chemical oxidation in water and wastewater treatment is to transform undesirable chemical constituents to a more oxidized state which reduces the pollution potential. It is often unnecessary to carry the oxidation of a compound to completion since, depending on the oxidant and oxidizing conditions, the intermediate oxidation products which may be formed will be of much lower toxicity or less objectionable characteristics than the original materials. Complete oxidation may not only be impractible from a treatment standpoint, but also represents a non-justified economical outlay. Subsequently, chemical oxidation might be considered as a selective modification or elimination of objectionable or toxic substances, including [1] :

1. Inorganic constituents, such as Mn^{++}, Fe^{++}, S^{--}, CN^-, SO_3^-; and
2. Organic compounds, such as phenols, amines, humic acids, other taste, odor, or color producing or toxic compounds, bacteria and algae.

The desirable characteristics of a chemical oxidant are that it be readily and economically available and that it not generate secondary pollutants into the

337

wastewater. The significant considerations in selecting an oxidizing agent and process include:

1. Integration with other existing or proposed unit treatment operations;
2. The treatment effectiveness;
3. The nature of the oxidation reactions;
4. The capital and operating economics; and
5. Storage and handling considerations.

Generally, the chemical oxidants which have been found most suitable for the oxidation of industrial wastewaters include ozone, hydrogen peroxide, potassium permanganate, chlorine or hyperchlorite, and chlorine dioxide. Of these oxidants, ozone, permanganate, and chlorine are the most commonly applied.

Generally, the effectiveness and economics of a specific oxidant depend on:

1. The concentration of reactants in the wastewater;
2. The initial temperature and changes of temperature upon reaction;
3. Waste characteristics; and
4. Influences of impurities.

A major influence on the rates of oxidation is the effect of pH which may result in:

1. Changes in free energy of the overall reactions;
2. Changes in the reactivity of reactants; and
3. Specific ion catalysts by OH^- or H_3O^+ ions.

The reaction rates and rate parameters of oxidation reactions generally cannot be predicted quantitatively and must be determined experimentally. Although it is difficult to categorize organics with respect to amenability to oxidation, the selection of a chemical oxidant and design of an oxidation system may be facilitated with the following classifications of organics [1]:

1. High reactivity: phenols, aldehydes, aromatic amines, and certain organic sulfur compounds;
2. Medium reactivity: alcohols, alkyl-substituted aromatics, nitro-substituted aromatics, and unsaturated alkyl groups, carbohydrates, aliphatic ketones, acids, esters, and amines;
3. Low reactivity: halogenated hydrocarbons, saturated aliphatic compounds, and benzene.

Since ozonation and chlorination offer the most effective means of wastewater oxidation and since the laboratory techniques for these compounds are similar to using other constituents, these oxidants are discussed in further detail in this chapter.

338

Ozone as a Chemical Oxidant

The reactions of ozone as a chemical oxidant appear to involve at least two distinct mechanisms [2]. One mechanism considers an electrophilic attack by ozone while the other mechanism involves an ozone-initiated oxidation whereby ozone serves as the reaction initiator and oxygen is the principal reactant. The reactions of ozone with tertiary amines, phosphines, arsines, sulfides and sulfoxides are examples of the electrophilic attacks as shown for the oxidation of dialkyl sulfide below:

$$R_2S + O_3 \longrightarrow R_2SO + O_2 \longrightarrow R_2SO_2 + O_2 \qquad (18\text{-}1)$$

Examples of ozone-initiated reactions are the oxidative reactions of ozone and aldehydes, ketones, alcohols, ethers, and saturated hydrocarbon groupings. It is postulated in these reactions that ozone serves as a radical reagent by mobilizing an additional number of oxygen molecules. For example, in the oxidation of benzaldehyde to benzoic acid and perbenzoic acid by oxygen-containing ozone, a significant quantity of unreacted ozone was observed which indicated less sensitivity of the aldehydes to ozone oxidation. However, an analysis of the aldehyde solution demonstrated a heavy oxidation and much more oxygen consumed than was indicated by the ozone reduction.

Since ozone reacts to certain bonds which are susceptible to cleavage, the products of oxidation may not be simply carbon dioxide and water, but intermediates formed by the mechanism. For example, phenolics are more reactive to ozone than most other aromatics with the products being carbon dioxide, formic acid, glyoxal, and oxalic acid. Alternative pathways for ozonation of phenol are shown in Figure 18-1 [2].

Wastewater treatment by ozonation may be influenced by many considerations, including [3]:

1. The nature and concentration of wastewater constituents will determine the amenability of ozonation.
2. The wastewater pH and temperature will control the efficiency of ozone reactivity. Ozone is more stable at acidic pH levels, probably because of the catalytic decomposition of ozone by hydroxide ions. Additionally, the pH may influence the reactivity of certain constituents with ozone. The temperature influences ozone solubility and stability, namely, higher wastewater temperatures result in decreased ozone stability.
3. The ozone application rate and contact time which is required by a specific wastewater is determined by the nature of the waste, the extent of

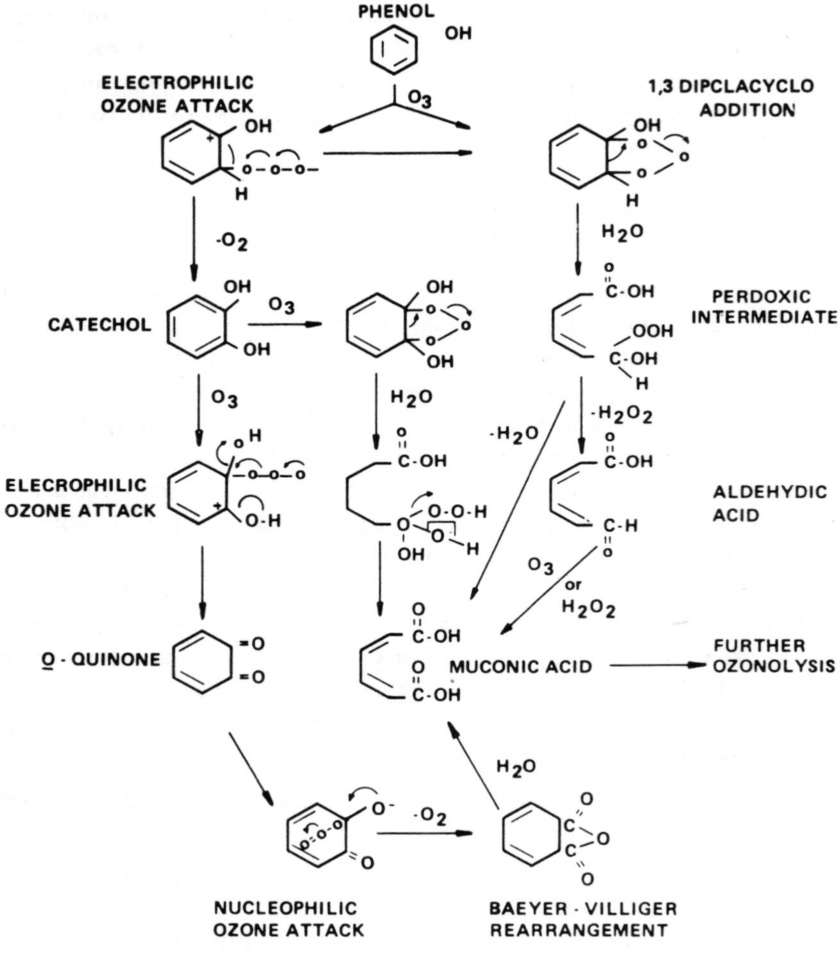

FIG. 18-1. POSSIBLE PATHWAYS FOR PHENOL OZONATION

chemical oxidation required, and the efficiency of the ozone-wastewater contactor.

4. The mechanism of contact of ozone with wastewater is a direct function of economics and will subsequently dictate the extent and efficiency of ozonation.

Ozone oxidation is applicable in color removal, phenol oxidation, cyanide oxidation, taste and odor removal, disinfection, and reduction of refractory materials which are resistant or are the by-products of biodegradation. This oxidant possesses the capability of oxidizing most elements and compounds to their highest oxidation state under ideal conditions. However, under most field conditions the complete degradation of relatively unreacted compounds, cannot always be anticipated.

Chlorine as a Chemical Oxidant

Chlorine has generally been accepted as a disinfectant and is more applicable in this area than in the actual oxidation of organic materials. When oxidizing wastewaters, chlorine has been more widely used for the oxidation of inorganic compounds, although in general the following materials are significantly reactive to chlorine oxidation:

1. Ammonia
2. Amino acids
3. Proteins
4. Carbonaceous materials
5. Nitrites
6. Iron
7. Manganese
8. Hydrogen sulfide
9. Cyanide
10. Phenols
11. Tannins

With industrial wastewaters, the use of chlorine in large dosages may generate undesirable chlorinated hydrocarbons. Moreover, a free chlorine residual may exert a deleterious effect on aquatic life. Therefore, caution must be exercised in its use. Chlorine is most frequently used to oxidize color, small concentrations of ammonia, hydrogen sulfide and cyanides. The most effective forms of chlorine for wastewater oxidation are hypochlorous acid, hypochlorite, or chlorine dioxide.

Hypochlorous acid is formed from the reaction of chlorine gas with water as shown below:

$$Cl_2 + H_2O \longrightarrow HOCl + HCl \qquad (18\text{-}2)$$

The concentration of HOCl formed depends on the total chlorine concentration and the pH as well as other variables [4]. The upper practical limit of chlorine solution from conventional aspiration equipment is set at 3,500 mg/l because of the associated low pH and corrosiveness of molecular chlorine on equipment. Sodium or calcium hypochlorite is formed by the reaction of chlorine, water, and sodium hydroxide or calcium hydroxide as shown below:

$$HOCl + NaOH \longrightarrow NaOCl + H_2O \qquad (18\text{-}3)$$

$$2HOCl + Ca(OH)_2 \longrightarrow Ca(OCl)_2 + H_2O \qquad (18\text{-}4)$$

The only difference between the reactions of hypochlorite and chlorine gas is the side reactions of the end products. The reaction of hypochlorite increases the hydroxyl ion concentration by forming sodium hydroxide or calcium hydroxide. The reaction of chlorine gas and water increases the hydrogen ion concentration by forming HCl. It is generally speculated that chlorine gas at a pH of 2 to 3 may be slightly more effective than a hypochlorite solution of pH 11 to 12 at the immediate point of application. This is because more of the HOCl and some extremely active molecular chlorine are present. It is well known that HOCl almost completely dissociates at a pH of 11 to 12 to the ineffective hypochlorite ion. The high pH is only momentary, but demonstrates why the hypochlorite solution should be as dilute as possible (in the range of 0.5 to 1.0 percent) rather than 5 to 15 percent.

The reactions of chlorine with ammonia in dilute aqueous solutions form three types of chloramines as follows:

$$HOCl + NH_3 \longrightarrow NH_2Cl + H_2O \qquad (18\text{-}5)$$

$$NH_2Cl + HOCl \longrightarrow NHCl_2 + H_2O \qquad (18\text{-}6)$$

$$NHCl_2 + HOCl \longrightarrow NCl_3 + H_2O \qquad (18\text{-}7)$$

All of these reactions can occur and compete, depending on pH, temperature, contact time and initial chlorine/ammonia ratio. When an excess of ammonia is present, the monochloramine is predominant. If sufficient chlorine is applied to produce the breakpoint phenomena, the ammonia-nitrogen is completely destroyed [4]. The monochloramine is converted to dichloramine and free chlorine begins to appear. This theoretically requires at least 10 mg/l of free chlorine per mg/l of ammonia-nitrogen. If the chlorine/ammonia ratio is greater than 15:1 or 20:1, some nitrogen trichloride is formed.

The reactions of chlorine with many inorganic compounds are described in detail in the applicable references at the end of this chapter and will not be discussed in detail herein [4].

Phenols can be completely oxidized at pH levels of 7 to 10 and a minimum of 100 mg/l of free chlorine residual. The destruction of phenol by chlorination is feasible up to 200 mg/l phenol. It is imperative that sufficient chlorine is applied or undesirable chlorinated hydrocarbons will be generated. The chlorine/ phenol ratio was estimated at 6 to 10/1 and will generally require large excesses due to other compounds which are usually associated with phenol in wastewater. Coke plant wastewaters have required as high as 5,000 mg/l chlorine to destroy 100 mg/l of phenol. The contact time for phenolic oxidation ranges from 5 to 10 minutes with chlorine residuals of 1,000 and 3,000 mg/l up to 2 to 5 hours with residuals of 10 to 100 mg/l. The equations for chlorine oxidation of phenol are given below [2]:

| Substituted Phenol | Substituted Trichlorophenol | Compound A Aliphatic Acid | Intermediate | Compound B Aliphatic Acid |

$$(18\text{-}8)$$

Due to the complexity of oxidation reactions, it is impossible to accurately predict the oxidant quantities based on a casual knowledge of the wastewater. Even a thorough characterization will fail to provide accurate estimates because of competing reactions and effects of the wastewater alkalinity, pH, temperature and inorganic constituents. Subsequently, thorough treatability studies are required. More effort is devoted herein to ozone experimentation because of its uniqueness and relatively recent entry into the wastewater treatment field. Although large scale pilot ozone plants have been operated, sufficient information can be obtained from bench-scale tests, both batch and continous, to ascertain the feasibility, the design parameters, and approximate economics of a prototype facility. Also, since the ozone must be applied in a gaseous form, the experimental techniques and equipment are much more involved than with chlorine or other oxidants which can be tested in a dry or liquid form.

EQUIPMENT REQUIRED

The equipment and associated apparatus required for batch and continuous ozonation are depicted in Figures 18-2 and 18-3 and are the same for either treatment mode except for the ozone-wastewater contactor. Ozone may be generated from the laboratory by a small ozonator constructed as shown in Figure 18-4. The apparatus required for both batch and continuous experimentation includes the following items.

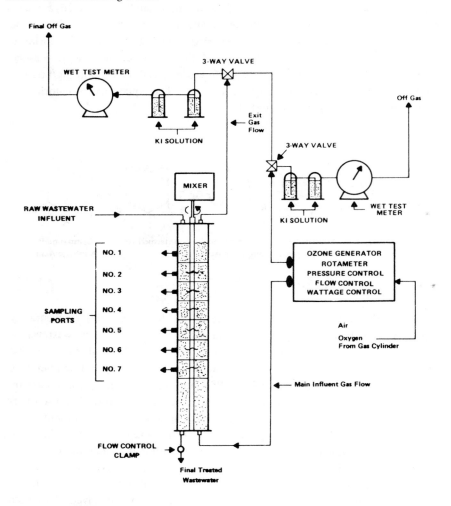

FIG. 18-2. OZONATION SCHEMATIC DIAGRAM

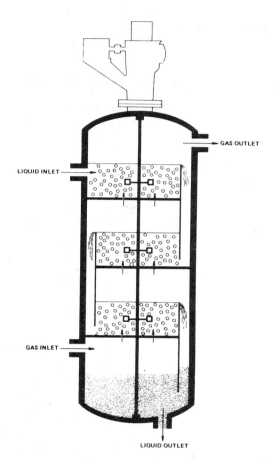

GAS OUTLET

LIQUID INLET

GAS INLET

LIQUID OUTLET

FIG. 18-3. SCHEMATIC OF EFFICIENT OZONE-WASTEWATER CONTACTOR   (Courtesy of Mixing Equipment Co.)

General Equipment

1. Four, 1-liter sealed glass containers for containing the analytical solution utilized for measuring ozone concentrations before and after wastewater contact.

2. Two standard wet test meters for measuring the flow of ozone gas before and after wastewater contact. One meter could be arranged to serve both purposes, but the switching of valves at the critical times is difficult.

3. Two rotameters for controlling and adjusting gas flow rates. The rotameters built into most commercial generators are not reliable for accurate measurement.

345

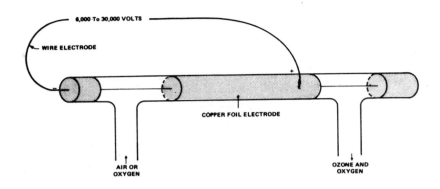

FIG. 18-4. LABORATORY OZONATOR (Ref. 4)

4. A commercial ozonator or a laboratory-constructed ozonator shown in Figure 18-4 [2],
5. An oxygen cylinder with the appropriate metering valves and a pressure regulator.
6. Miscellaneous tubing and glassware as required. The tubing should be glass, if possible, although Teflon and Tygon, in that order, could be used as conveyances for the ozone gas. Of the three materials, Tygon is the least acceptable.

Batch Reactor

1. One 3-liter glass reactor. One liter of volume is the minimum acceptable volume with the 3-liter volume being preferable.
2. One glass-fritted diffuser. The diffuser should not be the common aquarium type due to the presence of unstable, oxidizable adhesives used in many cheaper aquarium stones.
3. One 2-way glass valve for withdrawing periodic samples from the reactor.

Continuous-Flow Reactor

1. One 6-foot, 3-inch diameter glass column. The column is operated counter-currently with the ozone entering from the bottom and the waste-water from the top. For pilot and finalized design investigations, a manufacturer's contactor such as illustrated in Figure 18-3 should be used.
2. One glass-fritted diffuser as described above.

EXPERIMENTAL PROCEDURES

Analytical Methods for Ozone Detection

The most common method of measuring ozone in water at low concentrations is by the oxidation of potassium iodide in acidic solutions by:

$$O_3 + 2H^+ + 2I^- \longrightarrow O_2 + I_2 + H_2O \qquad (18\text{-}9)$$

Investigators have encountered serious problems with this method including non-stoichiometric iodine formation at neutral and alkaline conditions. Other work has inferred high iodine formation in acidic solutions. A summary of analytical methods for oxidant detection in water is shown in Table 18-1 [2].

TABLE 18-1. ANALYTICAL SUMMARY FOR OZONE MEASUREMENT

Analytical Method	Method of Oxidation	Interferences or Limitations
Potassium Iodide; alkaline, acid, and neutral conditions	$2\,KI \longrightarrow I_2$	Most oxidants, including oxygen, interfere
Ferrous ion oxidation	$Fe^{2+} \longrightarrow Fe^{3+}$	Results believed to be low
Manganese oxidation and orthotolidine	$Mn^{2+} \longrightarrow Mn^{3+}$	
Visible Region Spectrophotography	Molar absorptivity of 2,500 to 3,000 at 260 mμ	Detection limits for 1 cm cell 10^{-3} M
Leuco Crystal Violet	Redox indicator: Leuco Crystal Violet	Newest technique (under investigation)
Instrumental methods using KI oxidation	$2\,KI \longrightarrow I_2$	Same as KI above

347

The newest technique for ozone measurement is the leuco crystal violet test which is still under investigation. This test involves a colorimetric measure of the oxidation of leuco crystal violet at a wavelength of 592 mμ in acidic solutions. The color is very stable and has actually been monitored for 44 days.

The reagents required for the standard potassium iodide test are presented in *Standard Methods* [5]. The reagents required for the leuco crystal violet test are given by Black and Whittle [6].

Analytical Methods for Chlorine

There are several tests which have gained common use throughout the world for determining chlorine residuals in water and wastewater. The most prevalent methodology includes:

1. Iodometric (starch iodide method).
2. Orthotolidine method.
3. OTA (orthotolidine-arsenite) method.
4. Alternate OTA method (developed by U. S. Army).
5. Palin's method.
6. Stabilized neutral orthotolidine (SNORT) method.
7. Amperometric method.

Each of these methods is described in detail by White [4]. The orthotolidine method of chlorine residual determination is accepted in most of North America as the best procedure. However, Palin's OPD method is the most common procedure in Great Britain and parts of Europe.

Analytical Methods for Other Oxidants

Permanganate. Permanganate concentrations are generally determined by a photometric (wave length of approximately 526 mμ) or titrametric method. Morgan and Stumm have prepared a comprehensive discussion of the various methods for determining manganese compounds in dilute aqueous solutions [7]. It has also been shown that permanganate can be determined independently in the presence of MnO_2 and Cl_2 by amperometric titration with phenyl arsene oxide.

Chlorine Dioxide. Although chlorine dioxide will react adequately and quantitatively with reagents such as orthotolidine and potassium iodide, these reactions do not seem to be specific in the presence of other species such as chlorine, chlorite, chlorate, and chloride. A method of determining chlorine dioxide independently has been employed in which chlorine dioxide is reacted with Acid Chrome Violet K and determined spectrophotometrically without interference by Cl_2, OCl^-, ClO_2^-, and ClO_3^- [8].

Hydrogen Peroxide. The standard potassium iodide test described in *Standard Methods* is generally employed for the determination of hydrogen peroxide [5]. Of course, the use of this test assumes the absence of any oxidants, other than hydrogen peroxide.

Batch Procedures

The batch procedure for ozonating wastewater consists of measuring the ozone concentration in the ozone and oxygen gas stream from the ozonator and then monitoring the residual ozone in the gas stream after contacting a known quantity of wastewater with a measured quantity of gas. Subsequently, the amount of ozone which was used to oxidize a measured reduction in wastewater contaminants, such as COD, phenol or color can be determined. Different contact times and ozone loadings can be examined under various operating variables, such as pH and temperature. The procedures for the batch tests follow.

1. Connect the oxygen cylinder to the ozonator.
2. Fill the batch ozone reagent reactors with one liter of potassium iodide solution at 20 g/l concentration. Two contactors are operated in series on the exit gas stream to insure that all of the ozone is captured for subsequent analysis.
3. Fill the contactor with 3 liters of wastewater which have been analyzed for the specific constituents under study, such as COD, BOD or phenol.
4. Adjust the ozonator gas flow to the desired flow rate with the primary rotameter. Vent the gas stream to the atmosphere during this period.
5. Using the primary stopcock, divert the gas flow through the primary reagent reactors. Pass exactly 3 liters of gas, using the wet test meter as an indicator, through the primary reagent reactor.
6. When exactly 3 liters have passed through the reagent, divert the gas stream through the waste sample.
7. Ozonate the waste sample for the desired contact time (5 min. to 5 hr.), and pass the gas stream to the secondary reagent reactors.
8. At the end of the contact time, cut off the gas flow to the reactor with the primary stopcock and remove the primary and secondary reagent solutions for titration with standard 0.1 N $Na_2S_2O_3$ solution. Record the secondary wet test meter readings to obtain the total gas flow through the system during the oxidation test. Measure the residual COD or other pertinent constituents of the waste sample.
9. Repeat Steps 2 through 8, varying the contact time and the quantity of ozone applied. The amount of ozone can be controlled by employing a higher gas flow rate or by increasing the ozone concentration in the gas,

using a higher voltage on the ozonator. Generally, the gas flow is used to control the amount of applied ozone. However, by varying the gas rate through the system, it is possible that the bubble size and degree of turbulence may also be varied thereby changing the actual conditions of the test. Other conditions, such as pH, and temperature, can be evaluated at a constant ozone concentration.

The batch tests allow examination of the effect of ozone loading and contact time at various operating conditions. The batch tests can be used to delineate certain conditions of operation, but by no means can batch results be used for design of a final system.

Continuous Flow Procedures

After conclusion of the batch tests, the continuous-flow reactor can be used to determine optimum conditions under counter-flow, continuous operation as will be experienced in the field. Operation of the continuous column as shown in Figure 18-2 is identical to the batch tests except for the reactor. It is possible to use a small, continuous-flow reactor of approximately 3 to 6 in. in diameter and 3 to 4 ft in depth. A reactor of this type can be used to develop optimum design conditions. However, it is emphatically cautioned that a reactor of this type will not project identical conditions to a field system if a proprietary or manufacturer's contactor is utilized in the prototype. Most proprietary ozone contactors will give slightly different ozone utilization efficiencies and should be guaranteed by the manufacturer prior to a final system design. The contactor shown in Figures 18-2 and 18-3 was developed by a manufacturer and was employed with a 2 gpm pilot system for color reduction in a waste containing approximately 5,000 to 6,000 mg/l APHA units of color [9]. The procedures for the continuous study are described as follows:

1. Estimate the desired contact time by pumping the wastewater into the top of the column at the calculated flow rate. For example, with 4-ft of liquid level in a 3-in. diameter column and a desired contact time of 10 min, the flow rate would be:

Contact Area	$= \frac{\pi}{4}(3)^2 = 7.065$ sq in.
Volume	$= (7.065)(4 \times 12)$
	$= 339$ cu in.
	$= 2189$ ml
Pump flow rate	$= 2189/10$
	$= 219$ ml/min

2. Measure the ozone concentration in the gas flow as described under the batch procedures.

3. Divert the gas flow into the reactor column in which waste is being fed at the desired flow rate. Vent the exit gas from the column to the atmosphere.

4. After one detention time necessary to attain steady-state conditions, divert the gas using the stopcock, through the secondary reagent contactors and the wet test meter for measurement of the ozone concentration and the gas flow rate. The contactor is generally operated at 6 to 9 psig.

5. Continue the tests until the reagent in the first contactor indicates saturation. It is desirable to have sufficient reagent life for at least one detention time.

6. Shut off the influent gas flow and the waste flow simultaneously. Measure the volume of wastewater pumped during the test run and record the volume of gas passed through the sample. Analyze the wastewater sample for the specific constituents and measure the reagent solutions for ozone levels.

7. Repeat Steps 1 through 6 at various operating conditions. It may be desirable to examine the effects of contactor depth and bubble size on ozone efficiency in the event that a pilot contactor is not available.

CORRELATION OF RESULTS

After the equipment has been set up and the appropriate data collected, it is desirable to present the test results in a form suitable for interpretation and design. Generally, the major calculation required is the quantity of oxidant utilized in order to oxidize or destroy a specified quantity of pollutant, such as COD, BOD, and color.

Batch Ozonation Correlations

The results of the batch studies are correlated to delineate optimum conditions of operation, such as operating pH, temperature, and detention time. For example, suppose it is desired to examine the effects of contact time and ozone loading on oxidation of phenol from an activated sludge system. A matrix of batch oxidation calculations can be set up as shown in Table 18-2.

The results of the tests in Table 18-2 are plotted in Figure 18-5 (the examples of calculating ozone quantities are described in the continuous-flow correlations in the next section). From Figure 18-5, the minimum times to achieve residual

351

TABLE 18-2. MATRIX OF BATCH OZONATION STUDY

Bio-Effluent pH	Gas Flowrate (1/min)	Ozone Loading (mg O_3/min)	Contact Time (min)	Residual Phenol (ppb)
7.0	0.22	45.7	0	--
7.0	0.22	45.7	5	--
7.0	0.22	45.7	15	39
7.0	0.22	45.7	30	18
7.0	0.22	45.7	60	2
7.0	1.02	88.7	0	--
7.0	1.02	88.7	5	38
7.0	1.02	88.7	15	24
7.0	1.02	88.7	30	7
7.0	1.02	88.7	60	< 1

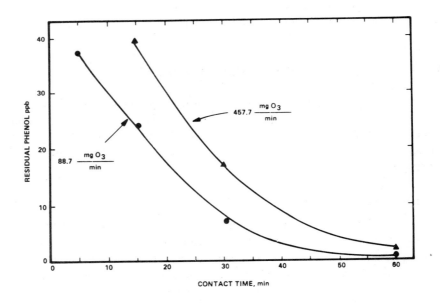

FIG 18-5. DETERMINATION OF MINIMUM CONTACT TIME BY BATCH OZONATION

phenol concentrations less than 2 ppb were approximately 40 and 60 min for ozone loadings of 88.7 and 45.7 mg O_3/min, respectively. Other ozone loadings can be examined and the results correlated as in Figure 18-6. If desired, effects such as temperature are similarly related as indicated in Figure 18-6.

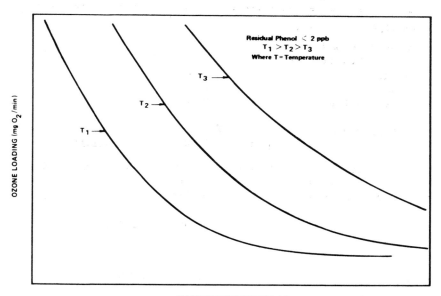

FIG. 18-6. EFFECT OF TEMPERATURE ON OZONE LOADING - CONTACT TIME RELATIONSHIP

Continuous-Flow Correlations

An example with ozone will serve to illustrate the calculations involved for a continuous test. A sample of wastewater was continuously contacted with various quantities of ozone for color removal. The results of one test are shown in Table 18-3 and it is desired to correlate the results as shown in Figure 18-7.

1. The data format, shown in Table 18-3, presents the initial operating conditions, the data collected during the test, such as total liquid and gas flow, removal of desired constituents, and the results of titration of the potassium iodide solution with a 0.1 N $Na_2S_2O_3$ solution. The influent gas sample is the gas stream coming directly from the ozonator. Bottles 1 and 2 refer to the reagent contactors for the exit gas stream as shown in Figure 18-2.

353

TABLE 18-3. DATA SHEET FOR CONTINUOUS OZONATION TEST

OPERATING CONDITIONS

Wastewater Flow Rate	33.2 ml/min
Contactor Detention Time	20 min
Voltage	90 Volts
Pressure	7.9 psig
Ozone Flow Rate	0.35 l/min

OBSERVED DATA

	Initial	Final	Elapsed
Time of Study	11:05 AM	3:20 PM	4 hr 15 min = 255 min
Total Wastewater Volume		8,520 ml	
Total Ozone Gas Flow		90 liters	

	Influent	Effluent[a]
BOD	20	24
TOC	257	208
Color	5,500	3,000

TITRATIONS OF OZONE SAMPLES

Sample No.	Sample Description	ml of 0.1 N $Na_2S_2O_3$	Liters of Gas Sampled
1	Influent O_3 gas	11.7	3
2	Bottle No. 1	144.8	90
3	Bottle No. 2	1.4	90

[a]Effluent represents sample of Total Wastewater Composite (8,520 ml).

2. The quantity of ozone in each sample can be determined as shown in Table 18-4. The total quantity of ozone (column 2 in Table 18-4) is determined by multiplying 1 by 2.4 (1 ml of 0.1 N $Na_2S_2O_3$ is equivalent to 2.4 mg O_3).

Influent ozone gas: 11.7/0.417 = 28.1 mg ozone

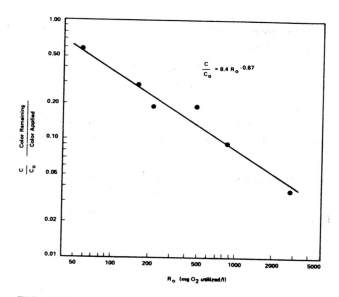

FIG. 18-7. CORRELATION OF COLOR REMOVAL
WITH OZONE UTILIZATION

TABLE 18-4. CALCULATION OF OZONE QUANTITIES

Column Sample Description	1 ml of 0.1 N $Na_2S_2O_3$	2 Total mg of O_3	3 Liters of Gas	4 mg of O_3 per liter of gas	5 mg of O_3 Applied
Influent Ozone Gas	11.7	28.1	3	9.36	842.4
Bottle No. 1	144.8	347.52	90	--	--
Bottle No. 2	1.4	3.36	90	--	--

3. The concentration of ozone in the influent gas stream (Column 4) can be calculated by dividing Column 2 by Column 3 in Table 18-4.

Concentration of ozone = 28.1/3
= 9.36 mg ozone/liter influent gas

4. Calculate the total mg of ozone applied. Since the total gas flow during the test was 90 liters:

$$\text{Total ozone applied} = 9.36 \text{ mg } O_3/\text{liter} \times 90 \text{ liters}$$
$$= 842.4 \text{ mg } O_3$$

5. Calculate the efficiency of ozone utilization
   a. The total ozone remaining in the exit gas stream is the sum of ozone captured in Bottles 1 and 2, i.e., the sum of Column 2 for Bottles 1 and 2:

   $$\text{Total ozone remaining} = 347.52 + 3.36$$
   $$= 350.9 \text{ mg } O_3$$

   b. Total ozone applied $= 842.4$ mg ozone (Step 4 above)
   c. Calculate the efficiency of ozone utilization

   $$\text{Percent ozone utilization} = (842.4 - 350.9)/842.4$$
   $$= 58.3 \text{ percent}$$

6. Calculate the concentration of ozone used in the wastewater
   a. mg ozone used $= 842.4 - 350.9$
   $$= 491.5 \text{ mg}$$
   b. Total wastewater volume $= 8,520$ ml
   c. Concentration of ozone used $= 491.5$ mg/8.52 liters
   $$= 57.6 \text{ mg/l}$$

7. Correlate the data for different runs as shown in Table 18-5 and Figure 18-7.

TABLE 18-5. OZONATION DATA SUMMARY SHEET

Date	Ozone Applied (mgO₃)	Ozone Not Utilized (mgO₃)	Percent Utilization	Color (APHA) Inf	Eff	TOC (mg/l) Inf	Eff	BOD (mg/l) Inf	Eff	Waste Flow (liters)	Ozone Usage (mgO₃/l)
Nov. 17	842	351	58.3	5,300	3,000	257	208	20	24	8.52	57.6
Nov. 20	1,766	525	70.3	5,300	1,500	181	171			7.63	162.6
Nov. 22	1,653	547	66.9	5,300	1,000	149	135	8	21	5.08	217.7
Nov. 24	2,660	455	82.9	5,300	1,000	192	159	15	38	4.54	485.7
Nov. 27	4,596	567	87.7	5,300	500	175	150	15	53	4.69	859.1
Nov. 28	4,435	537	87.9	5,300	200	179	149	11	86	1.35	2,887.4

LIMITATIONS AND SCALE-UP

The major limitation in designing a laboratory system for ozonation is the degree and efficiency of contacting afforded between the ozone gas and the wastewater to be oxidized. In order to scale-up from laboratory to prototype system, it is necessary that the contactor be adequately sized to obtain the required ozone utilization efficiency. In order to accurately predict this efficiency, it is necessary that the laboratory and pilot studies be conducted under identical turbulence and bubble size conditions. Otherwise, scale-up factors as high as 100 percent additional capacity might be required. Of secondary importance is the temperature of the liquid at which the experiments are conducted. Although the rate of chemical reaction increases with increasing wastewater temperature, the relative stability of ozone greatly decreases with increasing wastewater temperature so that the overall effect of increasing temperature might be to lower the rate of oxidation. Thus, it is essential that the effect of temperature be examined so that the efficiency of ozone utilization can be predicted as a function of seasonal variations in wastewater temperature.

REFERENCES

1. Weber, W. J., *Physiocochemical Processes for Water Quality Control*, Wiley-Interscience, New York (1972).

2. Evans, F. L., *Ozone in Water and Wastewater Treatment*, Ann Arbor Science Publishers, Inc., Ann Arbor, Michigan (1972).

3. "Tertiary Treatment of a High Strength Phenolic and Ammonia Wastestream," Industrial Report for the Westinghouse Electric Corporation, Associated Water and Air Resources Engineers, Inc., Nashville, Tn. (1972).

4. White, G. C., *Handbook of Chlorination*, Van Nostrand Reinhold Co., New York (1972).

5. *Standard Methods for the Examination of Water and Wastewater*, 14th Edition, APHA, AWWA, WPCF (1976).

6. Black, A. P. and Whittle, G. P., "New Methods for the Colorimetric Determination of Halogen Residuals. Part I: Iodine, Iodide and Iodate," *Jour. American Water Works Association*, 59, 471-490 (1967).

7. Morgan, J. J. and Stumm, W., "Analytical Chemistry of Aqueous Manganese," *Jour. American Water Works Association*, 61, 205 (1969).

8. Myhrstad, J. A. and Samdal, J. E., "Behavior and Determination of Chlorine

Dioxide," *Jour. American Water Works Association*, 61, 205-208 (1969).

9. "Pilot Plant Treatment Investigations of a Complex Industrial Effluent," Industrial Report for Toms River Chemical Corp., Toms River, New Jersey, Associated Water and Air Resources Engineers, Inc., Nashville, Tn. (August 1973).

19

GRAVITY THICKENING
OF SLUDGES

DISCUSSION OF PRINCIPLES

Thickening is generally the first step in most sludge handling systems and is accomplished by either gravity or dissolved air flotation. The primary objective of a thickener is to reduce sludge volumes by concentrating the sludge, thereby, increasing the effectiveness and lowering the costs of subsequent dewatering processes, such as vacuum filtration or centrifugation, or filter presses. Although gravity thickening has been used extensively in waste treatment, thickener design has not been formulated on a rational basis. The relationship of sludge settling characteristics and resultant thickener operation have not been developed and various alternative designs have not been examined on a true comparative basis.

The most important criteria in thickener design is the surface area required to accomplish the desired degree of thickening. The surface area must be sufficient so that the rate of solids application is less than the rate at which solids are able to reach the bottom of the tank. This area is found by establishing a limiting solids loading rate, or "solids flux," in units of lb solids applied /sq ft-day. After developing the limiting flux which will produce the desired underflow concentration, the thickener area is [1]:

$$A = \frac{8.34\,C_o Q_o}{G_L} = \frac{M}{G_L} \qquad (19\text{-}1)$$

where:

A   = thickener area, sq ft
Q_o = influent flow, mgd
C_o = influent solids concentration, mg/l
M   = solids load to thickener, lb/day
G_L = limiting solids flux, lb/sq ft-day

The capacity of a thickener for carrying solids downward at a given concentration by gravity under a batch situation is:

$$G_B = C_i V_i \qquad (19\text{-}2)$$

where:

G_B = batch solids flux, lb/sq ft-day
C_i = sludge concentration, lb/cu ft
V_i = settling velocity at C_i, ft/day

In a continuous thickener, the solids are transported downwards by both gravity and the velocity resulting from the removal of sludge from the tank bottom. Thus,

$$G_c = C_i V_i + C_i U \qquad (19\text{-}3)$$

where:

G_c = continuous solids flux, lb/sq ft-day
U   = average downward sludge velocity due to sludge removal, ft/day

The continuous flux, G_c, can be varied by the designer by controlling, U, since this is determined by the underflow concentration. The settling characteristics of the sludge determine the amount of solids transported by gravity subsidence $C_i V_i$. The amount of sludge transported by sludge withdrawal, $C_i u$, varies as controlled by the operation of the process. Assuming that most of the suspended solids are removed in the sludge:

$$U = \frac{Q_u}{A} = \frac{C_u Q_u}{C_u A} = \frac{M}{C_u A} = \frac{G_L}{C_u} \qquad (19\text{-}4)$$

where:

Q_u = underflow rate, cu ft/day
C_u = underflow concentration, lb/cu ft

Thus, from Equations 19-3 and 19-4, the capacity of a thickener can be increased by increasing the rate of sludge withdrawal; however, the resulting underflow concentration, C_u, will be less. To determine the area of a continuous thickener, it is necessary to develop the minimum flux, G_L, in Equation 19-4 for the range of suspended solids which could occur in the thickener. A method has been developed [1, 2, 3] which employs batch data to generate a batch flux plot shown in Figure 19-1. This plot is constructed by relating G_B in Equation

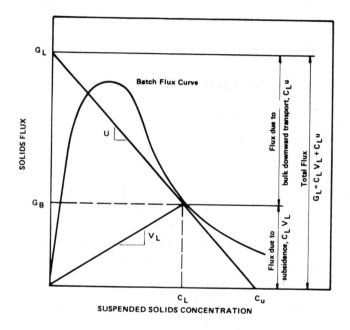

FIG. 19-1. BATCH FLUX PLOT WITH ILLUSTRATION OF USE OF PLOT TO DETERMINE LIMITING FLUX FOR A CONTINUOUS THICKENER

19-2 to solids concentration, C_L. Thus, from Equation 19-4 the slope of the line connecting G_L on the y-axis with C_u on the x-axis on the batch flux plot is the required underflow velocity, U. Therefore, the y-axis intercept of the tangent to the batch curve drawn from the desired underflow concentration on the x-axis is the limiting (minimum) flux, G_L, for a continuous thickener. The area can then be calculated by:

$$A = \frac{M}{G_L} \qquad (19\text{-}5)$$

$$A = \frac{M}{C_L V_L + C_L u} \qquad (19\text{-}6)$$

where:

C_L = concentration of sludge with the minimum ability to convey solids to the bottom of the thickener when thickened sludge is withdrawn at concentration C_u, lb/cu ft

V_L = settling velocity at C_L, ft/day

EQUIPMENT REQUIRED

The equipment needed for performing settling tests includes a graduated cylinder with stirrer. A typical arrangement is shown in Figure 19-2. Details of the equipment are outlined below:

1. **Graduated cylinder**: Cylinder should be at least 2 inches in diameter and preferably 4 inches or greater. A minimum depth of one foot, and preferably 3 feet, is desired. The cylinder can be graduated in milliliters or inches. If a one-liter graduated cylinder is used, the milliliters should be calibrated into inches. Each cylinder should be calibrated separately since the diameter and, thus, the ml/inch, vary among cylinders.

2. **Stirring mechanism**: A triangular stirring device, such as that illustrated in Figure 19-2, is sufficient for testing. The stirrer should not touch the sides of the cylinder, and should be constructed for ease of disconnecting from the stirring motor. The stirring motor should be capable of rotating the stirrer so that the tip speeds are approximately 10 in./min. This will result in rotational speeds of approximately 4-6 revolutions/hr. Small clock motors are ideal or a more elaborate arrangement can be constructed with gear arrangements to operate two to four cylinders at one time.

3. **Stopwatch**

4. **Stirring rod**: For certain sludges, particularly physical/chemical, it is desirable to mix the contents gently prior to settling so that sufficiently

sized flocs are formed. This flocculation step can be accomplished by slowly raising and lowering a perforated disc in the cylinder.

EXPERIMENTAL PROCEDURES

The most significant sludge characteristics which influence design are the zone settling velocity at various solids concentrations, the temperature, the biological properties, the specific gravity and the effects that shear forces have on the related sludge properties. In designing a thickener, it is essential to establish the relationship between settling velocity and suspended solids levels for all concentrations anticipated in the thickener [2].

For design purposes, it is necessary to construct a batch flux curve as shown in Figure 19-1. The settling velocity of the sludges can be determined by observing the subsidence of a zone interface under batch conditions in a transparent, graduated cylinder. After sufficient flocculation, the sludge-liquid interface will settle at a uniform rate until the sludge becomes so concentrated that the rate gradually decreases. The constant rate portion of the settling test is taken to be the correct zone settling velocity and can be determined by plotting the sludge-liquid interface versus time of settling. The test is repeated for the anticipated range of suspended solids concentrations. It may also be desirable to examine the settling ratio as a function of depth since a dependence sometimes exists for certain flocculant sludges.

The specific test procedures are outlined below:

1. Add the desired amount of sludge to the graduated cylinder. If a one-liter cylinder is used, then generally 1000 ml are added (the approximate depth is about 13 to 14 inches depending on the cylinder diameter).
2. With the stirring rod, gently mix the sludge so that large flocs are formed. A good rule-of-thumb is to raise and lower the rod every three seconds for 15-20 seconds (5-7 cycles).
3. Immediately insert the stirrer into the cylinder, taking care not to shear the flocculated sludge. Attach the stirrer to the stirring motor or gear quickly (see Figure 19-2).
4. Observe the sludge-liquid interface as the sludge mass subsides in the cylinder. Record the sludge interface at equally-spaced time intervals until the rate of settling begins to decrease. Frequently, it is difficult to observe a distinct interface, and the interface level must be approximated with regard to other dispersed flocs.

5. Repeat Steps 1 through 4 at different sludge concentrations. With excess activated sludges, the range of concentrations should be from 2,000 to 20,000 mg/l, if possible. With physical-chemical sludges, such as lime, the concentrations may range from 4,000 to 180,000 mg/l, depending on such factors as the suspended organic content.
6. Repeat Steps 1 through 4 at different depths in deeper cylinders of identical diameter, if possible. The depths should range from 1 to 4 feet.

CORRELATION OF RESULTS

The results of the settling tests are correlated to determine zone settling

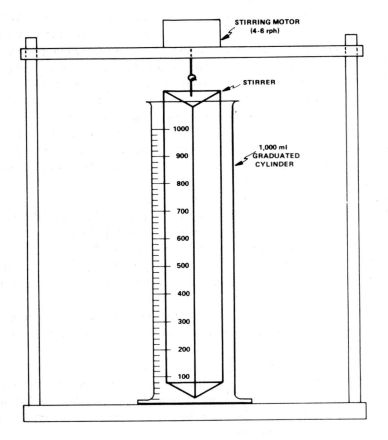

FIG. 19-2. DIAGRAM OF ZONE SETTLING APPARATUS

velocities at the various suspended solids concentrations. Subsequently, the batch flux curve is constructed. Additionally the relationship of settling velocity and initial sludge depth is desired.

1. Arrange the settling data at the various suspended solids concentrations as shown in Table 19-1.

TABLE 19-1. HEIGHT OF SLUDGE-LIQUID INTERFACE AS A FUNCTION OF SETTLING TIME

Time (min)	Suspended Solids Concentration (%)					
	0.1	0.4	0.8	1.2	1.6	2.0
0	1,000	1,000	1,000	1,000	1,000	1,000
1	840	940	985	990	998	999
2	675	880	965	985	995	998
3	570	820	945	980	990	997
4	490	765	920	970	985	995
5	425	720	900	960	983	994
6	380	680	880	950	980	993
7	360	640	860	940	978	993
8	335	600	840	935	977	992
9	310	560	815	925	975	991
10	295	535	795	915	970	990
15	210	425	695	880	950	985
20	155	355	625	840	940	980
25	115	305	-	-	-	-
30	85	275	525	770	915	975
40	60	240	480	740	900	960
50	55	230	455	725	885	960

2. Correlate these data by plotting the sludge-liquid interface with time as shown in Figure 19-3.
3. Calculate the zone settling velocity (ZSV) as the slope of the straight-line portion of the curve. This slope will be in ml/min and should be corrected to ft/hr by using the appropriate conversion factor for the specific cylinder (if one-liter cylinder is used). For ease of conversion, an inch scale can be taped to the cylinder so that conversion factors are unnecessary.
4. Correlate the ZSV to the respective suspended solids concentrations on plot as shown in Figure 19-4.
5. Develop the batch flux curve (Figure 19-5) by calculating the mass loading

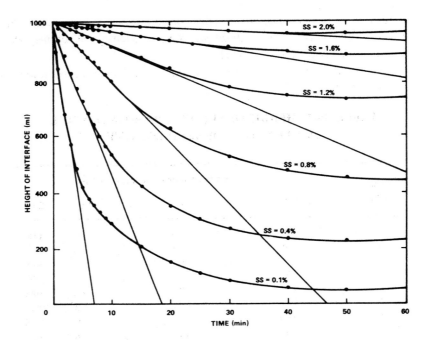

FIG. 19-3. SETTLING CURVES AT VARIOUS SUSPENDED SOLIDS CONCENTRATIONS

or solids flux as shown in Table 19-2. The batch flux curve is developed by plotting the solids flux (lb/sq ft-day) versus suspended solids concentration (%). For example, from Figure 19-4 the solids flux at a 1.0 percent solids concentration is:

$$\begin{aligned}
G_B &= C_i V_i \\
&= (0.01 \times 62.4 \text{ lb/cu ft}) \\
&\quad (1.48 \text{ ft/hr} \times 24\text{hr/day}) \\
&= 22.2 \text{ lb/sq ft-hr}
\end{aligned} \tag{19-2}$$

6. Various alternative designs can be evaluated using the batch flux curve in Figure 19-5. By drawing an operating line from a desired underflow concentration of solids (x-axis) which is tangent to the batch curve, the design solids flux is obtained on the y-axis. The required area is obtained by dividing the total pounds of solids to be thickened by the solids flux as in Equation 19-1.

7. Correlate the ZSV versus initial settling depth as shown in Figure 19-6.

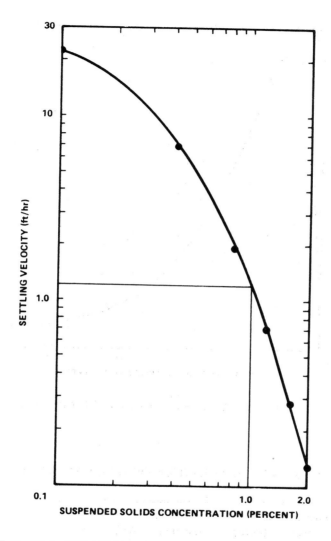

**FIG. 19-4. RELATIONSHIP OF SETTLING VELOCITY AND
SUSPENDED SOLIDS CONCENTRATION**

From this figure, it would seem that at least 4 feet of sludge depth are needed for obtaining the maximum settling rate. A better method for estimating sludge depth is not available although it is feasible that the depth requirements are determined by the need to store solids during overload situations [1].

367

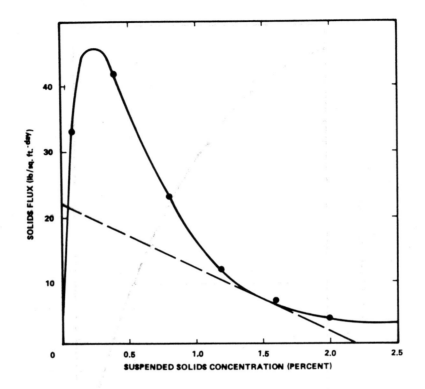

FIG. 19-5. BATCH FLUX CURVE FOR DESIGN

TABLE 19-2. CALCULATIONS OF SOLIDS FLUX VALUES

Suspended Solids			Settling Velocity			Solids Flux
(%)	(mg/l)	(lb/cu ft)	(ml/min)	(ft/hr)	(ft/day)	(lb/sq ft-day)
0.1	1,000	0.0624	314	22.0	528.0	33
0.4	4,000	0.250	100	7.0	168.0	42
0.8	8,000	0.499	27	1.9	45.6	23
1.2	12,000	0.749	13	0.9	21.6	12
1.6	16,000	0.998	4	0.3	7.2	7
2.0	20,000	1.248	2	0.13	3.1	4

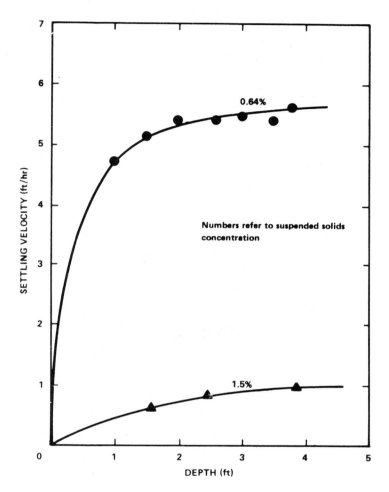

FIG. 19-6. INFLUENCE OF INITIAL SLUDGE DEPTH
SETTLING VELOCITY

LIMITATIONS AND SCALE-UP

Although the batch settling tests and development of the design batch flux curve is relatively simple, several factors warrant serious consideration in translating from laboratory to field conditions. Significant errors can result if the settling sludge is not stirred. The wall effects in small-diameter cylinders (3

369

inches) can cause the ZSV to be greater or less than the true value in large tanks depending on the solids concentration [4]. Slow mixing, as described herein, is essential to minimize bridging and other artificial effects of laboratory settling tests.

Because of the lack of adequate design procedures for depth determinations, it is desirable to perform the laboratory tests in the range of effective depths in the field (3 to 6 ft). Unfortunately, the available quantity of sludge for laboratory tests often makes this impossible. Detention time should be considered in scale-up, particularly with biological sludges. Excessive detention times will result in anaerobic conditions causing floating sludge and possible dissolution of precipitated phosphorus compounds.

At low suspended solids concentrations, the effects of temperature on settling velocities can be approximated as the corresponding ratio of fluid viscosities [1]; however, high concentrations of solids are less affected by temperature changes. With physical-chemical sludges, the specific gravity of the thickened sludge may be substantially greater than water and the dry weight volume estimates will need to be corrected accordingly.

REFERENCES

1. Dick, R. I., "Thickening," *Process Design in Water Quality Engineering: New Concepts and Developments,* E. L. Thackston and W. W. Eckenfelder, Jr., Eds., Jenkins Publishing Co., Austin, Texas and New York (1972).
2. Yoshioka, N. Y., Hotta, S. T., and Tsugami, S., "Continuous Thickening of Homogeneous Flocculated Slurries," *Chemical Engineering,* Tokyo, Japan, 21, 66-74 (1957).
3. Dick, R. I., "Role of Activated Sludge Final Settling Tanks," *Jour. San. Eng. Div.,* ASCE, 96, 423-436 (1970).
4. Vesilind, P. A., "The Effects of Stirring in the Thickening of Biological Sludge," Ph.D. thesis, University of North Carolina, Chapel Hill, N.C. (1968).

20

AEROBIC DIGESTION
OF BIOLOGICAL SLUDGES

DISCUSSION OF PRINCIPLES

Aerobic digestion may be defined as the destruction of degradable organic sludges by aerobic, biological mechanisms. Generally, aerobic digestion is most applicable to excess biological sludges, such as those generated by the activated sludge and trickling filter processes. In the absence of an external substrate, microorganisms enter the endogenous phase of the life cycle and deplete internal cellular carbon sources. Due to the presence of a heterogeneous population of microorganisms and an extremely complex ecosystem, various microbial species may serve as food sources for other members of the population. Eventually, some organisms undergo cellular lysis releasing protoplasm into the environment which is then utilized by other bacteria. The result is a net decrease in the degradable portion of the microbial population or sludge mass. A simplified representation of the aerobic digestion phase of biological waste treatment in relation to other processes is shown in Figure 20-1.

Several kinetic models have been proposed to estimate the required detention time for a desired destruction of organic sludge. However, many aerobic digester systems have been underdesigned due to the application of traditional first-order kinetics to a continuous-flow system.

In batch-fed reactors or continuously-fed plug flow systems, the destruction of volatile degradable organics may be approximated as follows [1, 4]:

$$\frac{(X_d)_e}{(X_d)_o} = e^{-k_b t} \tag{20-1}$$

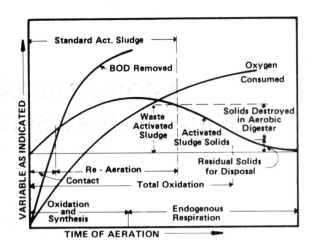

FIG. 20-1. SCHEMATIC DEPICTION OF AEROBIC BIOLOGICAL TREATMENT

where:

$(X_d)_e$ = degradable VSS remaining after batch aeration time, t, mg/l

$(X_d)_o$ = initial degradable VSS at time O, mg/l

k_b = batch reaction rate for degradable VSS destruction, day^{-1}

t = time of aeration, days

The degradable VSS, X_d, may be expressed as a function of total VSS, by incorporating the non-degradable residue, X_n:

$$(X_d)_e = (X_e - X_n) \qquad (20\text{-}2)$$

$$(X_d)_o = (X_o - X_n) \qquad (20\text{-}3)$$

where:

X_e = effluent total VSS remaining at time t, mg/l

X_o = influent total VSS at time zero, mg/l

X_n = non-degradable portion of VSS, assumed constant throughout aeration period, mg/l

Equation 20-1 may therefore be modified to consider total VSS rather than degradable VSS by incorporating Equations 20-2 and 20-3.

$$\frac{(X_e - X_n)}{(X_o - X_n)} = e^{-k_b t} \qquad (20\text{-}4)$$

Most conventional digesters are operated on a "flow-thru" basis where raw excess sludge enters the digester directly from the final clarifier of an activated sludge system. The digested sludge is aerated for a sufficient period to obtain the desired VSS destruction and passes from the digester to subsequent thickening and dewatering processes. As such, the digester is a completely-mixed reactor with no solids recirculation. Generally, design procedures have been comprised determining a rate coefficient, k_b, by correlating degradable VSS with aeration time on a batch basis as shown in Figures 20-2 and 20-3. The rate coefficient is then employed in Equation 20-6 along with the desired removal efficiency to calculate the required detention time, t.

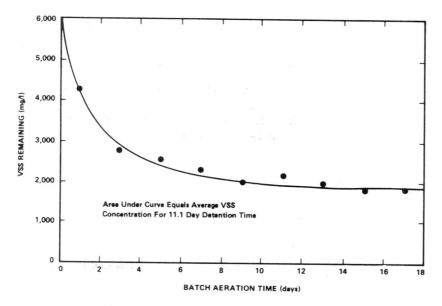

FIG. 20-2. CHRONOLOGICAL DESTRUCTION OF VSS
IN BATCH REACTOR

Unfortunately, this approach often results in an underdesigned system because the aeration basin is not operated as a batch or plug-flow reactor, but as a flow-thru, completely-mixed tank. A mass balance around a completely-mixed digester is depicted in Figure 20-4 and described below[5]:

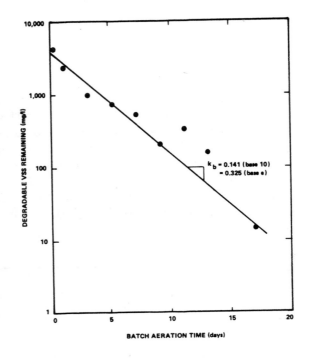

**FIG. 20-3. CORRELATION OF DEGRADABLE VSS WITH
DETENTION TIME**

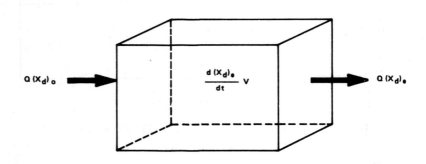

**FIG. 20-4. MASS BALANCE THROUGH A COMPLETELY-MIXED
AEROBIC DIGESTER**

374

Degradables In −Degradables Out = Degradables Destroyed

$$Q(X_d)_o - Q(X_d)_e = \frac{d(X_d)_e}{dt} V \qquad (20\text{-}5a)$$

and:

$$(X_d)_o - (X_d)_e = k_b(X_d)_e t \qquad (20\text{-}5b)$$

Substituting Equations 20-2 and 20-3 and solving for detention time:

$$t = \frac{X_o - X_e}{k_b(X_e - X_n)} \qquad (20\text{-}6)$$

Based on the above sequence of equations, it has been shown that a batch experimental procedure may be utilized to establish the reaction rate coefficient, k_b, but Equations 20-1 and 20-4 cannot be used to predict a completely-mixed flow-thru system [5]. Instead, the batch coefficient can be utilized in Equation 20-6 to predict the performance of the completely-mixed basin. In reality, the rate coefficient, k_b, will need to be corrected for temperature as shown below:

$$(k_b)_T = (k_b)_{20}\theta^{T-20} \qquad (20\text{-}7)$$

The value of θ has been found to range from 1.02 to values as high as 1.07.

EQUIPMENT REQUIRED

1. Batch reactors (8 to 20 liter volume) complete with aeration stones.
2. Dissolved oxygen probe for measurement of specific oxygen uptake rates.
3. Apparatus for determining total suspended and volatile suspended solids, such as gooch crucibles, filtering apparatus, drying oven and muffle furnace.
4. Graduated cylinders for monitoring daily increments of sludge to the continuous-flow digesters.

EXPERIMENTAL PROCEDURES

The laboratory or pilot studies are designed specifically to determine the rate of volatile suspended solids destruction, the maximum percent reduction of volatile suspended solids which can be expected, and the oxygen requirements for various degrees of volatile solids destruction. Either batch or continuous systems can be initiated. However, it is possible to accurately predict the continuous digester performance by correctly incorporating the batch digester results into Equation 20-6.

Batch Digesters

The batch reactors should be set up to cover anticipated ranges in suspended solids and temperatures.

1. Start two to four batch units with approximately 4 to 20 liters of excess activated sludge in each unit. The suspended solids concentration in the batch units should be varied in order to cover the entire range of anticipated concentrations and temperatures in the proposed digester.
2. Aerate the units and, after they are completely mixed, immediately perform the following analyses on each system:
   a. Suspended solids (SS), mg/l
   b. Volatile suspended solids (VSS), mg/l
   c. Oxygen uptake, mg/l-hr
3. Continue to aerate the systems for about 25 to 30 days and perform the above analyses every three days on each unit.
4. The above sequence of steps should also be performed with at least one reactor in a refrigerator at anticipated cold weather temperatures.

Continuous-Flow Digester

1. Set up at least three digesters with a volume of 4 to 20 liters. The detention times should be varied from 3 to 20 days. Generally, detention times of 3, 8, and 17 days will be sufficient for design purposes.
2. Each day the reactors are batch fed a specific amount of sludge to give the desired detention time.
   a. With the unit completely mixed, remove the required amount to give the desired detention time.
   b. Replace the digested sludge with fresh, raw sludge.
3. The same analyses, namely, SS, VSS, and oxygen uptake, should be performed on the continuous reactors as was specified for the batch systems. The tests should be performed at least every three days. These tests should also be conducted before the daily increment of fresh sludge is added to the reactor. The effluent VSS level, X_e, is taken as the VSS concentration

measured before the daily addition of raw sludge. The influent VSS level, X_o, is the actual concentration of the raw sludge which is added each day.

4. Continue operating the continuous systems until consistent and stabilized results are obtained. This will require at least 2 to 3 detention periods.

CORRELATION OF RESULTS

Batch Digesters

The results of the batch digesters are correlated to develop the batch rate coefficient, k_b, for use in Equation 20-6 and to estimate the approximate oxygen requirements.

1. Tabulate the results of the batch tests as shown in Table 20-1. The temperature at which these tests were run was 23°C.

TABLE 20-1. BATCH DATA USED TO DEVELOP REACTION RATE COEFFICIENT

Aeration Time (days)	VSS Remaining (mg/l)	Degradable VSS Remaining (mg/l)	%VSS Destroyed
0	6,115	4,355	-
1	4,220	2,460	31.0
3	2,770	1,010	54.7
5	2,510	750	58.9
7	2,280	520	62.7
9	1,975	215	67.7
11	2,105	345	65.6
13	1,925	165	68.5
15	1,760	<20	71.2
17	1,775	<20	71.0

2. Plot the VSS concentration remaining versus sludge age (aeration time) as shown in Figure 20-2. From this plot, the oxidizable or degradable fraction of the solids can be approximated. In other words, the residual volatile suspended solids remaining after 25-30 days of digestion can be taken

as the non-degradable portion of the volatile matter (1,775 mg/l in Table 20-1). The volatile solids which were destroyed during this aeration time are considered to be the maximum degradable portion of volatile matter.

3. For each sampling period, recalculate the degradable VSS remaining (third column in Table 20-1). Plot the degradable VSS remaining as a function of detention time and calculate the reaction rate coefficient, k_b, (Figure 20-3). Note the effect of initial VSS on the destruction rate and indicate this relationship, if significant.

4. Record the oxygen uptake rate as a function of sludge age or aeration time (Figure 20-5). When sizing aeration equipment, the oxygen utilization value can be estimated as the average value exerted during the aeration time required for the desired VSS destruction level. It should be realized that this average oxygen requirement may be slightly greater or lower than the actual demand at equilibrium conditions, but this average number is considered adequate for design purposes.

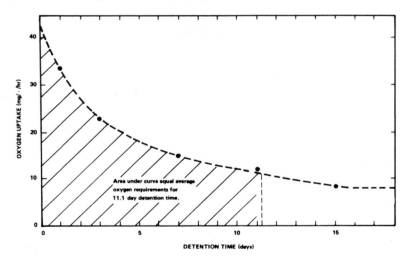

FIG. 20-5. CHRONOLOGICAL DATA FROM BATCH AEROBIC DIGESTER

After the required detention time (e.g., assume 11.1 days) has been determined from Equation 20-6, using k_b determined above, the area under the curve in Figure 20-5 can be determined to obtain the approximate oxygen requirement [2].

378

5. The average oxygen required is computed by calculating the area under the oxygen curve in Figure 20-5 at the required detention time and dividing by the design detention time. (Note: The oxygen uptake values on the y-axis are in mg/l-hr and must be corrected to mg/l-day to be consistent with "time" on the x-axis.)

Area under the curve (11.1 days)	=	7,310 mg/l O_2
Average daily use	=	7,310/11.1
	=	659 mg/l-day

Similarly, the average VSS during the test period must be estimated to determine the specific oxygen requirements.

Area under curve (11.1 days)	=	43,040 day-mg/l (See Figure 20-2)
Average VSS concentration	=	3,880 mg/l
Specific oxygen utilization	=	659/3880
	=	0.17 mg O_2/mg VSS-day

6. Thus, the design criteria developed from the batch system are:

$$X_n = 1,760 \text{ mg/l (See Table 20-1)}$$

$$= \frac{1,760}{6,115} = 29\% \text{ of influent sludge}$$

$$k_b = 0.141 \text{ (base 10) at } 23°C$$

$$= 0.325 \text{ (base e)}$$

The design equation is:

$$t = \frac{X_o - X_e}{0.325(X_e - 0.29X_o)}$$

The rate coefficient can be corrected for temperature by:

$$(k_b)_T = 0.325(1.05)^{T-23}$$

Oxygen requirements = 0.17 mg O_2 required/mg VSS-day
(These requirements are based on 65% VSS destruction in 18 days.)

Continuous-Flow Digesters

The continuous digester data are generally used as confirmation data for the batch test results.

1. Tabulate the data as shown in Table 20-2. The influent solids levels, X_o, are running averages of daily influent concentrations based on the detention time of each system. These data represent the stabilized periods only.

TABLE 20-2. CONTINUOUS-FLOW, COMPLETELY MIXED DIGESTER DATA

Day From Start (days)	Influent and Effluent VSS Levels (mg/l)							
	3-Day		5-Day		10-Day		15-Day	
	X_o	X_e	X_o	X_e	X_o	X_e	X_o	X_e
45	4,777	2,705	4,685	2,515	4,757	2,100	4,753	2,225
46	5,244	3,000	4,984	2,845	4,899	2,265	4,844	2,090
47	6,123	3,490	5,563	3,135	5,196	2,565	5,042	2,335
48	6,137	3,840	5,683	3,135	5,292	2,400	5,112	2,130
49	6,366	4,165	5,912	3,645	5,445	2,140	5,221	2,085
50	6,434	3,630	6,043	3,655	5,556	2,350	5,307	1,865
51	5,559	3,060	5,597	3,150	5,381	1,975	5,202	1,920
52	5,674	3,735	5,658	3,265	5,433	1,915	5,244	1,205
53	5,863	3,810	5,774	3,850	5,513	2,065	5,306	1,810
54	6,067	3,980	5,914	3,935	5,680	2,045	5,379	1,420
55	6,763	4,580	6,362	4,170	5,862	2,035	5,560	1,755
56	6,393	4,150	6,221	3,600	5,841	1,835	5,561	1,885
57	6,354	4,190	6,232	3,400	5,883	1,500	5,604	2,185
58	5,999	3,990	6,043	3,420	5,823	1,435	5,579	2,495
59	6,302	4,115	6,216	3,780	5,931	1,820	5,663	2,590
60	5,781	4,040	5,921	3,525	5,811	1,415	5,597	2,515
61	7,256	5,435	6,778	4,250	6,250	2,275	5,899	2,840
62	7,480	5,740	7,008	4,295	6,417	2,905	6,030	3,030

2. Average the influent and effluent VSS levels and calculate the percent removals as shown in Table 20-3.
3. Plot the percent VSS destruction versus detention time as shown in

TABLE 20-3. SUMMARY OF CONTINUOUS-FLOW DIGESTER DATA

Detention Time (days)	Average X_o (mg/l)	Average X_e (mg/l)	%VSS Destroyed
3	6,142	3,980	35.3
5	5,922	3,531	40.4
10	5,520	2,060	62.5
15	5,383	2,132	60.5

Figure 20-6. The resulting correlation will illustrate the minimum detention time required to achieve the maximum practical reduction in VSS concentration. In this example, the maximum practical reduction at 23°C would be about 65 percent which could be obtained in 11.1 days of digestion.

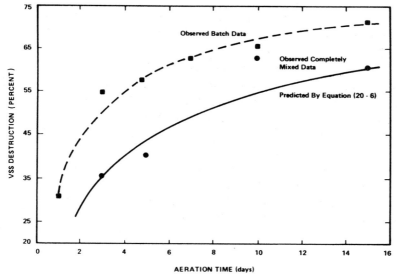

FIG. 20-6. COMPARISON OF OBSERVED AND PREDICTED VSS DESTRUCTION FOR COMPLETELY MIXED AEROBIC DIGESTER

LIMITATIONS AND SCALE-UP

The most significant limitation in the application of aerobic digestion is the effect of temperature. It is imperative that the effects of temperature be considered during design so that the digester can be sized for cold weather conditions. Alternatively, a lower destruction of VSS can be accepted during colder situations if the design capacities of subsequent dewatering and ultimate disposal processes so allow.

In translating from laboratory to field situations, the oxygen requirements must be carefully examined to avoid an undermixed situation. In most cases, the horsepower required to completely mix the digester will be much greater than the horsepower needed to supply the oxygen requirements. Thus, the oxygen requirements determined in the laboratory are not generally as significant as the detention time and temperature constraints [3].

REFERENCES

1. Eckenfelder, W. W., Jr., and Ford, D. L., *Water Pollution Control: Experimental Procedures for Process Design,* The Pemberton Press, Austin, Texas (1970).
2. Stein, R. M., Jewell, W. J., Eckenfelder, W. W., Jr., and Adams, C. E., Jr., "A Study of Aerobic Digestion Comparing Air and Pure Oxygen," Proc. 27th Industrial Waste Conference, Purdue University, West Lafayette, Ind. (1972).
3. Adams, C. E., Jr., "Partial Volatile Solids Destruction: Aerobic Digestion," *Environmental Engineers Handbook,* Vol. 1, Chilton Book Co., Radnor, Pennsylvania (1974).
4. Benedek, P., Farkas, P., and Literathy, P., "Kinetics of Aerobic Sludge Digestion," *Water Research,* 6, 91-97 (1972).
5. Adams, C. E., Jr., Eckenfelder, W. W., Jr., and Stein, R. M., "Modifications to Aerobic Digester Design," *Water Research,* 8, 212-218 (1974).

21

VACUUM FILTRATION

DISCUSSION OF PRINCIPLES

Vacuum filtration is used to dewater wastewater sludges in which the liquid phase is removed under an applied vacuum through a porous media which retains the solids. Media used may include Nylon or Dacron cloth, steel mesh or tightly-wound stainless steel coilsprings.

In vacuum filter operation, a rotary drum passes through a slurry tank in which solids are retained on the drum under an applied vacuum. The submergence of the drum in the slurry tank may vary from 10 to 60 percent. During the submergence portion of the cycle, solids are retained on the filter media and the water removed by filtration. This period of the filtration cycle is called the form time. After the drum emerges from the slurry tank, the deposited cake is further dried by liquid transfer to air drawn through the cake by the applied vacuum. At the end of the filter cycle, the cake is removed by a knife edge onto a conveyor belt for disposal, usually either to a collection hopper or to trucks for hauling, or directly to incineration. The filter media is washed with a water spray prior to again being immersed in the slurry tank. A vacuum filter operation is shown in Figure 21-1.

The variables that affect the dewatering process are:

1. Sludge feed solids concentrations that are determined by the nature of the sludge and by the thickening processes preceding the filtration step.
2. Sludge and filtrate viscosity that is usually the same as the viscosity of water at similar temperatures.
3. Sludge compressibility that is related to the nature of the sludge particles.

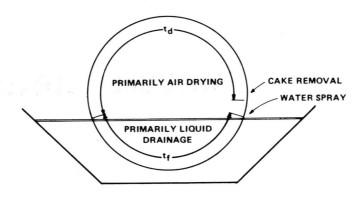

FIG. 21-1. MECHANISM OF VACUUM FILTRATION

4. Chemical and physical composition including such variables as particle size and shape, and water content.

The filter operating variables are:

1. Operating vacuum which usually varies from 10 to 20 inches of mercury (higher vacuums are more effective with incompressible cakes).
2. Drum submergence which may vary from 10 to 60 percent. High porosity sludges will use higher submergences.
3. Sludge conditioning by chemical addition. Many sludges require coagulant addition (ferric chloride, lime or polyelectrolyte) to coagulate smaller particles and minimize fine particle migration which results in binding of the filter media and cake. This binding will markedly reduce the filtration rate.
4. Type and porosity of the filter media. Where filtrate solids are not of significance, high porosity media can be used resulting in higher filtration rates.

The two major classes of sludge conditioners are physical (diatomaceous earth, fly ash, and ground blast furnace slag) and chemical (polyvalent metallic ions and synthetic organic polyelectrolytes). Physical conditioners are generally less expensive and less affected by variable conditions than chemical conditioners; however, the physical compounds increase the sludge volume significantly. The required conditioners and dosage are controlled by the characteristics of the sludge carrier water (pH, alkalinity, polyvalent cation concentration, and ionic strength) and the character of the sludge particles (suspended solids concentrations, surface charge, and particle size).

The basic filtration equation derived from Poiseilles and D'Arcy's law is [1]:

$$dV/dt = \frac{PA^2}{\mu(rcV + R_m A)} \qquad (21\text{-}1)$$

where:

V	=	volume of filtrate, cm^3
t	=	time, sec
P	=	applied vacuum, g/cm^2
A	=	filter area, cm^2
c	=	solids per unit volume of filtrate, g/cm^3
r	=	specific resistance, sec^2/g
R_m	=	initial resistance of the filter media, sec^2/cm^2
μ	=	filtrate viscosity, poises, g/cm.sec

Integration and rearrangement of this equation permits the calculation of specific resistance, r, which is a measure of the filterability of the sludge and is numerically equal to the pressure difference required to produce a unit rate of filtrate flow of unit viscosity through a unit weight of cake. Integration of Equation 21-1 yields:

$$\frac{t}{V} = \left[\frac{\mu rc}{2PA^2} \cdot V + \frac{\mu R_m}{PA} \right] \qquad (21\text{-}2)$$

An arithmetic plot of t/V versus V will generate a linear relationship with a slope equal to $\mu rc/2PA^2$ and an intercept of $\mu R_m/PA$. Thus, if the slope of the line is defined as "b," then:

$$b = \frac{\mu rc}{2PA^2} \qquad (21\text{-}3)$$

The specific resistance is therefore:

$$r = \frac{2PA^2 b}{\mu c} \qquad (21\text{-}4)$$

Specific resistance is primarily useful to compare the filtration characteristics of different sludges and to determine the optimum coagulant requirements of a specific sludge. The Buchner funnel apparatus is used to generate the data needed to determine the t/V versus V relationship and, subsequently, specific resistance. Many wastewater sludges from compressible cakes in which both the specific resistance and filtration rate are a function of the pressure difference across the cake, such that:

$$r = r_0 P^s \tag{21-5}$$

in which "s" is the coefficient of compressibility. The coefficient, s, can be determined from a log-plot of specific resistance, r, versus vacuum, P. The intercept at P = 1 psi will be the cake constant, r_0, and the slope will be equal to s.

The filtration design equation is developed from a modification of Equation 21-1 as shown below:

$$L = 35.7 \left[\frac{cP^{(1-s)}}{\mu R_0 t_f} \right]^{\frac{1}{2}} \tag{21-6}$$

where:

L	=	filter loading, lb/sq ft-hr
t_f	=	form time, min
P	=	applied vacuum, psi
c	=	solids deposited per unit volume filtrate, g/ml
R_0	=	$r_0 \times 10^{-7}$, sec²/g

The solids deposited per volume of filtrate, c, are determined by:

$$c = \frac{1}{[(100 - C_i)/C_i] - [(100 - C_f)/C_f]} \tag{21-7}$$

where:

C_i	=	initial solids content of influent sludge, % or g/100 ml
C_f	=	final solids content of cake sludge, % or g/100 ml

Since most sludges have irregular particulate characteristics, Equation 21-6 must be modified for the prediction of filtration performance:

$$L = 35.7 \left[\frac{P^{(1-s)}}{\mu R_0} \right]^{\frac{1}{2}} \left[\frac{c^m}{t_f^n} \right] \tag{21-8}$$

Evaluation of various sludge conditioners is performed in the laboratory by filtering the sludge through a filter paper using a Buchner funnel and measuring either the time required to collect a given volume of sample or the time required for the sludge cake to begin to crack.

Recently, a new technique, referred to as the capillary suction time (CST) test, has been found to be a rapid, easy, inexpensive and reproducible method of characterizing the dewaterability of a given sludge [2]. Either of these methods is used to calculate the specific resistance which is a measure of the sludge's resistance to filtration. The specific resistance allows relative comparisons of the effectiveness of various conditioners. After the type and dosage of coagulant has been determined, the laboratory filter leaf tests are performed to collect representative data for formulating the required design criteria.

The leaf test laboratory procedure to develop filtration design data involves the determination of the empirical exponents (1 - s), m, and n in Equation 21-8. It should be recognized that each of these exponents will vary with the type of sludge being investigated.

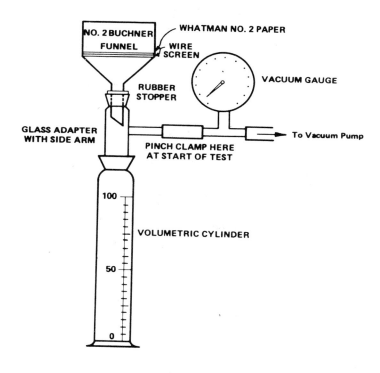

FIG. 21-2. BUCHNER FUNNEL ASSEMBLY

EQUIPMENT REQUIRED

Buchner Funnel (Figure 21-2)

1. 250 ml volumetric cylinder ground-glass with standard taper joint neck
2. Glass adapter with sidearm
3. Rubber stopper for volumetric cylinder with hole for Buchner Funnel

4. No. 2 Buchner funnel
5. Whatman No. 42 paper
6. Wire screen support for filter paper
7. Pinch clamp
8. ¼ hp vacuum pump with vacuum gauge, tubing and valves
9. Stop watch

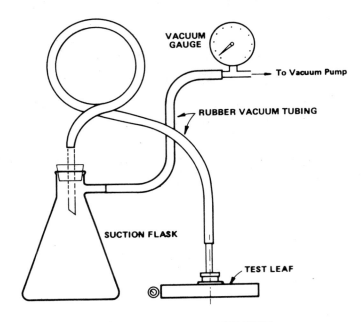

FIG. 21-3. LEAF TEST ASSEMBLY

Leaf Filter Apparatus (Figure 21-3)

1. Erlenmeyer flask with sidearm, 500 ml
2. Rubber stopper with one hole
3. ¼ hp vacuum pump with vacuum gauge, tubing and valves
4. Filter test leaf
5. Several types of synthetic or wire mesh media

Capillary Suction Time (CST) Apparatus (Figure 21-4)

1. One plexiglass plate 4-3/8 in. square by 5/8 in. thick. The underside of this top plate is recessed 1/16 in., to a radius of 1-7/8 in., and has concentric circles inscribed at 1/4 in. intervals out from the reservoir at the

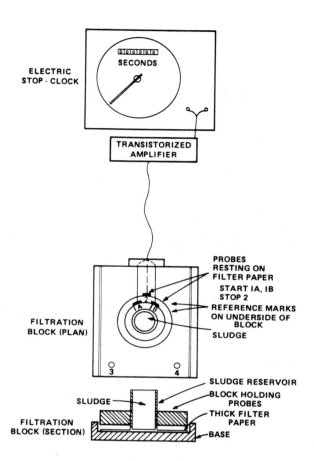

FIG. 21-4. CAPILLARY SUCTION TIME APPARATUS

center. The sample reservoir is a 1-in. length of 3/4 in. diameter, type "L", copper tubing coated with epoxy enamel. The bottom of the reservoir is set even with the bottom surface of the outer rim of the top plate.

2. One plexiglass plate 4-3/8 in. square by 5/8 in. thick. This is the bottom plate.

3. Whatman No. 17 chromatography paper.

4. Stop watch.

5. Automatic timer. In this case platinum wire electrodes are set in the bottom plates, one beneath each of the circles inscribed in the top plates. These electrodes are connected to a timer through appropriate relays and switches and protrude slightly into the filter media so that the timer may

be started when the filtrate reaches a selected electrode and stopped when the interface reaches the next electrode.

EXPERIMENTAL PROCEDURES

The general approach in vacuum filter laboratory tests is to evaluate various sludge conditioners using the Buchner funnel (Figure 21-2) or the capillary suction apparatus (Figure 21-4), and then delineate the filter design parameters with the filter leaf apparatus (Figure 21-3).

Buchner Funnel Test

1. Measure the initial solids content.
2. Prepare the Buchner funnel using a screen and filter paper (see Figure 21-2). Wet the paper with water and apply a vacuum to obtain a seal.
3. Close the valve and adjust vacuum to 15 or 20 inches of Hg.
4. Place 200 ml of the sludge sample in a 400 ml beaker and add the appropriate conditioners. If $FeCl_3$ and lime are used, add the lime about 30 seconds after mixing the $FeCl_3$ with the sludge. Mix for 2 minutes.
5. Add 200 ml sludge to Buchner funnel and allow sufficient time for a cake to form (usually about 10 seconds).
6. Release the pinch-clamp.
7. Record the filtrate volume until vacuum breaks or the rate of filtrate collection drops to about 1 ml per minute.
8. Repeat Steps 1 through 7 using varying concentrations of coagulant or polymer. Depending on the nature of the sludge, $FeCl_3$ and/or lime dosages may vary from 2 to 10% by weight and polyelectrolyte dosages may vary from 0.1 to 1.5% by weight.
9. Determine specific resistance for each situation and then delineate the optimum conditions that generate the minimum specific resistance as explained in CORRELATION OF RESULTS in this chapter.

Capillary Suction Filtration

The capillary suction time (CST) test simply involves measuring the time of travel of filtrate from a conditioned sludge through a known length of chromatography paper. The values can easily be correlated with specific resistance and the CST test used for routine testing. The procedures are as follows:

1. Place a sheet of Whatman No. 17 chromatography paper on the bottom plate of the apparatus, aligning the grain of the paper in the direction

selected for timing of the filtrate movement. If the electrical timer is utilized, the grain of the paper should be placed parallel with the line of platinum electrodes.

The chromatography paper should be placed in a desiccator to avoid interference from absorbed moisture.

2. Place the top plate over the filter media or paper on the bottom plate. If using the electrical timer, press the top plate firmly onto the bottom plate to implace the paper onto the platinum electrodes.
3. Place approximately 3 ml of conditioned sludge in the sample reservoir.
4. Time the filtrate movement between two reference marks in the top plate. Generally, a 1/4 inch length is sufficient.
5. Record the time of travel as the capillary suction time (CST) and record the temperature of the sludge in the reservoir. Duplicate determinations should be made.

Filter Leaf Test

The filter leaf test is used to develop the coefficients m, n, s and R_0, in Equation 21-8 by relating filter loading, L (lb/sq ft-hr) to form time, t_f, solids concentration, c and vacuum, P. Additionally, it is desired to relate final cake moisture to dry time, t_d. Several runs will be necessary in which the parameters above are varied. A single run will consist of submerging the filter leaf in a specific concentration of sludge for a selected form time. The leaf is then removed and allowed to dry for a selected dry time after which the quantity and percent moisture of the cake are determined. A minimum series of eight (8) runs should be performed to generate the desired design criteria.

The specific test procedures are as follows:

1. Using the results of the Buchner funnel test, add the optimum coagulant dosage as a percent by weight or lb/ton of dry solids.
2. Flocculate the mixture for 30 seconds (in some cases a series of tests should be run to determine the optimum flocculation time).
3. Submerge the leaf in the flocculated sludge mixture for the specified form time. Total cycle time can range from 1 to 6 minutes, with a variation in form time of 0.25 to 3.0 minutes. A possible series of runs is shown in Table 21-1. Maintain a gentle mixing of the sludge to avoid deposition.
4. Remove the leaf from the sludge and hold vertically for the specified dry time keeping it under full vacuum.
5. Transfer the entire cake from the filter leaf to a tared dish (compressed air may be gently applied to loosen the cake from the leaf). With thin cakes (<3/8 inch thick), it is generally necessary to scrape the cake from

TABLE 21-1. LEAF TEST EXPERIMENTAL VARIATIONS

Form Time (min)	Dry Time (min)	Solids Concentration (%)	Vacuum, (in. Hg)
0.25	1.5	C_1	20
0.50	1.0	C_1	20
1.50	0.5	C_1	20
0.50	1.5	C_2	20
0.50	1.5	C_3	20
1.50	1.0	C_1	10
1.50	1.0	C_1	15

TABLE 21-2. RESULTS OF BUCHNER FUNNEL TEST

Time (sec)	Volume (ml)	t/V (sec/ml)
14.5	66	0.22
29.5	92	0.31
45	112	0.40
59	129	0.46
70	134	0.52
89	156	0.57
105	167	0.63
120	174	0.69

the media with a knife blade.

6. Weigh the wet cake, dry at 103°C and reweigh the dried cake; measure and record the cake thickness and percent moisture.

7. Repeat Steps 2 through 6, varying vacuum (5 to 20 inches Hg), initial solids concentration, form and dry times.

CORRELATION OF RESULTS

Buchner Funnel Test

1. For each Buchner filter run, data were collected as shown in Table 21-2. The third column is the elapsed time, divided by volume.

2. The data are correlated by plotting t/V versus V as shown in Figure 21-5.

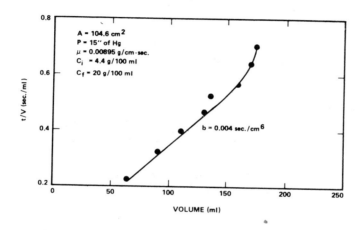

FIG. 21-5. CORRELATION OF BUCHNER FUNNEL RESULTS

3. The slope of the line is equal to "b" in Equation 21-3.

$$b = 0.004 \text{ sec/cm}^6$$

4. The specific conditions of the test were:

Filter paper area, A	= 104.6 cm²
Vacuum, P	= 15 inches of Hg
	= 526 g/cm²
Initial sludge concentration, C_i	= 4.4 g/100 ml = 4.4%
Final sludge concentration, C_f	= 20 g/100 ml = 20%
Filtrate viscosity, μ	= 0.00895 poises

393

5. Calculate the solids deposited per unit volume of filtrate (Equation 21-7).

$$c = \frac{1}{[(100 - C_i)/C_i] - [(100 - C_f)/C_f]}$$

$$= \frac{1}{(95.6/4.4) - (80/20)}$$

$$= 0.056 \text{ g/ml or } 5.6\%$$

6. Calculate the specific resistance, r (Equation 21-4).

$$r = \frac{2PA^2 b}{\mu c}$$

$$= \frac{2(526)(104.6)^2 (0.004)}{(0.00895)(0.056)}$$

$$r = 0.92 \times 10^6 \text{ sec}^2/\text{g}$$

7. By computing the specific resistance at varying polymer dosages, the optimum value is found by determining the minimum specific resistance as shown in Figure 21-6.

Therefore, the optimum conditioner concentration for dewatering is 6 lb/ton. The variation of specific resistance with polymer dosage as shown in Figure 21-6 would represent the best conditioner curve of all those tested.

Capillary Suction Data

CST data were collected at identical coagulant dosages to those of the funnel test. The CST can be correlated directly to conditioner dosage as shown in Figure 21-6. As seen in Figure 21-6, the coagulant producing the minimum specific resistance also produces the minimum CST. Thus, CST is just as effective and much simpler to apply in evaluating the applicability of various conditioners.

Filter Leaf Test

Using the optimum conditions from the Buchner funnel test, the filter leaf tests are performed.

1. Take the data collected from the various filter leaf runs and tabulate as shown in Table 21-3. The last column is the dry time, t_d, divided by the cake thickness, W.

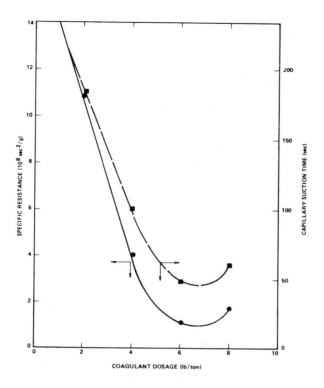

FIG. 21-6. EFFECT OF COAGULANT DOSAGE ON SLUDGE SPECIFIC RESISTANCE AND CAPILLARY SUCTION TIME

2. Develop the following graphical correlations:

   a. Filter loading, lb/sq ft-hr, versus form time, minutes, in Figure 21-7. The slope of this line is the exponent, n, in Equation 21-8 and equals 0.66.

   b. Filter loading, lb/sq ft-hr, versus initial solids (%) in Figure 21-8. The slope of this line is the exponent, m, in Equation 21-8 and equals 1.18.

   c. Filter loading, lb/sq ft-hr, versus vacuum, inches Hg, in Figure 21-9. The slope of this line is the exponent, $(1 - s)/2$, in Equation 21-8. The value of $1 - s$ equals 0.28.

   d. Filter loading, lb/sq ft hr, versus $[\dfrac{35.7\, P^{\frac{(1-s)}{2}}\, c^{m}}{\mu t_{f}^{n}}]$ in Figure 21-10.

   The slope of this line is $(1/R_{0})^{\frac{1}{2}}$. R_{0} equals 0.0004.

TABLE 21-3. DATA FROM FILTER LEAF TEST

Solids in Feed (%)	Vacuum (in. Hg)	Form Time (min)	Dry Time (min)	Cake (% Solids)	Thickness (inch)	Loading (lb/sq ft-hr)	t_d/W (min/cm)
2.18	20	1.5	2.0	20.0	5/8	21.8	1.27
2.43	20	0.5	1.0	19.0	1/2	54.5	0.79
2.55	20	0.25	0.5	17.4	3/8	84.0	0.53
2.43	20	0.25	1.0	19.2	3/8	84.3	1.05
2.37	20	0.13	0.3	16.6	5/16	126.7	0.384
1.85	20	0.25	0.5	16.6	1/4	70.5	0.80
1.87	20	0.50	0.5	17.2	3/8	48.5	0.53
1.85	20	1.0	1.25	18.9	1/2	29.2	0.98
1.87	10	0.5	0.75	18.2	3/8	44.2	0.79
1.90	5	0.5	0.75	18.7	3/8	45.2	0.79
1.89	5	0.5	0.75	16.0	3/8	39.2	0.79
1.89	5	0.5	0.75	16.6	3/8	39.5	0.79
1.89	15	0.5	0.75	19.5	3/8	46.0	0.79
1.88	15	0.5	0.75	20.0	3/8	46.0	0.79
5.63	20	0.5	0.75	15.6	7/8	156.0	0.33

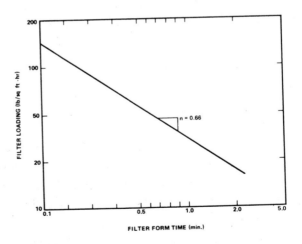

FIG. 21-7. DETERMINATION OF COEFFICIENT n

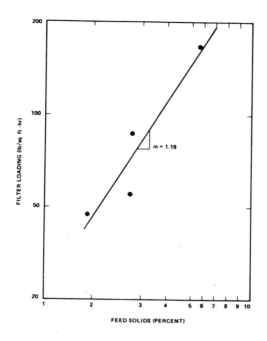

FIG. 21-8. DETERMINATION OF COEFFICIENT m

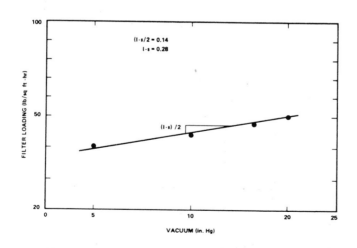

FIG. 21-9. DETERMINATION OF COEFFICIENT (1 – s)

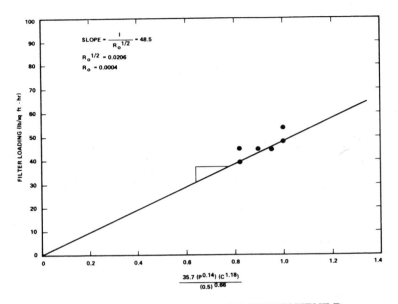

FIG. 21-10. DETERMINATION OF COEFFICIENT R_o

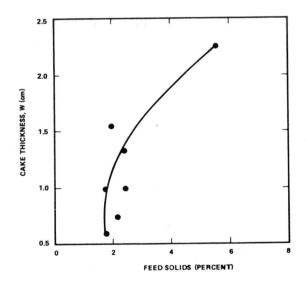

**FIG. 21-11. RELATIONSHIP OF CAKE THICKNESS TO INFLUENT
FEED SOLIDS CONCENTRATION**

f. The cake thickness, W, is a function of influent feed solids in Figure 21-11.

3. The equation for the filter design is therefore:

$$L = 35.7 \left[\frac{P^{0.28}}{(0.0004)} \right]^{\frac{1}{2}} \frac{c^{1.18}}{t_f^{0.66}}$$

4. From Figure 21-12, the maximum cake solids percent is determined to be 1.5 minutes.

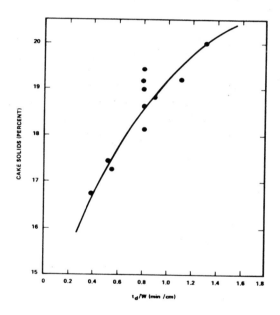

FIG. 21-12. RELATIONSHIP OF CAKE SOLIDS CONCENTRATION TO DRYING TIME

LIMITATIONS AND SCALE-UP

The laboratory results from the filter leaf test can be used directly in designing a full-scale filter. However, several factors must be considered in applying the results to actual design.

The total filter cycle time, t_c, is composed of the form time, t_f, the dry time, t_d, and the cake removal/wash time, t_w. The form time and dry time can be accurately determined from the leaf tests. The cake removal/wash time is generally taken as 20 percent of the total cycle time, or

$$t_c = \frac{t_f + t_d}{0.8}$$

The fraction of the drum area, which is submerged, is taken as the ratio of the form time to the total cycle time or t_f/t_c.

A scale-up factor of 0.8 is employed to the final calculated filter loading for conservative purposes.

REFERENCES

1. Tenney, M.W., "Vacuum Filtration," *Process Design in Water Quality Engineering: New Concepts and Developments*, E.L. Thackston and W.W. Eckenfelder, Eds., Jenkins Publishing Co., New York (1972).
2. Baskerville, R.C., and Gale, R.S., "A Simple Automatic Instrument for Determining the Filterability of Sewage Sludges," *Water Pollution Control*, 67, 233-241 (1968).

22

CENTRIFUGATION

DISCUSSION OF PRINCIPLES

Centrifuges are used to separate solids, liquids, and sometimes oil by accentuating the difference in density which is accomplished in a centrifugal field. A discrete solid particle or liquid drop settling in a continuous liquid phase under the acceleration of gravity increases in velocity until a terminal level is reached. At that point, the force resulting from gravitational acceleration is equal in magnitude to the force resulting from the frictional drag of the surrounding medium. The settling velocity of the discrete particle or drop in a gravity field is defined by Stokes Law as in Equation 22-1:

$$v_g = \frac{\Delta\rho d^2 g}{18\mu} \qquad (22\text{-}1)$$

where:

v_g = settling velocity of a particle or drop in a gravity field, ft/sec

$\Delta\rho$ = $\rho_s - \rho_L$ = the difference between the true mass density of the solid particle or liquid drop and that of the surrounding liquid medium, lb/cu ft

d = diameter of the solid particle or liquid drop, ft

g = acceleration of gravity, ft/sec^2

μ = viscosity of surrounding medium, lb/ft-sec

Equation 22-1 can be expanded to apply when settling takes place in a centrifugal field as shown in Equation 22-2:

Centrifugation

$$v_s = \frac{\Delta\rho d^2 \omega^2 r}{18\mu} = v_g \frac{\omega^2 r}{g} \qquad (22\text{-}2)$$

where:

v_s = settling velocity of a particle or drop in a centrifugal field

ω = angular velocity of the particle in the settling zone

r = radius at which settling velocity is determined

The combination of the surrounding liquid phase velocity vector and the settling velocity vector in a centrifugal field, g, as calculated in Equation 22-2 will describe the resultant velocity vector of the particle. This approach is used in analyzing the separation of phases by centrifugation.

There are three basic types of centrifuges employed for dewatering waste sludges and the centrifuge selection will depend on the sludge characteristics. Namely, the particle size and distribution, the concentration, the dewaterability and degree of bound water, the specific gravity, and the flow characteristics affect the applicability of centrifugation as a method of dewatering and influence the selection of the equipment. The three types discussed herein are those accomplishing solids separation by sedimentation in a centrifugal field against an imperforate surface or bowl. These include:

1. the conveyor or scroll solid bowl centrifuge;
2. the basket, solid bowl centrifuge; and,
3. the disc centrifuge.

Scroll Solid Bowl Centrifuge

The conveyor or scroll centrifuge is particularly suited for handling large quantities of solids, including fairly coarse material [1]. This solid bowl centrifuge, as illustrated in Figure 22-1 has large inlet pipes and solid discharge ports so that coarse material can be handled. The feed sludge enters the cylindrical bowl through the conveyor discharge nozzle and compacts against the bowl wall under centrifugal force while the centrate moves toward the axis of rotation. The compacted sludge is moved continuously by an internal scroll or conveyor which rotates just slightly slower than the bowl itself. The differential speed causes the scroll to act as a screw conveyor, pushing the sludge along the bowl wall to an inclined beach area and out. In some cases, a redispersion phenomenon occurs during the scroll conveyance if the sludge is compacted only to a soft cake at the bowl wall. This results in poor clarification and cake concentration and necessitates the addition of polymers to enhance the solid's separation and compaction and to minimize redispersion of suspended materials.

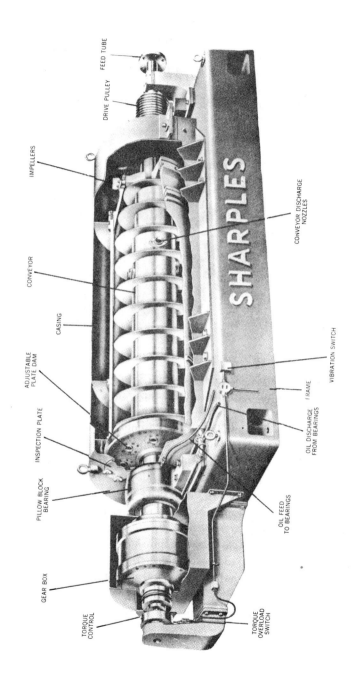

FEED TUBE

DRIVE PULLEY

IMPELLERS

CONVEYOR

CASING

ADJUSTABLE
PLATE DAM

INSPECTION PLATE

PILLOW BLOCK
BEARING

GEAR BOX

TORQUE
CONTROL

TORQUE
OVERLOAD
SWITCH

OIL FEED
TO BEARINGS

OIL DISCHARGE
FROM BEARINGS

FRAME

VIBRATION SWITCH

CONVEYOR DISCHARGE
NOZZLES

SHARPLES

FIG. 22-1. SOLID BOWL – SCROLL TYPE CENTRIFUGE
(Courtesy of Pennwalt Chemical Co.)

Disc Centrifuge

The disc centrifuge has been used for many years for handling large flows with relatively low concentrations of fine particles. As shown in Figure 22-2, the feed stream enters at the top and is divided among a multitude of stacked conical discs. The suspended particles have only a short distance to settle, so the

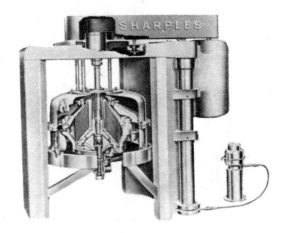

FIG. 22-2. DISC-NOZZLE TYPE CENTRIFUGE
(Courtesy of Pennwalt Chemical Co.)

particles are readily collected and discharged continuously through small orifices in the bowl wall. The solids are continuously flushed out of the bowl with a portion of the liquid medium, and the solids underflow concentration is therefore only 10 to 20 times that of the feed. The discharge of the sludge through nozzle orifices limits the size of particles which can be handled by the disc centrifuge and the feed should therefore be screened and degritted before being charged to the centrifuge. The disc centrifuge is generally used for the concentration of excess activated sludge or possibly oily sludge. The disc centrifuge can concentrate excess activated sludge from 0.5 to 1.0 percent up to five percent with 80 to 95 percent solids recovery at flow rates to 350 gpm per unit. There are many variables, however, which affect the disc centrifuge performance and pilot plant studies should first be performed for process evaluation.

Basket Centrifuge

The basket centrifuge, as shown in Figure 22-3, is a relatively simple device

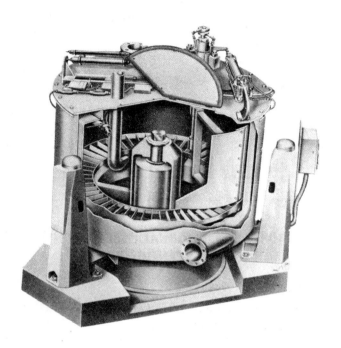

FIG. 22-3. IMPERFORATE BOWL BASKET CENTRIFUGE
(Courtesy of Pennwalt Chemical Co.)

and widely used in the dewatering of sludges, particularly activated sludge. The feed sludge is introduced to the bottom of the basket and the solids collect at the bowl wall while the centrate overflows the lip ring at the top. As there is no moving element such as a scroll conveyor during the centrifugation cycle, the recovery for all types and sizes of suspended particles are generally good. Recovery levels of 90 to 95 percent are generally obtained, even without the use of coagulants. Unlike the scroll or disc centrifuge, the basket centrifuge does not have facilities for a continuous discharge of the collected cake. The operation is, therefore, batch and requires an interruption of the feed sludge when the cake is unloaded. This generally requires only two minutes for a 20 to 30-minute cycle time as shown in Figure 22-4. There are provisions for cake removal by both skimmer and knife as indicated in Figure 22-3. The basket centrifuge is therefore very flexible in its application and well suited as a dewatering process for many sludges because of its low speed, low maintenance, high recovery efficiency, and high degree of cake compaction [2].

405

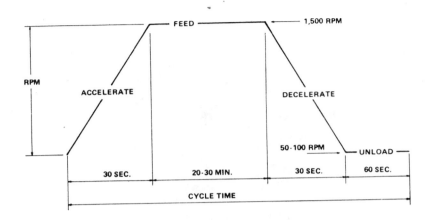

FIG. 22-4. TYPICAL OPERATIONAL CYCLE FOR SOLID-BOWL
BASKET CENTRIFUGE

Centrifuge Performance

Centrifuge performance is affected by both machine and process variables which influence centrifuge evaluation, scale-up, and actual performance. The significant machine variables for the scroll type centrifuge are bowl speed, pool speed, pool volume, and conveyor speed. Disc centrifuge machine variables include bowl speed, recycle mode of operation, disc spacing, and nozzle configuration. Basket centrifuge machine variables are bowl speed, cycle feed time, skimmer nozzle travel rate, and skimmer nozzle dwell time. The process variables for all machines include feed rate, nature of the solids, influent solids concentration, coagulant aids, and temperature. For example, the effects of increasing the machine and process variables on performance for the scroll machine are given in Table 22-1.

The three major classifications of centrifuges were discussed above. A review of the applications for each and an indication of their performance is shown in Table 22-2.

As seen in the previous discussion, different centrifuges have specific applicability for given sludges. For this reason, two-stage centrifugation often is efficacious when the waste sludge is classified into two types. A scroll centrifuge followed by a basket centrifuge, for example, has been effective in many instances when the sludge is comprised of both coarse (free draining) and compactible particles. Two-stage centrifugation is also used for oily solids handling in both dewatering the sludge and breaking the emulsion.

The amount of sludge removed from the carrier stream during centrifuga-

TABLE 22-1. CENTRIFUGE RESPONSE TO SIGNIFICANT MACHINE AND PROCESS VARIABLE

	Machine Variables			Process Variable			
	Bowl Speed	Pool Depth	Conveyor Speed	Temperature	Feed Rate	Feed Concentration	Polymer Addition
Increase in Sludge Concentration	Yes	No	No	Yes	Yes	No	No
Increase in Effluent Clarity (Solids Capture)	Yes	Yes	No	Yes	No	Yes	Yes

TABLE 22.2. SCROLL CENTRIFUGE APPLICATION TO VARIOUS WASTEWATERS

Application		Solids		Cake	Polymer added*
Effluent	Treatment	As fed	As discharged	(% solids)	(lb/ton)
		Solid Bowl Scroll Centrifuge			
Paper mill; paper	Primary; primary, secondary	Coarse, fibrous, claylike	Relatively dry	28-40	None
Municipal	Primary raw	Coarse, fibrous claylike	Relatively dry	30-40	1.5-2.5
Municipal	Primary digested, mixed digested	Coarse, fibrous slimy	Slimy to dry; depends on primary-secondary ratio	20-30	3-6
Municipal	Primary raw, secondary	Coarse, fibrous, slimy	Slimy to dry; depends on primary-secondary rate	18-22	4-6
Refinery	· · · ·	Gritty, coarse	Dry to pudding	20-25	None
Paper mill, municipal	· · · ·	Slimy, thickened	Thick pudding	18-22	10-20
Paper mill, water treatment	Lime sludge; water softening	Claylike	Dry	40-60 (depends on % hydroxide)	None
Steel mill	Pickle liquor, neutralized	Some floccy, some clay	Very thick pudding (can be shoveled)	20-30	1-2

TABLE 22.2. SCROLL CENTRIFUGE APPLICATION TO VARIOUS WASTEWATERS (continued)

| Application | | Solids | | Cake | Polymer added* |
Effluent	Treatment	As fed	As discharged	(% solids)	(lb/ton)
Disc-Type Centrifuge with Nozzles					
Paper, municipal	Waste activated	Slimy	Thickened (for further dewatering or digestion)	6-7	None (or 1)
Refinery	Liquid-liquid solids	Oil-water emulsion; some fine clay-like solids	Oil water emulsion split solids, concentrated	Oil (1%) water; solids (7-10%)	None
Water treatment plant	Alum floc	Slimy, floccy	Thin, floccy	5-7	1
Solid Bowl Basket (Imperforate) Centrifuge					
Municipal	To improve recovery	Floccy, slimy	Thick pudding	10-14	None
Water treatment chemical waste	Alum floc, hydroxide waste	Floccy	Very thick pudding	15-25	None (or 1)

*Recovery 85-90%
Following solid bowl scroll

tion can be calculated as the "solids recovery." It is mathematically defined as follows:

$$SR = \frac{S_s(S_i - S_c)}{S_i(S_s - S_c)} \qquad (22\text{-}3)$$

where:

SR   =   solids recovery, percent
S_s =   percent solids in discharged sludge, by wt.
S_i =   percent solids in influent, by wt.
S_c =   percent solids in centrate, by wt.

The effect of the nature of the sludge on centrifuge performance as measured by solids recovery for feed rates, for example, is shown in Figure 22-5. These are typical operating curves for a 14-in. scroll solid bowl centrifuge. The maximum

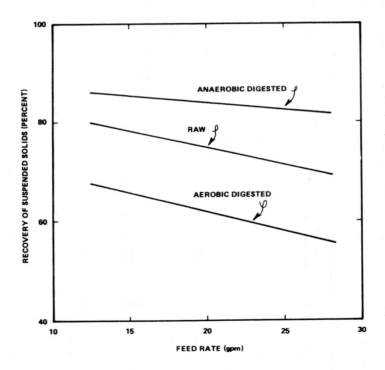

FIG. 22-5. EFFECT OF SLUDGE CHARACTERISTICS
ON SOLIDS RECOVERY FOR SCROLL CENTRIFUGE

cake concentration obtainable in a basket centrifuge is related to the mean solids recovery as indicated in Figure 22-6 which means that the improvement of one parameter is accomplished at the expense of another. As basket centrifugation systems are usually automated, proper control settings and operation are required to optimize the performance as evidenced by maximizing the solids recovery and cake concentration at the selected feed cycle time.

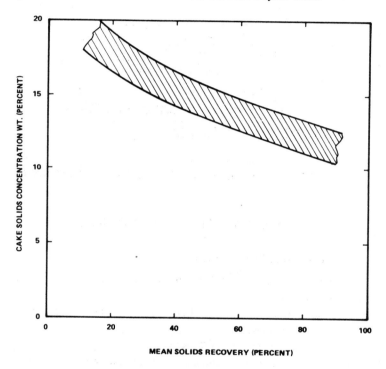

**FIG. 22-6. RELATIONSHIP BETWEEN CAKE CONCENTRATION
AND MEAN SOLIDS RECOVERY FOR BASKET CENTRIFUGE**

EQUIPMENT REQUIRED

The testing of centrifugation needs to be performed on a pilot scale before meaningful results can be obtained. Lab scale testing is of only limited value and cannot be used as a basis for process decisions. Pilot-scale centrifuges are available commercially, and the various types should be tested in the evaluation program. Typical pilot-scale centrifuges are skid mounted and equipped with the necessary electrical equipment for operation. Ancillary equipment such as sludge storage tanks and chemical addition facilities are also required for complete pilot plant operation. A flow diagram for pilot-scale centrifuge testing is shown in Figure 22-7.

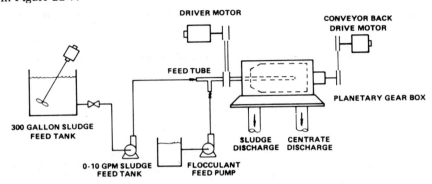

FIG. 22-7. CENTRIFUGE PILOT PLANT FLOW DIAGRAM

EXPERIMENTAL PROCEDURES

Scroll or Conveyor Solid Bowl Centrifuge

1. Fill the sludge feed tank with a representative mixture of the sludge composite to be tested.
2. Pre-set the rotation speed, backdrive speed, pool level, and conveyor pitch to the desired settings.
3. Start the centrifuge and bring it up to the desired operational speed.
4. Start the sludge feed pump and chemical feed pump (if applicable).
5. Allow a minimum of 10 minutes equilibrium time for each run before taking samples.
6. Collect samples of the feed, centrate, and sludge for each run and analyze for suspended solids content. If oily sludges are being tested, analyze for oil.
7. Establish material balances for each run.

Disc Centrifuge

The procedure for evaluating the disc centrifuge is essentially the same as that for the scroll or conveyor unit. The underflow or cake concentration can be varied, however, by changing not only the feed rate but also the recycle rate using the recycle clarifier bowl assembly.

Basket Centrifuge

1. Fill the sludge feed tank with a representative mixture of the test sludge.
2. Start the centrifuge and bring it up to the desired speed.
3. Start the sludge feed pump and chemical feed pump (if applicable).
4. Collect samples of the feed pump and centrate at five minute intervals following feed pump start-up.
5. Measure feed and centrate suspended solids (and oil) content. As the basket accumulates sludge around the periphery, the centrate suspended solids level will start to increase. When this exceeds the desired level, stop the feed.
6. Following feed shut-off, the sludge skimming and unloading operation is initiated. Measure the solids (and oil) concentration of the dewatered sludge.
7. Establish a material balance for the run. A new cycle can then be initiated.

CORRELATION OF RESULTS

The results of the pilot studies can be resolved in several ways. The most common approach is to plot solids recovery calculated in accordance with Equation 22-3 as a function of feed rate applied to the scroll or disc type centrifuge. Comparisons of dewatering various sludge types of combinations as well as effects of polyelectrolyte addition can be illustrated in a similar manner. A graphical depiction of a typical relationship for a scroll and disc type centrifuge is shown in Figure 22-8. The basket centrifuge, which unloads sludge on a cyclic basis as previously described, is evaluated by measuring solids recovery as a function of feed cycle time. The effect of feed cycle time on cake solids and solids recovery for excess activated sludge is illustrated in Figure 22-9 [3]. Another factor which is important in many applications is the nature of the centrate following the dewatering of oily solids. If the centrate emulsion is broken, then this liquid can be rerouted through a gravity separator and oil can be recovered. The addition of chemicals, however, is usually necessary to effectively break the emulsion. The effectiveness of chemical dosage in breaking the emulsion can be measured by the respective volumes of water and oily emulsion in a graduated cylinder following a specified time allowance for phase separation. This is depicted in Figure 22-10 where an optimum dosage is inferred.

413

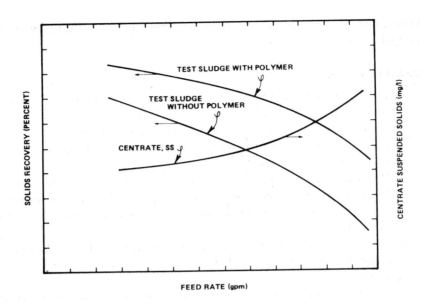

FIG. 22-8. PERFORMANCE RELATIONSHIP FOR SCROLL AND DISC TYPE CENTRIFUGE

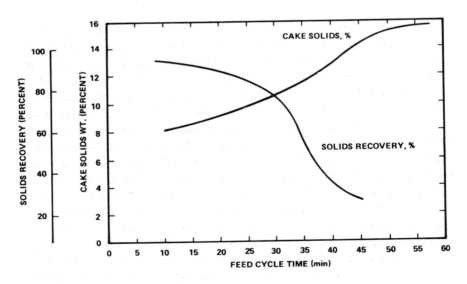

FIG 22-9. PERFORMANCE RELATIONSHIP FOR BASKET CENTRIFUGE

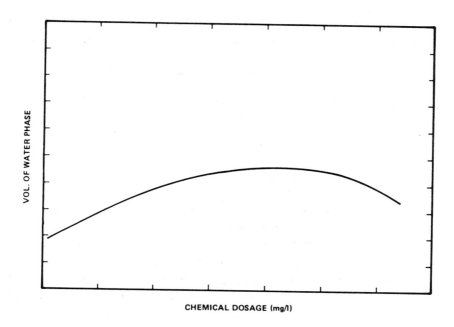

FIG. 22-10. EFFECT OF CHEMICAL DOSAGE ON EMULSION
SEPARATION

LIMITATIONS AND SCALE-UP

There are both machine and process variables which affect centrifuge evaluation, scale-up, and actual performance. Machine variables for the scroll centrifuge include bowl speed, pool volume, and conveyor speed. Disc centrifuge machine variables include bowl speed, recycle mode of operation, disc spacing, and nozzle configuration. Basket centrifuge machine variables are bowl speed, cycle feed time, skimmer nozzle travel rate, and skimmer nozzle dwell time. Process variables include feed rate, nature of the solids, solids concentration, coagulant aids, and temperature. It is necessary that each of the machine and process variables be defined to the maximum possible extent in the pilot studies to enhance the accuracy of scaling up to actual performance.

A centrifuge capacity factor, S, is used comparing centrifuge performance. This value is a theoretical capacity based entirely on the physical dimension, speed, and liquid flow pattern of the centrifuge bowl. Complete mathematical derivations may be found in *Encyclopedia of Chemical Technology* [4]. It reflects capacity as the area of a gravity settling system of clarification capability equal to that of the centifuge: namely, a large Σ value indicates a high capacity [5].

The capacity factor for a basket centrifuge can be defined mathematically:

$$\Sigma = \frac{\omega^2 V}{2g \ln 2r_c/(r_c + r_\varrho)}$$

(22-4)

where:

Σ = centrifuge capacity factor
ω = angular velocity, radians/sec
V = volume occupied by the slurry, cm³
g = acceleration of gravity, cm/sec²
r_c = interface radius, cm
r_ϱ = radius at bottom of centrifuge basket, cm

Flow rates to the centrifuge are divided by the pertinent Σ value to produce the generalized correlation parameter, Q/Σ. This parameter can be defined mathematically:

$$Q/\Sigma = \frac{2g \ln 2r_c/(r_c + r_\varrho)}{\omega^2 t}$$

(22-5)

The Q/Σ parameter is convenient for scaling one size of centrifuge to another or for comparing different types of centrifuges by multiplying the Q/Σ parameter at the required solids recovery level by the appropriate Σ value of the machine under consideration.

The capacity factor for an imperforate bowl centrifuge, Σ_T, is:

$$\Sigma_T = 2\pi l \frac{\omega^2}{g} (3/4 \, r_3^2 + 1/4 \, r_\varrho^2)$$

(22-6)

where:

l = effective clarifying length of the centrifuge bowl
r_3 = radius at the inside wall of the cylinder, cm
r_ϱ = length of the settling zone, cm

The capacity factor for a disc centrifuge, Σ_D, is:

$$\Sigma_D = \frac{2\pi n}{3} \frac{\omega^2}{g} \cot \theta \, (r_2^3 - r_1^3)$$

(22-7)

Moreover, adding thickened, oily flotation sludges as shown in Run 10 did not significantly influence the dewaterability of the cake. In Test Runs 6, 7, and 8, the effects on decreased oil content in the cake were examined by washing the cake with hot water. These results inferred that by washing the cake with hot water, much lower oil contents could be obtained than the corresponding Tests 1, 2, and 3 with lime.

The appearance of the filtrate was similar in all tests with the oily sludges and, in all cases, the filtrate was readily separated into a water and oil phase. Selected tests which were run on certain filtrates are shown in Table 23-2.

TABLE 23-2. CHARACTERISTICS OF FILTER PRESS FILTRATE

Run No.	Feed Mixture	Water Phase		Oil Phase				Comments
		TSS (mg/l)	COD (mg/l)	Viscosity	Specific Gravity at 60°F	API Gravity	Chlorides	
6	Base Oily Sludge Mixture	24	...	...	0.914	23.3	...	
11	Base Oily Sludge Mixture	20	614	...	0.918	22.6	158 ppm on 150 - 450°F of distilled fraction	
14	Non-contaminated API Separator Sludge	600	...	...	...	...	...	
16	Base Oily Sludge Mixture	... ...	... ...	340 S.U.S. @ 100°F	0.921	22.2	...	Oil Phase Sulfur Content=0.34%

These tests indicated that the water phase would not create any problem in the wastewater facility and could be routed back to the biological system. The oil phase was deemed to require further processing through a high chloride slop system.

The final conclusions from the pressure filter operation were:

1. The solids stabilized emulsions could be broken by high pressure filtration.
2. Other emulsions, such as white water, can be broken if mixed with sludge and spent clay.
3. The filtrate can be separated into oil and water phases and with no major problems anticipated.
4. Cake solids levels in excess of 50 percent can be achieved under proper conditions.
5. Depending on the operating conditions, 5 to 20 percent of the cake can be oil.
6. High pressure hot water can be utilized to wash the cake and significantly reduce the cake oil concentrations.

LIMITATIONS AND SCALE-UP

In performing laboratory and pilot operations on the pressure filter, the most critical control measure is to ensure that all pressure plates are sealed tightly so that no leaks occur and the sludge is truly subjected to the desired pressure. It is also essential when precoating the filter to avoid introducing air. The precoat mixture must be properly suspended prior to introduction to the filter so that a uniform coating is applied within the filter itself.

In scaling-up from the pilot results, generally a 20 percent scale-up factor is applied to the plate area required for filtration. Most full scale systems can be constructed to allow for future capacity expansion of 30 to 40 percent at very nominal installation cost. When the expansion is required, additional filter plates can be installed at normal costs, with no changes in piping, controls, or material handling equipment.

24

AIR DRYING OF SLUDGES

DISCUSSION OF PRINCIPLES

The air drying of sludge on sand beds is one of the most economical methods of dewatering sludges if adequate land area is available and climatic conditions are favorable. The specific area requirements will depend on rainfall and evaporation rates as well as sludge characteristics. Generally, the drying beds contain 8 to 18 inches of graded gravel or stone covered by 4 to 9 inches of sand. The sand has an effective size of 0.3 to 1.2 mm and a uniformity coefficient less than 5.0. The gravel is graded from 1/8 to 1 inch. The under-drainage system usually consists of vitrified clay tile, laid with open joints, with a minimum diameter of 4 inches and a minimum slope of 1 percent. The drains are normally spaced between 9 and 20 feet apart.

Wet sludge is generally applied to the drying beds at depths of 8 to 12 inches. The degree of dryness at which sludge can be removed from the bed in a liftable state will be determined based on methods of pickup as well as individual experience. In many cases, the bed turnover time can be reduced substantially by the addition of chemical coagulants. For example, the proper use of polymers can increase both the rate of bed dewatering and the depth of application.

Dewatering of sludge on sand beds occurs by two mechanisms: filtration of water through the subsurface underdrain, and evaporation of water due to radiation and convection. The filtration phase is usually complete in one to three days, resulting in solids concentrations as high as 15 to 25 percent [1]. The rate of air drying is usually slower and is related to temperature, relative humidity, and wind speed.

435

Evaporation will proceed to a critical moisture content at a constant rate, followed by a decreasing rate to some equilibrium moisture content. Critical moisture content is defined as when the rate of water migration to the surface is less than the rate of evaporation. During the constant rate period, the sludge surface is wetted and the rate of evaporation is relatively independent of the nature of the sludge. However, this rate is less than that which would be observed from a free water surface, probably due to the fact that the plan of evaporation is below the sludge surface [2].

The drying phases of sludge are illustrated in Figure 24-1.

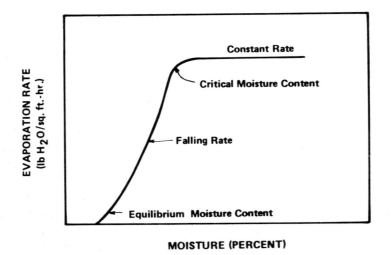

FIG. 24-1. PHASES OF SLUDGE DRYING

When the critical moisture content is obtained, water no longer migrates to the surface of the sludge as rapidly as it evaporates and the falling rate period occurs. The rate of drying during this period is related to the thickness of the sludge, its physical and chemical properties, and ambient conditions. Subsurface drying continues until an equilibrium moisture content is obtained. The rate of drying can be related mathematically to the heat transfer required to evaporate the water and to the mass transfer of internal water to the surface.

There are various approaches to the design of sludge drying beds, but the method presented herein is a rational procedure based on observed dewatering of a variety of sewage and industrial waste sludges [3].

EQUIPMENT REQUIRED

The apparatus required for this test is simple and consists of a plexiglas or glass tube filled with sand and gravel as shown in Figure 24-2.

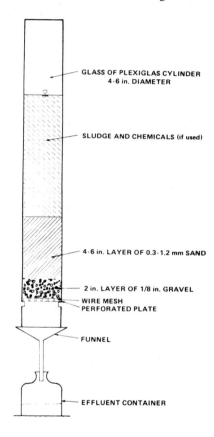

GLASS OF PLEXIGLAS CYLINDER
4-6 in. DIAMETER

SLUDGE AND CHEMICALS (if used)

4-6 in. LAYER OF 0.3-1.2 mm SAND

2 in. LAYER OF 1/8 in. GRAVEL
WIRE MESH
PERFORATED PLATE

FUNNEL

EFFLUENT CONTAINER

FIG. 24-2. DIAGRAM OF SLUDGE DRAINAGE CYLINDER

1. Glass or plexiglas cylinder. This tube should preferably be 4 to 6 inches in diameter, although a 1 to 2 inch diameter will suffice. The cylinder should have provisions for holding a 6 to 8 inch layer of coarse sand and gravel in the bottom on a wire mesh or perforated plate.
2. Sand and Gravel. A 2-in. layer of 1/8 in. gravel should be covered with a 4 to 6 in. layer of 0.3 to 1.2 mm sand.
3. A corer is useful for the larger diameter cylinders (greater than 4-in.). The

corer may be a thin-walled cylinder which can be pushed into the drained sludge to withdraw a core for further drying.

EXPERIMENTAL PROCEDURES

1. Fill the glass cylinder or tube, which contains the gravel and sand base, with the test sludge to a depth of 12 to 18 in. The appropriate chemical additions should be added to the sludge before filling the tube.
2. Allow complete free drainage of the water from the sludge. This drainage will generally require approximately 1 to 3 days, depending on the sludge characteristics and the initial moisture content.
3. After the free drainage is complete, remove the sludge from the cylinder. The sludge is most effectively removed from cylinders of less than 2 inches in diameter by releasing the sand and gravel base from the lower end of the tube and pushing the sludge core out with a plunger. In larger diameter cylinders, a sludge core may be obtained by inserting a corer of at least 2 inches in diameter and removing a core section from the drained sludge.
4. Measure the initial moisture content of a sample from the sludge core.
5. Place the core in an open dish and allow air evaporation to proceed.
6. Periodically measure the moisture content of the sludge. An effective way to monitor the moisture content is to use a small glass tube to remove small cores from the depth of the sludge core sample. Remove the small sludge core from the glass tube for the moisture content determination. Continue to monitor the moisture content until the pre-selected terminal moisture content is attained. This terminal moisture content must be based on obtaining a "liftable" cake. This judgment will have to be based on the experience of the designer or investigator. Generally, for biological sludges a cake is liftable at 15 to 20 percent solids content. The characteristics of physical-chemical sludges might vary considerably from these values.
7. This procedure may be repeated at various sludge depths and chemical additions to determine the optimum dewatering characteristics. The value of these laboratory procedures is to determine the maximum lift which can be applied to the bed and still obtain free drainage of the water. Consequently, careful observation by the investigator is required. If free water is still on top of the sludge layer after 5 to 8 hours, the sludge application depth was probably excessive.

CORRELATION OF RESULTS

It is desired to develop cumulative plots of rainfall and evaporation as shown in Figure 24-3.

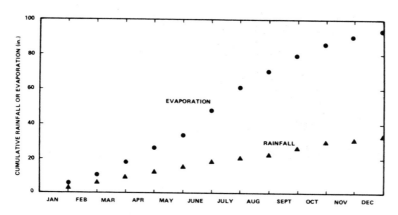

FIG. 24-3. CUMULATIVE RAINFALL AND EVAPORATION

Then the time of drying is calculated as that time required to evaporate the rainfall plus the water from the sludge. In this example, assume that it is required to dewater 2,000 lb/day (dry weight) of sludge with 4 percent solids content. A 12-in. application of sludge was considered liftable at 24 percent solids content. Determine the area requirements of the drying beds.

1. Obtain the local rainfall and evaporation meteorological records on a monthly basis as shown in Table 24-1. Tabulate these data as shown in Columns 2 and 3 of Table 24-2.

TABLE 24-1. RAINFALL AND EVAPORATION RECORDS

	Jan	Feb	March	April	May	June	July	August	Sept	Oct	Nov	Dec
Rainfall (inches)	3.50	2.46	2.63	3.50	3.34	3.16	1.58	2.46	3.69	2.46	2.10	2.28
Evaporation (inches)	5.34	6.00	7.20	8.27	10.70	10.50	12.69	10.80	8.54	5.87	4.11	2.54

TABLE 24-2. SUMMARY OF EVAPORATION TIME REQUIREMENTS

Month	Evaporation Rate (in/days of month)	Rainfall (in.)	Evaporation Rate x 0.75 (in/days of month)	Rainfall x 0.57 (in.)	Average Evaporation Rate (days/in.)	Time Required To Evaporate 0.67" (days)	Time Required To Evaporate Rainfall (days)	Total (days)
Jan	5.3	3.5	4.0	2.0	7.75	5.2	15.5	20.7
Feb	6.0	2.5	4.5	1.4	6.25	4.2	8.7	12.9
March	7.2	2.6	5.4	1.5	5.75	3.8	8.6	12.4
April	8.3	3.5	6.2	2.0	4.85	3.2	9.7	12.9
May	10.7	3.3	8.0	1.9	3.88	2.6	7.4	15.0
June	10.5	3.2	7.9	1.8	3.80	2.5	6.7	9.2
July	12.7	1.6	9.5	0.9	3.27	2.2	3.0	5.2
Aug	10.8	2.5	8.1	1.4	3.83	2.5	5.3	7.8
Sept	8.5	3.7	6.4	2.1	4.69	3.2	9.9	13.1
Oct	5.9	2.5	4.4	1.4	7.05	4.7	9.9	14.6
Nov	4.1	2.1	3.1	1.2	9.70	6.5	11.6	18.1
Dec	2.5	2.3	1.9	1.3	16.3	10.9	21.2	32.1

2. Multiply each evaporation rate by 0.75 and each rainfall value by 0.57. These multipliers are based on experimental evidence that the average evaporation of wet sludge is 75 percent of free water evaporation and that 43 percent of the rainfall is drained through the cake, leaving 57 percent to be evaporated [3]. The rainfall fraction to be evaporated will vary according to rainfall patterns and intensity. A value less than 57 percent, for example, might be expected in areas where rainfall is intense and of short duration.

3. Calculate the amount of water to be evaporated from the sludge as follows:

   a. The laboratory results indicated that a 12-in. application depth of sludge would drain freely and allow sludge evaporation to 24 percent solids content at a constant rate as shown in Figure 24-4.

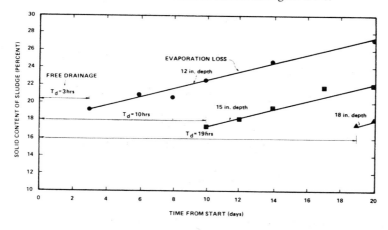

FIG. 24-4. SLUDGE DRYING CURVES

Greater depths did not drain freely and time was required to evaporate the free water above the sludge before evaporation of the sludge itself could begin.

   b. At a 12-in. application layer, the total weight of sludge per square foot of bed area including water is:

   (1 sq ft) (1 ft) (62.4 lb/cu ft) = 62.4 lb
   62.4 lb x 0.04 = 2.5 lb/sq ft of dry solids

   c. The total weight of water plus solids after drainage to 18 percent solids and evaporation to 24 percent is:

   At 18 percent (initial free drainage):

$$\frac{2.5 \text{ lb/sq ft}}{0.18} = 14.0 \text{ lb/sq ft}$$

At 24 percent (after required evaporation):

$$\frac{2.5 \text{ lb/sq ft}}{0.24} = 10.5 \text{ lb/sq ft}$$

Consequently, the water to be evaporated after drainage to 18 percent is:

$$14.0 - 10.5 = 3.5 \text{ lb/sq ft of water}$$

or $\quad (3.5 \text{ lb/sq ft}) (1/62.4 \text{ lb/cu ft}) = 0.056 \text{ cu ft/sq ft}$

or $\quad (0.056 \text{ cu ft/sq ft}) (12\text{in./ft}) = 0.67 \text{ in. of water to be evaporated}$

5. Calculate the time to evaporate the rainfall plus 0.67 in. of water per month.

   a. Calculate average evaporation rate in days/inch as shown in Column 6 of Table 24-2. For example, in January:

$$\text{Average evaporation rate} = (\text{days of month}) / (\text{Evaporation rate} \times 0.75)$$
$$= 31 / (5.3 \times 0.75)$$
$$= 7.8 \text{ days/in.}$$

   b. Calculate time to evaporate 0.67 in. of water (Column 7):
For January:

$$T_{0.67} = (7.8 \text{ days/in.}) (0.67/\text{in.})$$
$$= 5.2 \text{ days}$$

   c. Calculate time to evaporate the rainfall (Column 5 x Column 6):
For January:

$$T_{R.F.} = (7.8 \text{ days/in.}) (2.0 \text{ in.})$$
$$= 15.6 \text{ days}$$

   d. Thus, total evaporation time equals sum of Columns 7 and 8:
For January:

$$T_T = 5.2 + 15.5$$
$$= 20.7 \text{ days}$$

   e. Repeat the above steps for each month and use the month with the largest time for design.

      For example, with December as the controlling month and 2,000 lb/day of sludge:

$$\text{Area} = (2{,}000 \text{ lb/day}) (1/2.5 \text{ lb/sq ft}) (32.1 \text{ days})$$
$$= 25{,}700 \text{ sq ft}$$

REFERENCES

1. Eckenfelder, W. W., *Industrial Water Pollution Control*, McGraw-Hill Co., New York (1966).

2. Quon, J. E., and Ward, G. B., Convective Drying of Sewage Sludge, *International Journal Air & Water Pollution*, 9, 311-322 (1965).

3. Swanwick, J. D., Lussignea, F. W. and Baskerville, R. C., "Recent Work on the Treatment and Dewatering of Sewage Sludge," Proc., First International Conference on Water Pollution Research, London (September 1962).

25

THERMAL CONTENT OF SLUDGES

DISCUSSION OF PRINCIPLES

The design of incineration equipment for waste treatment sludges and waste combustible liquids requires that the thermal content of these materials be determined. This heat content of materials is often referred to as heat of combustion, thermal value, heating value, or calorific value, and may be broadly defined as the number of heat units liberated by a unit mass of substance when combined with oxygen in an enclosure of constant volume. Thus, the term, heat of combustion, refers to the heat liberated by the combustion of all carbon and hydrogen with oxygen to form carbon dioxide and water, including that heat which may be liberated by the oxidation of other compounds, such as sulfur and nitrogen, which may be present in the sample. This unit is commonly expressed in either calories per gram (cal/g) or British Thermal Units per lb (BTU/lb). The British Thermal Unit equals 251.99 calories (1055.07 absolute joules) and is roughly equivalent to the heat energy required to raise one lb of water one degree Fahrenheit at 60° F.

Calorimetry is the art of measuring "quantities" of heat, as distinct from measuring "temperature," and employs an instrument known as a calorimeter. The most common calorimeter utilized for waste treatment application is referred to as the "oxygen bomb" calorimeter and is the only type which will be discussed herein. The procedure using the oxygen bomb device involves burning a weighted sample in an oxygen-filled metal "bomb" which is submerged in a measured quantity of water with the entire apparatus being contained in a thermally-insulated chamber. By observing exactly the rise in water temperature which results from combusting the sample, the number of heat units which are liberated may be calculated. Probably the most important unit in the oxygen bomb calorimeter is the "bomb" itself. This device is probably called a "bomb" because it is filled with gas under high pressure and, when the charge is ignited, the combustion reaction takes place with an equivalent of explosive force, although there is no external evidence of such a reaction. The heat of combustion increases the temperature of the gases within the "bomb" very rapidly with a corresponding rapid increase in the internal gas pressure. This increased pressure is rapidly reduced since the heat is dissipated by the bomb to the surrounding media. However, the cooling rate is so much slower than the heating rate that the internal pressures remain significantly high. Despite mechanical problems caused by this condition, the oxygen "bomb" type of calorimeter has been accepted as the standard device for accurately determining heats of combustion.

A typical temperature rise curve for a plain calorimeter is shown in Figure 25-1.

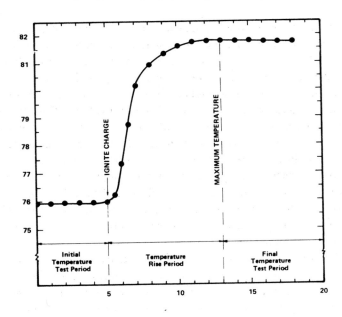

FIG. 25-1. TYPICAL TEMPERATURE RISE CURVE FROM PLAIN CALORIMETER

As is indicated, there are three major phases during the determination of the heat rise:

1. The initial temperature stabilization and test period;
2. The ignition and temperature rise period;
3. The final stabilization of temperature test period.

Computation of the gross heat of combustion, H_g, in calories per gram is accomplished by the following equation:

$$H_g = \frac{tW - e_1 - e_2 - e_3}{m} \qquad (25\text{-}1)$$

where:

t	=	the net corrected temperature rise, °F.
W	=	the energy equivalent of the calorimeter, calories/°F.
e_1	=	correction for heat of formation of nitric acid, calories.
e_2	=	correction for heat of formation of sulfuric acid, calories.
e_3	=	correction for heat of combustion of fuse wire, calories.
m	=	mass of sample, grams.

The net corrected temperature rise, t, can be calculated by the following equation:

$$t = t_c - t_a - r_1(b-a) + r_2(c-b) \qquad (25\text{-}2)$$

where:

a	=	time of firing, min.
b	=	time (to nearest 0.1 min) when the temperature reaches 60 percent of the total temperature rise, min.
c	=	time at beginning of period (after temperature rise) in which the rate of temperature change becomes constant, min.
t_a	=	temperature at time of firing, corrected for temperature scale error, °F.
t_c	=	temperature at time of firing, corrected for temperature scale error, °F.
r_1	=	rate (temperature rise per min) at which temperature was increasing during the 5 min period previous to firing, °F/min.
r_2	=	rate (°F/min) at which temperature was decreasing during the 5 min period after time, c. If the temperature was rising instead of falling after time, c, subtract the quantity $r_2(c-b)$

447

instead of adding it when computing the corrected temperature rise.

The energy equivalent of the calorimeter, W, represents the combined heat capacity of the water bucket, the water itself, the "bomb" and its contents, and parts of the thermometer, stirrer and supports for the bucket. If calculated, this factor would be equal to the sum of the heat capacities of all these parts. In practice, it is generally determined by a series of standardization tests as explained in a subsequent section of this chapter. The standardization tests should be performed after receiving the calorimeter from the manufacturer, upon changing any part of the calorimeter, and occasionally as a check on both the calorimeter and operating technique. The standardization procedure uses a standard benzoic acid pellet and follows the same procedure as the normal procedure for testing any fuel sample. The energy equivalent can be calculated by the following equation:

$$W = \frac{Hm + e_1 + e_3}{t} \qquad (25\text{-}3)$$

where:

H	=	heat of combustion of standard benzoic acid, calories/gram
m	=	mass of standard benzoic acid sample, grams
t, e_1, e_3	=	as previously defined in Equation 25-1.

EQUIPMENT REQUIRED

An oxygen "bomb" calorimeter consists of three major parts:

1. The "bomb" or chamber in which combustion takes place;
2. A container which holds the previously measured quantity of water in which the "bomb," thermometer, and stirring device are immersed;
3. The jacket which protects the container from effects in variation in room temperatures, drafts, or other environmental changes.

The "bomb" consists of a thick-walled, metal container, with a mechanical, screw-on cover which can be easily removed for inserting the sample and cleaning. The top of the "bomb" also contains provision for filling with oxygen under pressure, for supporting and igniting the sample, and for releasing the expanded gases after combustion is completed. The strength of the bomb must be sufficient to withstand normal working pressures of 100 atmospheres, and overload pressures up to 200 atmospheres (300 lb/sq in.). Since nitric and sulfuric acid are formed under the high temperatures and pressures developed within the bomb, the materials of construction should be resistant to corrosion. Generally, a nickel alloy, high in chromium content, is used in oxygen bomb construction.

The calorimeter container provides for total immersion of the bomb in a measured quantity of water. It must be highly polished to inhibit the adsorption or emission of radiant heat and must possess a stirrer for circulating the water and maintaining the temperature equilibrium. The stirrer must operate at a constant speed and must create sufficient turbulence to rapidly adsorb the heat from the bomb and must not introduce excessive heat from expended mechanical energy.

The jacket which encloses the bomb and container must provide a thermal shield to prevent heat transfer between the calorimeter and its environmental surroundings during the test, or means for controlling and measuring such heat transfer. There are two major jacketing methods which are most commonly employed and differ not only in jacket construction, but also in the temperature observation required during a test run. The first jacket device is the isothermal system in which the jacket temperature remains constant while the container temperature rises. This device requires temperature observation before, between, and after the initial and final temperature reading in order to calculate a radiation correction. The second device is an adiabatic system in which the temperature of the jacket may be adjusted continually during the test in order to maintain a temperature equal to that of the container at all times. The adiabatic method eliminates the need for a radiation correction and requires only the observation of initial and final calorimeter temperature. The major components necessary to accurately estimate the heat of combustion of a material are listed below with pertinent comments following:

1. The oxygen bomb;
2. The calorimeter, either with an isothermal jacket or an adiabatic device;
3. Thermometer, either mercurial or electric;
4. Reagents for standardizing the calorimeter and for determining acid correction factors;
5. An oxygen filling connection for transferring oxygen from a pressurized tank into the bomb;
6. A pellet press for forming pellets to insert into the bomb;
7. Combustion capsules for containing non-volatile samples. These capsules are approximately one inch inside diameter and 7/16 inch deep. They are generally made from chromium-nickel stainless steel or from mastalloy steel. They should be discarded when the wall or bottom thickness has been reduced by 25 percent. Also, a capsule with a thin rim should not be

utilized because of the danger that it may ignite and burn with an intensity that will damage the bomb;

8. Sample holder for volatile liquids. This holder eliminates the disadvantages of using a large correction factor for combustible gelatin capsules or tediously-formed glass capsules, which are otherwise required for measuring heat content on volatile liquids; and

9. A support stand for holding the bomb device while the sample is being prepared and inserted.

Several of the items above require further elaboration and are discussed in detail below.

Calorimeter

Both types of calorimeters, adiabatic and isothermal, are in wide practice. The adiabatic calorimeter is more expensive and will not be described in detail here. This design employs a container of special oval shape, holding the bomb

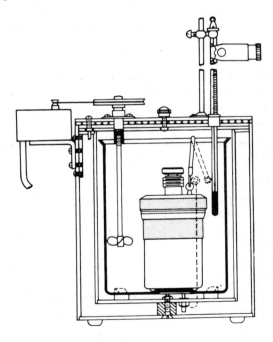

FIGURE 25-2. CROSS SECTION OF ISOTHERMAL JACKET CALORIMETER

and a measured quantity of water within a chamber which is completely enclosed by a circulating water jacket. By manual operation of a hot or cold water valve from an external source, the investigator can maintain the temperature of the jacket equal to that of the container during the rise after ignition. This produces adiabatic conditions which will reduce heat transfer between the calorimeter and its surroundings to a negligible quantity. This procedure eliminates the task of correcting for radiation loss, thus simplifying calculations. The isothermal jacket calorimeter, shown in Figure 25-2, is relatively simple in construction with a jacket which ensures low heat loss. Although this type of jacket will not completely eliminate thermal losses during the test run, its properties are so consistent that the quantity of heat which may be gained or lost during a test can be accurately calculated.

Water is circulated around the bomb by a stirrer mounted on the calorimeter cover. The impeller is insulated by non-metallic bushing to minimize heat conduction from the water to the outside drive wheel. The thermometer is supported by a rod attached to the cover.

Oxygen Bomb

The oxygen bomb, illustrated in Figure 25-3, is closed simply by screwing the cap down finger tight then, during the charging, the head is automatically sealed to the cylinder. The internal volume of the bomb with the head in place is 22 cu. in. or 360 ml. When charging the bomb, the oxygen enters through the spring check valve into a groove around the periphery of the bomb head in order to minimize disturbing the sample in the combustion capsule. When exhausting the bomb, the gases must leave in the same peripheral groove thus reducing the possibility of entrainment and loss of condensates.

Two electrodes are attached to the underside of the head and serve as binding posts for the fuse wire, which may be strung between them and bent down into contact with the sample.

Thermometers: Mercurial and Electric

Temperature measurements are the most critical determination during the calorimetric determination, yet generally they receive the least attention. Thermometers with a temperature range of 66 to 95°F (19 to 35°C) are sufficient for most thermal determinations. Readings should always be taken with a magnifying lens so that the operator should be able to estimate temperatures to 1/10 of the smallest scale division (0.005°F).

Unless operators are trained in the use of electric thermometers and the

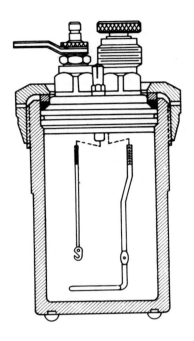

FIG. 25-3. 1101 DOUBLE VALVE BOMB

specific calorimeter is modified to accommodate these devices, it is recommended that mercurial thermometers be employed in all cases.

Standard Reagents

Benzoic acid is the material most commonly employed for standard combustion purposes. It is not appreciably hygroscopic, burns easily and completely, and may be readily compressed into pellets. Its heat of combustion is 6,318 calories/gram or 11,373 BTU/lb, subject to verification. Primary standard grade benzoic acid can be obtained from calorimeter manufacturers with the calorific value reported on the label. The form may be crystalline powder or pellets weighing approximately 1 gram each. The pellets are recommended for standardizing oxygen bomb calorimeters because of the convenience.

Naphthalene is sometimes used for a combustion standard, because it is not hygroscopic; however, its volatility requires care in use to avoid error. The heat of combustion is 9,614 calories/gram or 17,305 BTU/lb.

Sucrose or cane sugar has been used for a standard with a heat of combustion of 3,949 calories/gram or 7,108 BTU/lb. This substance is neither volatile nor strongly hygroscopic, but is sometimes difficult to ignite and may not burn completely. It should be ground into a powder before use. The U.S. National Bureau of Standards offers 2, 2, 4-trimethylpentane (Isooctane) as a standard for checking calorimeters to be used for volatile fuels.

The contents of an oxygen bomb dissolved in water after use are titrated with a standard alkali solution to determine an acid correction factor. A 0.0725 normal sodium carbonate solution is recommended. This solution is prepared by dissolving 3.84 grams sodium carbonate in water and diluting to one liter. Sodium or potassium hydroxide solution of equivalent normality are acceptable. Methyl orange or methyl red indicators are also needed for the acid-alkali titration.

EXPERIMENTAL PROCEDURES

There are four major phases which comprise the experimental sequence for determining the heat content of a substance: standardizing the calorimeter, preparing the sample, assembling the oxygen bomb, and operating the calorimeter. These phases are discussed in detail below.

Standardizing the Calorimeter

In standardizing the calorimeter, the objective is to obtain the energy equivalent (water equivalent factor) of the system. This factor has been discussed previously and represents the combined heat capacity of the various components of the system. The manufacturer generally furnishes a certificate with each complete calorimeter indicating the energy equivalent as determined by their laboratory. However, it is recommended that the investigator also standardize each new calorimeter before initiating tests with unknown materials. It is recommended that benzoic acid pellets be used for the calorimeter and a minimum of 6 tests spaced over a period of at least three days be used for standardization.

The procedure for standardization is exactly the same as testing a sample material and is explained in detail in the following sections. A standard benzoic acid pellet should be used which weighs not less than 0.9 grams nor more than 1.1 grams. The corrected temperature rise, t, is obtained from the observed test data and the bomb washings are also titrated to determine the nitric acid correction factor. The unburned fuse wire must also be measured and a correction applied. The energy equivalent, W, is obtained by substitution into Equation 25-3.

Sample Preparation

Care in sampling is of the utmost importance. Since the samples employed in the bomb calorimeter are very small in volume, it is essential that a representative sludge or liquid sample be employed. Of particular importance is examining samples from bench-scale dewatering devices such as a high pressure filter or vacuum filter leaf test. For example, if a precoat was used on a leaf test, one must be extremely cautious not to include too much of the precoat material in the sample being analyzed for thermal content since this will obviously lower the heat content per lb of sludge analyzed.

It is necessary that the solid samples be air dried and ground until all particles will pass a 60-mesh screen. Generally, when working with wastewater sludges the solids content has been previously determined by drying in a drying oven at 103 to 106°C. If this is the case, the oven-dried material may be used for the heat content analyses. After drying, the sludge can be ground by a mortar and pestle into a fine powder for subsequent pelletizing.

The powdered sludge is generally pelletized in a special pellet press with a one-half inch diameter punch and dye. Caution should be taken to avoid too much pressure on the pellet as making it too hard will cause inefficient burning in the bomb. Only enough force should be used to bind the particles together so that the pellet will not disintegrate when handled. It is recommended that several pellets weighing approximately one gram each be made from the same sludge sample for subsequent testing. The pellets can be stored in a glass vial or other bottle prior to use and should be handled with forceps or a small pair of tongs and not touched with the fingers.

Care must be taken to avoid overcharging the bomb because the peak pressure developed during combustion is proportional to the size of the sample. The maximum heat liberated in any test should be less than 10,000 calories and it is recommended to work with less than 7,000 calories. This will generally limit the quantity of combustible material to less than 1.1 grams. It is emphasized that this mass of material includes the sample plus any other combustion aids which may be with it including benzoic acid, gelatin, or firing oil.

The sample is then placed in a metal combustion capsule prior to assembling the bomb. The capsules generally develop a hard oxide tarnish or coating after repeated use. This coating will not affect their usefulness unless the unburned sample or other carbonaceous materials are attached to the unpolished surface. It is generally recommended that these capsules be polished with an emery cloth after each use. They may be then held over a Bunson burner or placed in a muffle furnace at 600°C for a few minutes to burn any remaining combustible material. For maximum corrosion resistance, platinum capsules may be obtained and used, although they are extremely expensive.

Volatile liquid samples can be weighted and handled in specially prepared gelatin capsules, sealed glass ampoules, or special volatile sample holders available through some manufacturers. The gelatin capsules consist of two gelatin cups which will telescope together with a friction fit to retain most liquids. Corrections must be made for the heat of combustion of the gelatin when used in calorimetry and for sulfur when used for analytical purposes. The gelatin generally contains 0.35 plus or minus 0.05 percent sulfur by weight and the heat of combustion is approximately 8,150 plus or minus 150 BTU per lb. The gelatin is subject to absorbing moisture and the heat of combustion values will change with moisture content. Blank tests must be performed to determine the exact corrections. Glass ampoules are excellent for handling volatile samples but require considerable skill in preparing and using. Probably the most satisfactory method of handling volatile liquids is the volatile sample holder available from the Parr Instrument Company. This holder is a small metal cup sealed with a disc of cellulose tape (Scotch tape) and eliminates the disadvantages of using a large correction factor for combustible gelatin capsules or the tedious operation for handling sealed glass ampoules. The volatile sample holder is approximately 9.5 mm inside diameter by 23.8 mm deep, and holds approximately 1.5 ml and weighs about 12.5 grams. The top ring of the device weighs 2.7 grams and a disk of "Scotch Brand" tape sufficient to cover the top of the cup will weigh approximately 0.013 grams. The technique is simple:

1. Weigh the empty cup and ring.
2. Cut a disc of tape and weigh it with the metal part. The mass of the tape is determined by the difference. The tape may be cut with a cork borer or by holding the end of the cup against a strip of tape and trimming with a razor blade.
3. Place the liquid sample in the cup and quickly apply the tape and the ring, twisting the ring slightly to seal the tape to the ring of the cup.
4. Weigh the complete assembly and the mass of the sample can be determined by the difference.
5. Place the cup in the loop electrode (a special electrode for the volatile sample holder) and use a 10-centimeter length of fuse formed into a hairpin shape so that it just touches the center of the tape. The bomb is then assembled as usual, except that the tape must be punctured with a sharp needle just before the bomb is closed. Oxygen is slowly added to 35 atmospheres and the bomb is fired according to standard instructions.

For accurate calorimetric determination, it might be desirable to remove the ring just before the capsule is lowered into the bomb, otherwise a trace of un-burned tape will remain in the joint. It is necessary to deduct a correction for the heat of combustion of the disk when using the volatile sample holder in the calorific test. This is generally accomplished by making a blank determination using about one-half gram of tape. The heat of combustion of the tape is generally 5 to 8 calories per milligram of tape.

Assembling and Pressurizing the Bomb

The head and electrodes of the bomb should be placed in the sample holder in order to perform the various procedures prior to closing the bomb as shown in Figure 25-4.

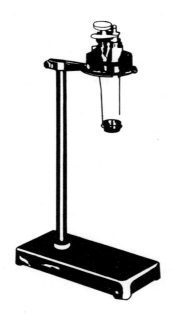

FIG. 25-4. SUPPORT STAND FOR OXYGEN BOMB HEADS

1. Attach the fuse by cutting a piece of wire 10 centimeters long and attach it to the electrodes as shown in Figure 25-5. Bend the wire up, as in detail "i" of this Figure and insert the capsule into the loop holder. Then bend

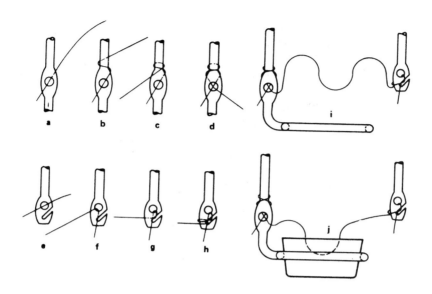

ASSEMBLING AND PRESSURIZING THE BOMB

FIG. 25-5. STEPS IN BINDING FUSE WIRE TO ELECTRODES

the wire down so that it just touches the surface of the charge as in detail "j". With pelleted samples, the wire should be bent so that the loop presses against the edge of the pellet firmly enough to hold it against the side of the capsule. If platinum wire is used, it may be employed as just described, or it may be formed into a small coil around a rod 1/16 inch in diameter and the rod removed. The resulting coil may then be connected between the electrodes and placed to one side of the cup, with the axis of the coil pointing towards the sample. A short piece of cotton or nylon thread can then be inserted through the coil and into the cup on the sample to carry the ignition flame. By this manner, it is possible to use the same wire for a considerable number of tests.

2. Place 1.0 ml of distilled water into the bomb accurately, using a volumetric pipette.
3. Close the bomb taking care not to disturb the sample when fitting the bomb head into the cylinder. If an internal pressure greater than 5 atmospheres cannot be maintained when the screw cap has been tightened firmly by hand, it can be assumed that the sealing ring or some other part of

the mechanism is not functioning properly. This malfunction should be found and corrected before proceeding further with the test. Attach the pressure filling connection from the oxygen cylinder to the bomb inlet valve and slowly admit oxygen to 30 atmospheres gauge pressure at room temperature. The bomb may be operated anywhere within the range of 26 to 35 atmospheres; however, the same pressure must be used for all tests, including standardization. Do not try to remove entrapped air by purging the bomb and, if the bomb is overfilled to greater than 35 atmospheres, do not proceed with combustion. Remove the filling connection, exhaust the bomb, remove the head, and reweigh the sample before repeating the filling operation.

Operating the Isothermal Jacket Calorimeter

Now that the calorimeter apparatus has been standardized (See CORRELATION OF RESULTS), the sample has been prepared, and the bomb assembled, the determination of heat content can proceed.

1. Weigh the oval container in a completely dry condition.
2. Add 2,000 plus or minus 0.5 grams of distilled or demineralized water. The water may be measured in a volumetric flask instead of weighing, if care is taken to perform the volumetric measurement at exactly the same temperature for each test and to maintain the flask in a very clean condition and allow the same drainage time. Prior to weighing or measuring, the water should be brought to a temperature of 3 to 3.5 °F below that of the calorimeter jacket. This initial adjustment should allow a final temperature slightly above that of the jacket. It is cautioned that the calorimeter water must be heated or cooled in a separate container from the calorimeter container since it is essential that the calorimeter container maintain its high finish, which would be impossible if it were heated over a burner or submerged in cooling water. The temperature of the air within the calorimeter should be used as a reference for adjusting the water temperature. This temperature should be determined just prior to each test by wiping all moisture from the thermometer bulb and closing the jacket with the thermometer in place. Read the jacket temperature after filling the bomb and bring the water into this range minus 3.0 to 3.5°F.
3. Assemble the calorimeter by placing the filled container into the jacket taking great care that no moisture is on the outside surface of the container. Lower the bomb into the water taking great care to avoid jarring or disturbing the contents. Attach the thrust terminal to the bomb electrode

and shake back into the container all water drops which were collected on the finger. Place the jacket cover on the calorimeter according to the manufacturer's instructions. Make sure that the electrical supply for the stirrer corresponds to the number stamped on the motor name plate. If any other drive motor is used, adjust the stirrer to the RPM designated on the name plate.

4. Operate the calorimeter motor for 5 minutes prior to testing in order to obtain a thermal equilibrium, but do not record temperature during this initial period.

   a. As soon as the calorimeter temperature has stabilized, record the calorimeter temperature at one minute intervals for exactly 5 minutes to the nearest 0.005° F (0.002°C).

   b. Press the button for ignition at the start of the sixth minute, recording the exact time and temperature at the firing point.

   c. After firing, record the rise of temperature in 15 second intervals. After firing, approximately 20 seconds will elapse before the temperature begins to rise. The rise rate will be rapid in the first few minutes and then decrease as the calorimeter stabilizes at a maximum temperature. During the period of rapid rise (4 to 5 minutes) the temperature can be read without the magnifying lens.

   d. After the period of rapid rise, use the magnifying lens and record the temperature to the nearest 0.005° F at one minute intervals until the difference between successive readings has been constant for 5 minutes. Generally, the temperature will reach a maximum and then begin to drop very slowly. This defines the stabilized period in Figure 25-1.

5. After the calorimeter has stabilized at a maximum temperature, the stirring motor can be stopped and the cover removed from the jacket. Disconnect the firing connection from the bomb terminal and lift the container and relieve all residual pressure with the pressure valve slowly and at a uniform rate so that the entire operation will not require less than one minute. Remove the screw cap, lift out the bomb head and place it in the support stand. Examine the interior of the bomb for evidence of incomplete combustion and discard the test if any is observed.

6. The interior surfaces of the bomb should be washed with a distilled water jet and the washings collected for titration with the standard sodium carbonate solution. This step is referred to as the "acid titration." After the titration phase of the test, the solution should be saved for determining the sulfur content of the sample.

7. The sulfur content of the sample should be analyzed if it is expected to

exceed 0.1 percent. The sulfate content can be accomplished by gravi-
metric or turbidimetric methods as explained in *Standard Methods* [1].

8. The net amount of wire burned should be determined by carefully removing all the remaining pieces of fuse wire from the bomb electrode.
Straighten these pieces and measure their combined length and subtract
this length from the initial 10 centimeters to get the net amount burned.
The length which was burned is used in obtaining the "fuse correction."

CORRELATION OF RESULTS

Using the procedures outlined previously, the gross heat of combustion, H_g,
can be calculated using Equation 25-1. All time in minutes should be recorded
as tenths of seconds.

Standardization of the Calorimeter

Assume the calorimeter was standardized with a 1.0062 grams benzoic acid
sample (6,318 calories/gram) and produced a net corrected temperature rise
of 4.701° F. The acid titration required 10.7 ml of standard alkali, and 7.8 cm
of fuse wire with 2.3 cal/cm were consumed during the combustion. Therefore,
the energy/equivalent can be calculated by Equation 25-1,

where:

H = 6,318 calories/gram
m = 1.0062 gram
e_1 = (10.7 ml) (1 calorie/ml) = 10.7 calories
e_3 = (7.8 centimeters) (2.3 calories/centimeter) = 17.9 calories
t = 4.701°F

therefore:

$$W = \frac{(6,318)(1.0062) + 10.7 + 17.9}{4.701}$$

= 1.358 calories/°F

Computation of Net Corrected Temperature Rise

Assume the data have been collected as shown in Table 25-1. From this table,
the parameters a, b, c, t_a, t_c, r_1, and r_2 can be calculated as explained below.

The time of firing, a, was initiated 5 minutes from the start of the test and
the maximum temperature (81.780) was reached 13 minutes after the test

TABLE 25-1. EXPERIMENTAL TEMPERATURE DATA FROM CALORIMETER

Time (min)	Temperature (°F)
0.00	75.925
1.00	75.930
2.00	75.935
3.00	75.940
4.00	75.945
5.00	75.950
5.50	76.205
6.00	77.345
6.50	78.775
7.00	80.165
8.00	80.945
9.00	81.325
10.00	81.600
11.00	81.770
12.00	81.775
13.00	81.780
14.00	81.779
15.00	81.778
16.00	81.777
17.00	81.776
18.00	81.775

began (8 minutes from firing). Therefore:

$$a \quad = \quad 5.00 - 0 \quad = \quad 5.00 \text{ min}$$
$$c \quad = \quad 13.00 - 0 \quad = \quad 13.00 \text{ min}$$

The thermometer reading at the time of firing (5.0 min) was 75.950 and the maximum reading at time, c, was 81.780. Correcting these readings for thermometer scale errors from a standard chart gives:

$$t_a \quad = \quad 75.950 + 0.026 = 75.976°F$$
$$t_c \quad = \quad 81.780 + 0.012 = 81.792°F$$

Thus, the total rise was equal to $81.792 - 75.976 = 5.816°F$. Sixty percent of this rise is $0.6 (5.816) = 3.490°F$. The time, b, to reach this value can be

461

interpolated between the temperature readings at 6.50 and 7.00 min and equals 6.75 min. Thus:

$$b \quad = \quad 6.75 \text{ min}$$

Therefore, the net temperature rise is:

$$t \quad = \quad t_c - t_a - r_1(b - a) + r_2(c - b)$$

$$= \quad 81.792 - 75.976 - (\frac{75.950 - 75.925}{5})(6.75 - 5.00) \; +$$

$$(\frac{81.780 - 81.775}{5})(13.00 - 6.75)$$

$$= \quad 81.792 - 75.976 - (0.005)(1.75) + (0.001)(6.25)$$

$$= \quad 5.814°F$$

Calculation of Gross Heat of Combustion

The milliliters of standard alkali (0.0725N) required to titrate the bomb washings was 23.9 ml and the sample, after titration with the alkali, was taken and the sulfate content was gravimetrically determined as 1.02 percent sulfur as S.

Therefore:

$$c_1 \quad = \quad 23.9 \text{ ml}$$
$$c_2 \quad = \quad 1.02 \text{ percent}$$
$$c_3 \quad = \quad 7.6 \text{ cm of wire remaining}$$

Correcting the above:

$$e_1 \quad = \quad c_1 \quad = \quad 23.9 \text{ calories (since standard alkali used)}$$
$$e_2 \quad = \quad 14(c_2)(m)$$
$$= \quad 14(1.02)(0.09936)$$
$$= \quad 1.42 \text{ calories}$$
$$e_3 \quad = \quad 2.3(c_3)$$
$$= \quad 2.3(7.6)$$
$$= \quad 17.5 \text{ calories}$$

Finally:

$$H_g \quad = \quad \frac{tW - e_1 - e_2 - e_3}{m}$$

$$= \quad \frac{5.814(1,358) - 23.9 - 14.4 - 17.5}{1.0062}$$

$$= \quad 7,791 \text{ cal/gram}$$

= 7,838 (1.8)
= 14,109 BTU/lb

LIMITATIONS AND SCALE-UP

One of the major sources of error in the combustion test procedures is incomplete combustion in the oxygen bomb. Incomplete combustion may be caused by one of the following:

1. Excessive rapid injection of the oxygen gas into the bomb during charging, blowing part of the sample from the cup.
2. Over-powderly condition of the sample in the cup prior to ignition causing ejection due to the violence of combustion.
3. The sample particles being too large.
4. Over-pressurizing of the pellet, making it too hard and causing spilling and ejection of fragments during heating.
5. Use of an ignition current which is too low to ignite the charge, or too high, causing the fuse to break before combustion is well under way.
6. Insertion of the fuse wire too far below the surface of a loose sample. Best results are obtained by barely touching the surface of the sample.
7. Insufficient oxygen to completely burn the charge or, conversely, the use of a very high initial gas pressure which may retard development of the required turbulence during combustion. As a rule, it is desirable to use the lowest gas pressure which will give complete combustion. Generally, it is best practice to use a lower gas pressure in the range of 20 to 25 atmospheres when initiating tests on a new sample. The pressure can be increased for subsequent tests if it is found that the sample is difficult to ignite or does not burn completely at the lower pressures. The lower pressures tend to permit higher gas temperatures and turbulence thus resulting in better combustion.

It is essential that a high grade thermometer be employed for all temperature readings. The thermometer which is used to calculate the energy equivalent of the calorimeter apparatus should also be used in all subsequent tests. If a new or different thermometer is employed, the energy equivalent should be recalculated.

The acid correction procedure is required because side reactions occur during the combustion process and generate a significant amount of heat which cannot be credited to the sample. Sulfur and nitrogen gases react with water vapor to form sulfuric and nitric acid which require correction to account for the heat liberated during their formation. In computing the correction for acid formation, it is assumed that all acid is in the form of nitric acid and that the heat of formation of 0.1N nitric acid under bomb conditions is 13.8 kcal/mole. If significant sulfuric acid is present, it is adjusted by separate computation based on the sulfur content of the sample. This adjustment uses a correction of 1.4 kg/cal for each gram of sulfur converted to sulfuric acid.

The correction for the wire which takes part in the combustion is computed for the burned portion by assuming a heat of combustion based on the type of wire used. This heat of combustion is 2.3 cal/cm for Parr 45C10 or 2.7 cal/cm for No. 34 B&S gauge iron wire.

The American Society for Testing and Materials specifies that duplicate results by the same operator should not vary more than 55 BTU/lb material to be considered acceptable. No values should vary more than 175 BTU/lb, regardless of who performs the test.

REFERENCES

1. *Standard Methods for the Examination of Water and Wastewater*, 14th Edition, American Public Health Association, Inc., New York (1976).

26

RECOVERY OF
PHYSICAL-CHEMICAL SLUDGES

DISCUSSION OF PRINCIPLES

The experience to date in sludge handling with conventional waste treatment schemes has been concerned with the processing and disposal of primary and secondary organic sludges. In advanced wastewater treatment schemes, the use of chemical coagulating agents generates tremendous quantities of sludge different in nature than these organic sludges. However, the disposal and recovery of chemical sludges is not a new or novel experience. Many industries and water treatment plants have been dealing with similar sludges for years and much of the present experience was gained from these facilities.

Excluding spent activated carbon, the two major sources of sludges originating from physical-chemical treatment systems are those generated during chemical addition to primary clarification facilities and those sludges which result from addition of chemicals in polishing units to reduce effluent suspended solids and phosphorus levels. The major difference between these two sludges, assuming the same chemicals are utilized, is the higher organic content in the primary sludges which results from influent and colloidal suspended materials removed by the chemical coagulation. The addition of chemicals directly to the aeration basin in an activated sludge process has been suggested as a possible method of phosphate removal; however, the resulting sludge will not be categorized as a physical-chemical sludge since it exhibits similar characteristics and requires similar treatment as a normal waste activated sludge.

The most commonly employed coagulants are the salts of calcium, aluminum, and iron. Generally, calcium is the most widely applied material when clarification and pH adjustment are required for subsequent processing such as

465

ammonia stripping and phosphorus removal. Aluminum, usually in the form of alum (aluminum sulfate), is used for clarification and phosphorus removal at lower pH ranges, such as pH 5 to 7. The resulting sludges settle slower and are more difficult to dewater than lime sludges. Iron, generally in the form of ferric chloride, has been used similarly for both coagulation and phosphorus removal. Normally, the iron requirements for phosphorus removal are considerably higher than alum and often will impart an undesirable yellowish color to the treated water. Disposal and recovery options with iron sludges are very limited and will not be discussed in detail herein.

In considering the various alternatives of sludge handling, the most single important factor involves the ability of the sludge to be dewatered. The drier sludges, particularly lime, are more amenable to recovery due to the economy of energy input. Many times the difficulty in dewatering one type of sludge will generate high costs for a dry method of recovery, thereby, encouraging the use of another coagulant, such as alum, which can be recovered by wet processing. With advanced waste treatment schemes oriented toward recovery, some form of dewatering is essential and must be considered.

Recovery of Alum Sludges

The use of alum in waste treatment has been primarily directed toward phosphorus removal and for final polishing ahead of filtration. Alum is an excellent coagulant for many wastes and will not only clarify turbidity and remove suspended materials, but forms a stable precipitate with phosphorus. Higher concentrations of alum are required for phosphorus removal than for clarification and the resulting sludges are different in nature and dewaterability.

The sludges generated from the use of alum are gelatinous in structure with a feathery, bulky nature. The moisture content is approximately 98.5 to 99 percent and, although it settles fairly readily, it is extremely difficult to dewater. The economics of dewatering alum and alum-sewage sludges often prohibit its use in wastewater treatment. The most feasible techniques of recovering alum sludges are by alkaline and acidic methods described as follows.

Alkaline Recovery of Alum. The alkaline methods of alum recovery have derived from the original work conducted by Lea et al. [1]. Slechta and Culp evaluated this method on a laboratory scale at South Tahoe, Nevada, and concluded that the economics were not favorable based on chemical costs alone [2].

Basically, the alkaline recovery method consists of adding sodium hydroxide to raise the pH above 12 and dissolve the aluminum hydroxide sludge. The aluminum hydroxide is converted to sodium aluminate at the high pH and the precipitated phosphate ions are released back into solution. Calcium chloride is then supplemented to precipitate the phosphate as insoluble calcium phosphate (hydroxyapatite). The following reaction describes the process:

$$Al(OH)_3 \cdot PO_4{}^{3-} + 4NaOH \longrightarrow NaAlO_2 + Na_3PO_4 + 2H_2O + 3OH^-$$

$$(26\text{-}1)$$

$$NaAlO_2 + 2Na_3PO_4 + 3CaCl_2 \longrightarrow NaAlO_2 + Ca_3(PO_4)_2 + 6NaCl$$

$$(26\text{-}2)$$

The sodium aluminate, which is thus generated, is not as effective a coagulant as aluminum sulfate and sufficient sulfuric acid must be added to adjust the pH downward and reform aluminum sulfate. Figure 26-1 indicates that the effi-

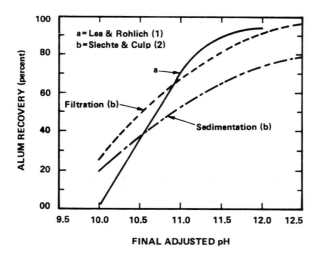

FIG. 26-1. ALUM RECOVERY BY THE ALKALINE METHOD

ciency of alum recovery may be as high as 90 to 94 percent depending on whether sedimentation or filtration is used to recover the alum [2]. The pH must be initially adjusted to greater than 12 or side reactions will occur with the calcium chloride to precipitate the aluminum ion. Slechta and Culp obtained 78 percent recovery by sedimentation and required 50 percent makeup alum to achieve the same turbidity removals as fresh alum [2]. Therefore, the process was deemed uneconomical and was not pursued further at South Tahoe.

Another method of alkaline recovery of alum, which is reported by Slechta and Culp, employs lime for both the pH adjustment and phosphorus precipitation. Lime is much cheaper than sodium hydroxide and facilities would only be needed for one chemical. The recovery efficiency was only about 35 percent. However, the overall costs were lower per ton of reclaimed alum than the alkaline method. However, fresh alum can be purchased for approximately 10 percent less than the reclaimed material. Thereby, on a strict chemical cost the recovery method is uneconomical. If the economics of sludge handling are included, these recovery techniques will become much more feasible.

Acidic Method of Alum Recovery. Generation of aluminum sulfate from the addition of sulfuric acid to aluminum hydroxide or hydrous aluminum oxide sludges has been practiced at several water treatment plants throughout the United States and Great Britain. Extensive studies by Roberts and Roddy at the Tampa, Florida, water treatment plant paved the way for successful demonstration of reuse and recovery of alum [4]. The equation of the process is:

$$2Al(OH)_3 + 3H_2SO_4 \longrightarrow Al_2(SO_4)_3 + 6H_2O \qquad (26\text{-}3)$$

Approximately 1.9 lb of sulfuric acid are required per lb of aluminum hydroxide recovered. Slechta and Culp found greater than 98 percent recovery at pH levels of 1 to 2 as shown in Figure 26-2 [2]. More refined alum can be formed by drying the sludge to form aluminum oxide prior to the sulfuric acid addition. The subsequent reaction is:

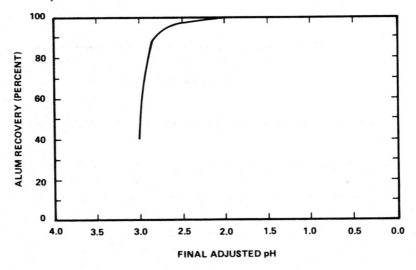

FIG. 26-2. ALUM RECOVERY BY THE ACIDIC METHOD

$$Al_2O_3 + 11 H_2O + 3H_2SO_4 \longrightarrow Al_2(SO_4)_3 + 14 H_2O \quad (26\text{-}4)$$

In experimental studies by Roberts and Roddy [4], an air dried sludge contained 25 to 30 percent aluminum oxide while an oven dried sludge at 105°C contained about 45 to 50 percent which is similar to low grade bauxite. These investigators decided that the wet method of treating thickened, clarified sludge involved the least amount of equipment and was cheaper than subsequent dewatering and drying methods. Slechta and Culp [2] estimated that the cost of the acidic recovery method is approximately one-third the cost of buying fresh alum.

The major disadvantage of the acidic recovery method of alum is the dissolution of phosphorus, which returns to the supernatant of the sludge handling system. Phosphate removal from the supernatant by ion exchange and activated silica was examined and found to be economically prohibitive [3]. Therefore, the acidic method of alum recovery can be very effective, but only if phosphate removal is not required.

Recovery of Calcium Sludges

The cost of lime has favored use of this chemical in wastewater treatment for coagulation of suspended and colloidal organic materials and also precipitation of phosphate compounds. At the proper pH, insoluble calcium carbonate is formed as shown below:

$$Ca(OH)_2 + Ca(HCO_3)_2 \longrightarrow 2 CaCO_3 \downarrow + 2H_2O \quad (26\text{-}5)$$

Calcium carbonate floc entraps suspended organics and is useful for primary clarification. The sludge which is produced has a very high lime and organic content. Calcium phosphate or hydroxyapatite is formed by the reaction of lime and phosphate as follows:

$$5Ca^{2+} + 4OH^- + 3HPO_4^{2-} \longrightarrow Ca_5OH(PO_4)_3 \downarrow + 3H_2O \quad (26\text{-}6)$$

As primary coagulation and primary and tertiary phosphate removal systems become more prevalent in waste treatment, the recovery and reuse of lime will undoubtedly receive considerable attention. The most commonly used method of reclaiming lime is by the process of recalcination where lime sludges are heated to regenerate calcium oxide. Basically, the process of calcination involves incineration of sludges to convert carbonates and hydroxides to oxides. The recalcination of lime sludges consists of burning the dewatered sludge in the temperature range of 1,800 to 2,000°F in order to drive off water and carbon dioxide leaving the calcium oxide as shown in the following equation:

$$CaCO_3 \xrightarrow{\text{2,000°F}} CaO + CO_2 \qquad (26\text{-}7)$$

The CO_2 which is released is generally reclaimed and employed for recarbonation and pH adjustment. Major processes which have found the most frequent application in recalcining lime sludges are the rotary kiln, the pellet-seeding calciner, and the multiple hearth furnace. Each of these processes has been compared and described for use in waste sludge reclamation by Adams [5]. Typical schematics of these processes are shown in Figure 26-3.

Previous studies have indicated that recalcining plants with capacities as low as 6 tons per day may be feasible where sludge disposal is a critical and costly problem. The use of the rotary kiln is limited to larger operations of greater than 50 tons per day while the fluidized beds are more useful for small installations. The rotary kiln requires a greater land area and dissipates more heat because it is less compact. The multiple hearth furnace satisfies intermediate needs between the small and large operations. A summary of existing data from various water and wastewater recalcining plants in the United States is shown in Table 26-1 [6].

General Considerations for Lime Recycle. Probably the most important consideration in reclaiming lime is the quantity of inert materials which accumulate through the continuous recycling. The wastage rate and the degree of lime makeup required are controlled by the quantity of inerts which must be removed from the system. With primary sludges, a tremendous quantity of inert materials accumulates from the residue of burning organics. This large quantity of inert residue generally will render the recycle of lime infeasible. However, two centrifuges in series can be employed to correct the situation. The first centrifuge is used to classify the solids by separating the more dense calcium carbonate solids into the cake. This calcium carbonate sludge then goes to incineration for recalcining and reclaiming. The centrate from the first centrifuge, consisting of organic and phosphate solids, is passed to the second centrifuge for concentration and eventual burning in a biological sludge incinerator.

In both primary and tertiary applications of lime, the reaction pH of 9.5 results in phosphorus removals on the order of 85 to 95 percent but exhibits high effluent turbidity due to colloidal and pin floc particles. As the pH is increased above 9.5, magnesium hydroxide will precipitate until the reaction is essentially complete at a pH of 10.5 to 11.0 The magnesium hydroxide precipitate will remove the majority of the colloidal materials resulting in a clear

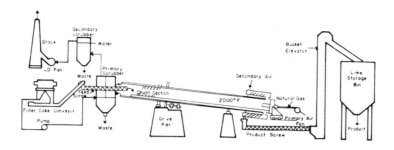

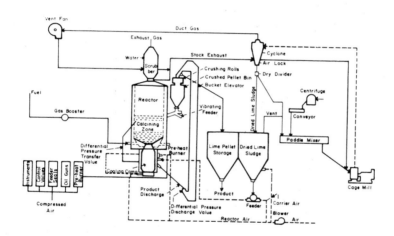

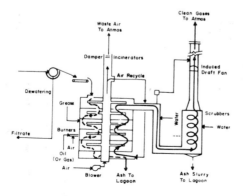

FIG. 26-3. RECALCINING PROCESSES FOR LIME RECOVERY

471

TABLE 26-1. LIST OF RECALCINING PLANTS IN UNITED STATES

Location	Approximate Construction Year	Capacity Product Output tons/day	Type of Dewatering Equipment*	Type of Recalciner**	Requirement mil Btu/ton of Output	CO₂ Recovered	Water Plant Rated Capacity MGD	Lime Feed Mil Gal	Sludge/Lime Ratio
Marshall, Iowa	--	4.2	C	FC	9.66	--	3.5	--	--
Pontiac, Mich.	--	--	C	FC	--	--	10	2,200	2.50
Miami, Fla.	1948	80	C	RK	8.5	Yes	180	1,800	2.20
Lansing, Mich.	1954	30	C	FB	8.0	--	20	2,200	2.27
Salina, Kan.	1957	--	C	FC	--	--	--	--	--
Dayton, Ohio	1960	150	C	RK	9.0	Yes	96	2,140	2.47
San Diego, Calif.	1961	25	VF	RD	9.0	--	--	--	--
S. D. Warren Co.†	1963	70	C	FB	7.2	Yes	--	--	--
Merida, Yucatan	1965	40	C	RK	--	Yes	24	--	--
Ann Arbor, Mich.	1968	24	C	FB	--	--	--	--	--
Lake Tahoe, Nev. ††	1968	10.8	C	MH	7.0	Yes	7.5	3,300	--
St. Paul, Minn.‡	1969	50	C	FB	8.2	Yes	120‡‡	990	2.40

* C - centrifuge; VF - vacuum filter

** RK - rotary kiln; FM - fluidized bed; FC - flash calcination; MH - multiple hearth

† paper mill owned by Scott Paper Company

†† activated sludge disposal plant

‡ now under construction

‡‡ lime recalcining plant designed to accommodate future water treatment plant capacity of 170 MGD.

supernatant; however, the hydrous nature of this precipitate has adverse effects on subsequent thickening and dewatering processes. Recarbonation of the resulting sludges to a pH of 9.5 will redissolve much of the magnesium hydroxide and precipitate the remaining free calcium as calcium carbonate.

Three investigations have evaluated the characteristics of lime with regard to reuse and waste treatment systems. Rand and Nemerow [8] performed laboratory studies with raw wastewater and found no change in the ability to remove phosphates with recovered lime and measured an average makeup demand of 13 percent. Slechta and Culp [2] worked with secondary effluent and recovered lime through 11 cycles. The results indicated an average makeup of 36 percent. The accumulation of inert materials, such as hydroxyapatite in the recalcined ash resulted in a decrease of the percent calcium oxide in the ash. The phosphorus removal was not hindered by returning reclaimed lime. Mulbarger *et al* [7] observed that recycled lime sludges dewatered better than raw sludges, probably due to the accumulation of inert materials. In the same studies, the characteristics of lime sludges, both before and after three recycles, were examined in soft and hard waters. The phosphate content and the alkalinity of the raw waste were varied in order to examine the accumulative affect of these qualities on the recycled lime. These results are presented in Figure 26-4 and several conclusions derived from these results are summarized below:

1. The quantity of sludge generated is directly proportional to the lime dosage, as would be expected.
2. The combustion loss and calcium oxide production will remain constant

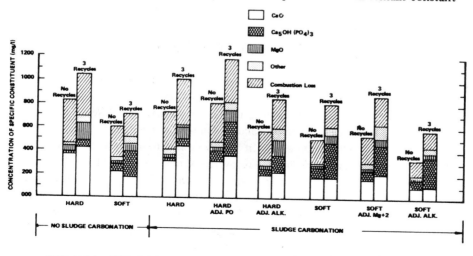

FIG. 26-4. CHARACTERISTICS OF RECALCINED LIME SLUDGE

with multiple lime reuse under consistent water quality and system performance. Therefore, lime makeup can be expected to be relatively constant under steady-state conditions.

3. Under constant conditions, magnesium hydroxide, hydroxyapatite and other inert materials will accumulate at constant increments with each recycle. In order to control the inert buildup, a wastage rate must be established for each situation, after which the sludge mass and composition can be closely predicted for any number of recycles.

4. Carbonation of the sludge will dissolve the magnesium hydroxide, resulting in slightly less sludge production.

5. In hard waters with a low phosphorus content, lime recovery may exceed lime usage. Consequently, lime wastage will control the wastage of other inert constituents.

6. In wastewaters of low alkalinity and high phosphate content, hydroxyapatite accumulates rapidly and may reach levels found in low grade phosphate rock.

The hydroxyapatite levels in recalcined lime ash have been found to have negligible solubility in distilled water [7]. Therefore, disposal in landfill sites should not cause a pollutional discharge due to phosphate runoff. The citrate solubility, which measures phosphate availability to plants, in the recalcined ash was measured to be in the range of 80 to 94 percent which is the range of good phosphate fertilizers. Thus, the sale of sludges for fertilizer value might be feasible in some locations.

EQUIPMENT REQUIRED

The equipment required for investigating physical-chemical sludge recovery consists of simple laboratory glassware and common laboratory reagents. For the alum recovery methods only glassware, reagents, and filter paper are required. The lime recalcination procedures will require a muffle furnace capable of heating to 2,000° F. Occasionally, it will be desired to measure the accumulation of specific compounds in the recovered sludge, such as MgO, CaO and $Ca_5OH(PO_4)_3$. The investigator is referred to *Standard Methods* or a standard inorganic analytical text for specific techniques of measuring calcium, magnesium, and other compounds [9]. The equipment needed for the tests is outlined below:

Alkaline Recovery of Alum

1. Several 500-ml graduated glass beakers.

2. Graduated burets for monitoring addition of reagents to sludge.
3. 10 percent NaOH solution.
4. 10 percent H_2SO_4 solution.
5. 10 percent calcium chloride solution.
6. 10 percent lime solution.
7. Filter paper and funnel for gravity filtering.
8. Reagents for measuring aluminum.

Acidic Method of Alum Recovery

1. Several 500-ml graduated glass beakers.
2. Graduated buret for measuring sulfuric acid solution.
3. 10 percent sulfuric acid solution.
4. Reagents for measuring aluminum.

Recalcination of Lime

1. Normal laboratory glassware, such as graduated beakers and burets.
2. Muffle furnace capable of heating to 2,000°F.
3. 10 percent lime solution.
4. Porcelain crucibles to contain sludge while heating in muffle furnace.
5. Reagents for measuring specific constituents, such as calcium, phosphate and magnesium.
6. Carbon dioxide cylinder for recarbonating sludge if desired.

EXPERIMENTAL PROCEDURES

Alkaline Method of Alum Recovery

The procedures for this method consist of determining the pH for maximum solubilization of the aluminum hydroxide sludge followed by determining the optimum amount of calcium chloride to add for phosphorus removal. Then, the coagulating properties of the recovered alum and various ratios of make-up with fresh alum are evaluated. Specifically, the procedures are:

1. Develop a titration curve so that a quantity of NaOH can be calculated to adjust the aluminum hydroxide to desired pH levels.
2. Adjust the pH of 100 ml samples of raw sludge to 10.5, 11.0, 11.5, 12.0, and 12.5.
3. Filter the pH-adjusted samples and measure the soluble aluminum and phosphorus content of the filtrate. The soluble aluminum represents the

conversion of aluminum hydroxide sludge to soluble sodium aluminate ($NaAlO_2$).

4. Select a pH value, based on the desired conversion of aluminum hydroxide, and adjust a 1,000 ml sample of raw sludge to this value.

5. To 100 ml samples of pH-adjusted sludge (Step 4), add various dosages of calcium chloride. Mix thoroughly, allow to settle and measure phosphate content of supernatant.

6. At the desired pH and optimum dosage of calcium chloride, prepare two liters of raw sludge. Divide the treated sludge sample into four equal portions of 500 ml each.

7. Add various percentages of fresh alum to the recovered aluminate solution (from Step 6) and evaluate the effectiveness with regard to coagulation properties.

Recovery of Lime Sludge by Recalcination

The procedures for recalcination of lime consist of air drying the sludge, recalcining in a muffle furnace, and evaluating the degree of fresh lime makeup based on the accumulation of inert materials, and slaking properties of the recovered lime. A schematic illustration of the sludge generation and recalcining procedures is shown in Figure 26-5. Specifically:

1. Determine the optimum dosage of lime (CaO) to coagulate the wastewater.

2. Coagulate 5 gallons of the raw wastewater. Flash mix for 1 to 5 min, flocculate for 5 to 15 min and settle for 1.5 to 2.5 hr.

3. After settling, decant the supernatant to a separate container. Filter the sludge in a Buchner funnel and add the filtrate to the decanted supernatant. Recarbonate the decant and filtrate liquor to a pH of 9.5.

4. Filter the calcium carbonate sludge from the recarbonation step (Step 3) and measure the calcium content of the filtrate.

5. Recalcine the lime (Step 3) and calcium carbonate (Step 4) sludges in a muffle furnace to produce a "soft-burned" lime.
   a. Air dry the lime and calcium carbonate sludges.
   b. Place the dried sludges in a crucible and insert into a cold muffle furnace.
   c. Gradually raise the temperature to 1,800°F (1,000°C) and hold for 1.5 hours.
   d. Allow the furnace to gradually cool.

6. Measure the available CaO content of the recalcined sludge using the rapid sugar determination for calcium [5]. It may also be desired to measure

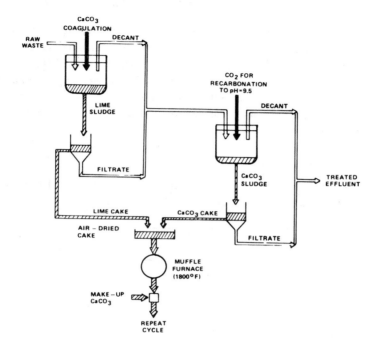

**FIG. 26-5. LABORATORY PROCEDURES FOR RECALCINING
LIME SLUDGE**

specific inert constituents such as magnesium, and phosphate, in order
to estimate the accumulation of MgO or calcium phosphate.

7. To the recalcined sludge, add the required amount of makeup lime to
   provide the initial lime requirement for coagulation (determined in Step
   1) of 5 gallons of raw wastewater.

8. Repeat Steps 2 - 7, measuring the accumulation of inerts and the required
   amount of makeup for each cycle.

9. It may be desirable to monitor the effects of recycle on the slaking characteristics of the recalcined lime:

   a. Add 5 g of recalcined lime to 35 ml of water.

   b. Record the change of temperature with time.

477

CORRELATION OF RESULTS

In correlating and evaluating the data from sludge recovery investigations, the significant factors include the quantity of recovery chemicals required (with alum recovery), the efficiency of primary coagulant ($Al_2(SO_4)_3$ or CaO) recovery obtained under varying operating conditions, and the accumulation of inert materials in the recovered sludges which will require a periodic blowdown or wastage in order to maintain the desired coagulation properties of the recovered coagulants.

Alkaline Recovery of Alum

1. A 500 ml sample of 1% $Al(OH)_3$ sludge is titrated with a 10% solution of NaOH as shown in Figure 26-6.

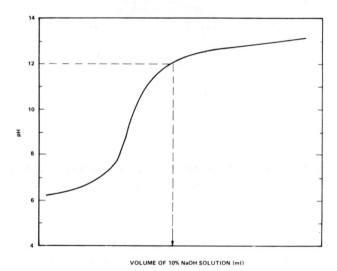

VOLUME OF 10% NaOH SOLUTION (ml)

FIG. 26-6. TITRATION CURVE FOR THICKENED ALUM SLUDGE

2. Using the results of Figure 26-6, five, 100 ml samples of the raw sludge are adjusted to pH levels of 10.5, 11.0, 11.5, and 12.5.
3. The supernatant is measured for aluminum and phosphate (if phosphorus removal is a criterion). The results are plotted in Figure 26-7. For example, if the raw sludge contained an aluminum concentration of 2,450 mg/l, then a 100-ml sample would contain 245 mg of aluminum or 2,695 mg of alum (aluminum sulfate, $Al_2(SO_4)_3 \cdot 14H_2O$).

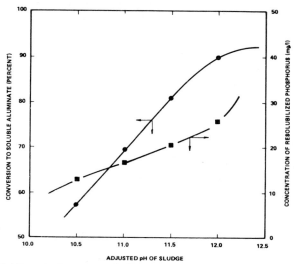

FIG. 26-7. ALUM SLUDGE RECOVERY AS A FUNCTION OF pH

At a pH of 11.5, the filtered supernatant contained 2,210 mg/l of aluminum (equivalent to 24,310 mg/l of alum). If the supernatant volume was 90 ml, then:

Aluminum content	=	2,210 mg/l x 0.09
	=	199 mg
	=	199 (594/54)
	=	2,188 mg of alum equivalent
% Conversion of Recovery	=	(2,188/2,695) 100
	=	81%

4. Suppose a 90% conversion is desired. From Figure 26-7 the required pH will be 12.0. Therefore, adjust a 500-ml sample of raw sludge to 12.0 using the quantity of NaOH indicated in Figure 26-6.

5. Add 25, 50, 75, 100, and 150 mg/l of calcium chloride to the 100 ml samples of the sludge from Step 4. The supernatant phosphate is correlated to the calcium chloride dosage in Figure 26-8. The optimum $CaCl_2$ dosage is selected at 100 mg/l.

6. Adjust several liters of the raw sludge to a pH of 12.0 and add 100 mg/l of $CaCl_2$ to the supernatant. Filter and divide the supernatant into 500 ml aliquots. The concentration of aluminum was found to be 235 mg/l (which is equivalent to 2,585 mg/l of aluminum sulfate or 714 mg/l of sodium aluminate).

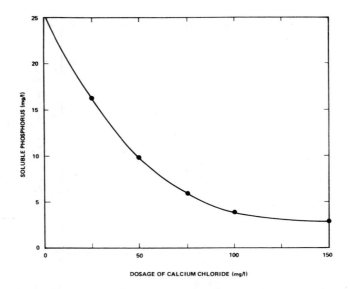

FIG. 26-8. PRECIPITATION OF PHOSPHORUS WITH CALCIUM CHLORIDE

7. Add fresh alum to the sodium aluminate samples in the following proportions:

0% fresh alum:	100% sodium aluminate solution
20% fresh alum:	80% sodium aluminate solution
40% fresh alum:	60% sodium aluminate solution
60% fresh alum:	40% sodium aluminate solution
100% fresh alum:	0% sodium aluminate solution

The relative proportions are based on equivalent ratios of alum $(Al_2(SO_4)_3 \cdot 14H_2O)$. For example, at the 20 percent fresh alum: 80 percent recovered sodium aluminate solution:

500 ml of recovered solution	=	714 mg/l $NaAlO_2$
	=	2,585 mg/l alum
	=	1,293 mg alum
	=	80% of total alum

Therefore, total alum content in 500 ml	=	1,293 mg alum/0.8
	=	1,616 mg alum

Fresh alum proportion	=	$1,616 - 1,293$
	=	323 mg alum
Assume stock solution of alum	=	30% $Al_2(SO_4)_3 \cdot 14H_2O$
	=	300 mg alum/ml
Thus to get 323 mg alum	=	323 mg alum/(300 mg alum/ml)

By adding 1.1 ml of 30 percent fresh alum solution to 500 ml of recovered sodium aluminate solution, the resultant liquid will contain:

20% of alum as fresh $Al_2(SO_4)_3 \cdot 14H_2O$
80% of alum as recovered $NaAlO_2$

The alum concentration is thus

Alum	=	1,293 mg + 323 mg
	=	1,616 mg
Volume	=	500 ml + 1.1 ml
	=	501.1 ml
Alum concentration	=	1,616 mg/0.5011 ℓ
	=	3,225 mg/l
	=	0.32%

8. Add 0, 100, 200, 300, 400, 500, and 600 mg/l as equivalent $Al_2(SO_4)_3 \cdot 14H_2O$ to the raw wastewater with each of the solutions given in Step 7. For example, suppose there is 501.1 ml of the 20% fresh alum: 80% sodium aluminate solution at 3,225 mg/l alum (see Step 7).

   1 ml of solution contains 3.23 mg of alum on a dry weight basis. Thus, to get 300 mg/l of alum with the 20%:80% solution in 500 ml of raw waste:

Alum quantity:	=	0.5 liters x 300 mg/l
	=	150 mg
Amount of 20%:80% solution	=	150 mg/3.23 mg/ml
	=	46.5 ml

9. After adding the desired quantities of alum in Step 8, thoroughly mix (and adjust pH if desired) and allow to settle. Measure the supernatant parameters of significance and correlate the results as shown in Figure 26-9.

10. As can be interpreted from Figure 26-9, 600 mg/l (as aluminum sulfate) are required of the 60%:40% solution to achieve the same results as the fresh alum at 400 mg/l. An economic evaluation can subsequently be made to determine the most feasible alum recovery efficiency and the degree of makeup desired with fresh alum.

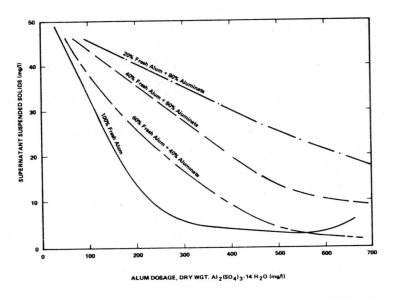

FIG. 26-9. COAGULATION PROPERTIES OF RECOVERED ALUM

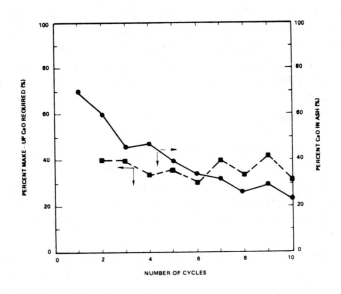

FIG. 26-10. EFFECTS OF RECYCLING ON CaO CHARACTERISTICS OF ASH

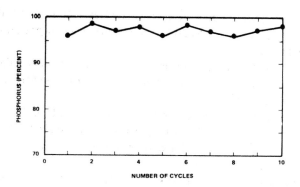

FIG. 26-11. EFFECT OF CaO RECYCLE ON PHOSPHORUS REMOVAL

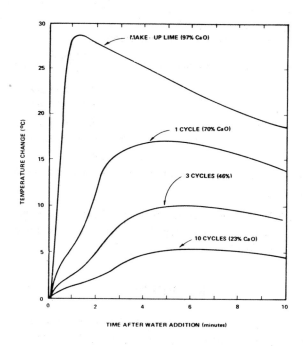

FIG. 26-12. EFFECTS OF CaO RECYCLE ON SLAKING TEMPERATURE

Recovery of Lime by Recalcination

1. The optimum dosage of CaO for coagulation was determined to be 450 mg/l.

483

2. Five gallons of wastewater were coagulated at 450 mg/l of CaO and the resulting sludge volume was 20% (one gallon) at a concentration of 6.2% suspended solids.

3. The sludge was filtered and air dried. The filtrate of 0.206 gallons (0.782 liters) was added to the decant volume of 4 gallons from Step 2 for a total volume of 4.206 gallons.

4. The decant and filtrate liquor was recarbonated to a pH of 9.5 and allowed to settle. The resultant $CaCO_3$ sludge was filtered and air dried.

5. The sludges from Steps 3 and 4 were recalcined in accordance with Step 5 of the "Procedures" section.

6. The CaO content of the combined recalcined sludges was equal to 0.7 mg CaO/mg ash. The total weight of ash was 4,480 mg.

7. Calculate the amount of makeup CaO required to maintain 450 mg/l of CaO in the raw wastewater. In 4 gallons of waste, 450 mg/l is equal to:

$$CaO = 450 \text{ mg/l} \times 4 \text{ gal} \times 3.785 \text{ } \ell/\text{gal}$$
$$= 6,830 \text{ mg per 4 gal of wastewater}$$

Calcium content of recalcined sludge $= \dfrac{0.7 \text{ mg CaO}}{\text{mg ash}} (4,480 \text{ mg ash})$

$$= 3,140 \text{ mg CaO}$$

Makeup CaO required $= 6,830 - 3,140$
$$= 3,690 \text{ mg CaO}$$

Thus, % makeup $= (3,690/6,830) \ 100$
$$= 54\%$$

8. These cycles can be repeated and the results correlated as shown in Figures 26-10 and 26-11.

9. With each cycle, the temperatures of the recalcined lime including makeup)was recorded with time (see Step 9 of "Procedures") and correlated as shown in Figure 26-12.

REFERENCES

1. Lea, W. L., Rohlich, G. A. and Katz, W. J., "Removal of Phosphates from Treated Sewage," *Sew. and Ind. Wastes*, 26, 261-275 (1954).

2. Slechta, A. F. and Culp, G. L., "Water Reclamation Studies at the South Tahoe Puplic Utility District," *Jour. Water Pollution Control Federation*, 39, 787-814 (1967).

3. Culp, R. L., Wesner, G. M. and Culp, G. L., *Handbook of Advanced Wastewater Treatment*, 2nd Ed., Van Nostrand Reinhold Co., New York (1978).

4. Roberts, J. M. and Roddy, C. P., "Recovery and Reuse of Alum Sludge at Tampa," *Jour. American Water Works Association*, 52, 857-866 (1960).

5. Adams, C.E., Jr., *Applications of New Concepts of Physical-Chemical Wastewater Treatment*, Pergamon Press (1972).

6. Dick, R. I. and Dean, R. B., "Disposal of Wastes from Water Treatment Plants," AWWA Research Foundation Report, *Jour. American Water Works Association*, 61, 543-546 (1969).

7. Mulbarger, M. C., Grossman, E., III, and Dean, R. B., "Lime Clarification, Recovery and Reuse for Wastewater Treatment," Project for U.S. Dept. of Interior, FWPCA, Cincinnati, Ohio (June, 1968).

8. Rand, M. C. and Nemerow, N. L., "Removal of Algal Nutrients from Domestic Wastewaters," Report No. 9, Dept. of Civil Eng., Syracuse University, Syracuse, New York (1965).

9. *Standard Methods for the Examination of Water and Sewage,* 14th Edition, American Public Health Association, Inc., New York (1976).

INDEX

Adsorption, activated carbon,
291-307
    equipment required for,
        carbon column, pilot-scale,
        308
        isotherm evaluation, lab-scale,
        308
    experimental procedures for,
        carbon columns, pilot-scale,
        310-311
        isotherm evaluation, lab-scale,
        309
        powdered activated carbon
        (PAC), 311
    limitations and scale-up, 311
    results, correlation of, 311
Aeration. *See* Oxygen transfer and
aeration equipment selection
Aerobic digestion of biological
sludges, 399-410
Anaerobic treatment of organic
wastes, 255-277

Centrifugation, 401-402
    centrifuge, types of,
        basket (solid bowl), 404-405
        disc, 404
        scroll solid bowl (conveyor),
        402
    equipment required for, 411-412
    experimental procedures for
    centrifuge,
        basket, 413
        disc, 412-413
        scroll solid bowl, 412
    limitations and scale-up, 415-417
    performance of, 406-411
    results, correlation of, 413-414
Centrifuge. *See* Centrifugation
Coagulation and precipitation,
    coagulation, with
        aluminum compounds, 74-75
        iron, 75
        lime, 73-74

considerations for, 73
equipment required for, 76
experimental procedures for,
  coagulation,
    jar test, defining the opti-
      mum operating condi-
      tions for, 78-81
    zeta potential, defining the
      optimum operating con-
      ditions for, 81-82
  solids recirculation, bene-
    ficial effects of, 82-84
  limitations and scale-up, 89-90
  polyelectrolytes, role of in,
    75-76
  results, correlation of,
    jar test, 84-87
    solids recirculation, 89
    zeta potential, 87-89
  zeta potential, 72-73
  jar test, 92-95
Dissolved air flotation (DAF).
  See Flotation, dissolved air
  zeta potential, 95-97
Filter, trickling, 223-224
  ammonia removal performance,
    229-230
  equipment required for, 232
  experimental procedures for,
    ammonia removal, 235-238
    organic removal, 233-235
  fixed-media system, 231-232
  limitations and scale-up, 238-239
  organic removal performance,
    224-228
  results, correlation of, 238
Filtration, granular media, 279-282
  equipment required for, 282-283
  experimental procedures for,
    284-285

limitations and scale-up, 288-290
  results, correlation of,
    backwash, bed expansion
      during, 288
    headloss and solids disposition
      characteristics, 287-288
    suspended solids removal
      characteristics, 285-286
Filtration, pressure, 419-420
  equipment required for,
    bench-scale, 421-423
    Buchner funnel apparatus,
      420 *See* 387-388
    pilot-scale, 424
    specific resistance meter,
      420-421
  experimental procedures for,
    424-426
    bench-scale test, 427
    Buchner funnel test, 426
    pilot-scale test, 428-429
    specific resistance test meter,
      426-427
  limitations and scale-up, 434
  results, correlation of, 429-433
Filtration, vacuum, 383-387
  equipment required for,
    Buchner funnel, 387-388
    capillary suction time appara-
      tus, 388-390
    leaf filter apparatus, 388
  experimental procedures for,
    Buchner filter test, 390
    capillary suction filtration,
      390-391
    filter leaf test, 391-392
  limitations and scale-up, 399-400
  results, correlation of,
    Buchner funnel test, 393-394
    capillary suction data, 394

filter leaf test, 394-396
Flotation, dissolved air (DAF),
107-114
  equipment required for,
    induced air, 114-115
    pressurized, 114
  experimental procedures for,
    induced air flotation, 119
    pressurized, DAF,
      full-flow, 115-118
      recycle, 118-119
  limitations and scale-up, 120-129
  results, correlation of, 120

Hydraulics and mixing characteristics, 131-139
  equipment required for, 139
  experimental procedures for,
    139-140
  limitations and scale-up, 141

Ion exchange
  experimental procedures for,
    pH effects on exchange,
      evaluation of, 321
    regenerants, evaluation of,
      321-322
    regenerant use, optimization
      of, 322-323
    resin, determination of attri-
      tion characteristics of,
      323-324
    resin exchange capacity,
      determination of, 320-321
  limitations and scale-up, 334
  resin description, 313-315
  results, correlation of,
    pH effects on exchange,
      evaluation of, 324-325

regenerants, evaluation of,
  325-327
regenerant use, optimization
  of, 327-333
resin, attrition characteristics
  of, 333-334
resin exchange capacity,
  determination of, 324
systems,
  DESAL process, 317-319
  mixed-resin exchange opera-
    tion, 316-317
  two-stage cation-anion
    exchange, 316

Lagoon, aerated, 209
  biochemical oxygen demand
    (BOD), removal characteristics
    of, 210-213
  equipment required for, 217
  experimental procedures,
    217-219
  limitations and scale-up, 221-222
  nutrient requirements, 217
  oxygen requirements, 213-214
  results, correlation of, 219-221
  settling basin, final, 215-217
  sludge production, 214-215

Mixing. *See* Hydraulics and mixing
  characteristics

Neutralization, 57-59
  control system,
    cascade, 60
    feedforward, 60
    multimode or proportional, 60
    two-position (on-off), 59-60

equipment required for,
alkaline or acid, liquid,
bench-scale, 63
limestone, bench-scale, 63
pilot-scale, 64
experimental procedures for,
alkaline or acid, liquid,
bench-scale, 64-65
limestone, bench-scale,
65-66
pilot-scale, 66-67
limitations and scale-up, 69
pH,
as pretreatment, control of, 61
in biological systems,
increase of, 62-63
reduction of, 61-62
results, correlation of, 67-68

Organic wastes, anaerobic treatment
of, 255-261
anaerobic degradation, kinetics
of, 261-265
denitrification, biological,
265-267
equipment required for, 267-271
experimental procedures for,
271-275
limitations and scale-up, 276-277
results, correlation of, 275-276
Oxidation, chemical, 337-338
chlorine as chemical oxidant,
341-343
equipment required for,
general, 345-346
reactor, batch, 346
reactor, continuous-flow, 346
experimental procedures for,
batch, 349-350

chlorine, detection of, 348
continuous flow, 350-351
oxidants, detection of,
chlorine dioxide, 348
hydrogen peroxide, 349
permanganate, 348
ozone, detection of, 339-341
limitations and scale-ups, 357
ozone as chemical oxidant,
339-341
results, correlation of,
continuous flow, 353-356
ozonation, batch, 351-353
Oxygen transfer and aeration equipment selection, 143-147
aeration systems,
diffused bubbler, 147-149
mechanical, 151-154
static, 149
turbine, 149-151
experimental procedures for,
field performance, 161-163
oxygen transfer coefficient,
laboratory procedure for
determination of the,
164-166
reaeration, 154-161
limitations and scale-up, 166-167

pH,
control of, as pretreatment
biological systems, 61-63
Ponds, waste stabilization, 241-248
equipment required for, 248-
249
experimental procedures for,
249-252
limitations and scale-up, 252-
253

Precipitation. *See* Coagulation and precipitation

Sampling
  manual and automatic,
    duration of, 26-27
    equipment for, 30-36
    frequency of, 26-27
    handling and preservation of, 27-29
  program, organizing, 21-23
  results, correlation of, 36-38
  techniques for,
    composite, 25-26
    grab, 25
  wastewater, 23
  waste survey, 23-24
Screening and toxicity methodology, 39-41
  equipment required for,
    batch reactor, 45
    Hach apparatus, 43, 44
    Warburg apparatus, 41-43, 44
  experimental procedures for,
    batch, 53
    batch acclimation, 45-47
    Hach, 51-52
    Warburg, 47-51
  limitations and scale-up, 56
  results, correlation of,
    batch, 56
    Warburg, 54-55
Sedimentation
  equipment required for, 98
  experimental procedures for,
    settling,
      discrete, 98
      flocculant, 98-99
  limitations and scale-up, 104-105

results, correlation of,
  settling,
    discrete, 99-101
    flocculant, 101-103
settling, types of
  compression, 92
  discrete, 91, 92-95
  flocculant, 91, 95-96
  zone, 91-92, 96-97

Sludge, activated, 169-171
  equipment required for,
    activated sludge systems,
      bench-scale,
        aeration basin mixers, 188
        diffused air supply, 189
        heating and cooling, 189-190
        multi-stage, 185-188
        reactor-clarifier, single-stage combined, 184-185
        sludge pumps, influent feed and recycle, 188
        waste containers, influent and effluent, 188
    activated sludge systems,
      pilot scale,
        aeration tank, 190-191
        clarifier, secondary, 191-192
    monitoring equipment and apparatus,
      chemicals and materials, 192
      oxygen uptake rate test, 193
      zone settling velocity apparatus, 192-193

experimental procedures,
193-194
  activated sludge methodology,
  batch, 199-200
  activated sludge method- ˙v,
  ology, continuous, 194-199
  limitations and scale-up, 206-207
  nitrification, biological, 180-183
  organic loading, 178-180
  organic removal, 171-174
  oxygen requirements, 174-176
  sludge production, 176-177
  results, correlation of, 200-205
Sludge, aerobic digestion of biological, 371-375
  equipment required for, 375
  experimental procedures for,
    digesters,
      batch, 376
      continuous-flow, 376-377
  limitations and scale-ups, 382
  results, correlation of,
    digesters,
      batch, 377-379
      continuous-flow, 380-381
Sludge, air drying of, 435-436
  equipment required for, 437-438
  experimental procedures for, 438
  results, correlation of, 439-443
Sludge, gravity thickening of, 359-
362
  equipment required for, 362-363
  experimental procedures, 363-
  364
  limitations and scale-up, 369-370
  results, correlation of, 364-368
Sludge, recovery of physical-
chemical, 465-466
  alum sludges, recovery of,

acidic method of, 468-469
alkaline method of, 466-468
calcium sludges, recovery of,
469-470
lime recycle, 470-474
equipment required for,
  alum, recovery of,
    acidic method of, 475
    alkaline method of,
    474-475
lime, recalcination of, 475
experimental procedures for,
  alum recovery, alkaline
    method of, 475-476
  lime sludge recovery, recal-
    cination of, 476-477
results, correlation of,
  alum, alkaline recovery of,
    478-483
  recalcination, recovery of
    lime by, 483-484
Sludge, thermal content of,
445-448
  equipment required for, 448-450
    calorimeter, 450-451
    oxygen bomb, 451
    standard reagents, 452-453
    thermometers,
      mercurial, 451-452
      electric, 451-452
  experimental procedures for,
    bomb, assembling and press-
      urizing, 456-458
    calorimeter,
      isothermal jacket, opera-
        ting the, 458-460
      standardizing the, 453
    sample preparation, 454-456
  limitations and scale-up, 463-464

results, correlation of,
    calorimeter, standardization
    of the, 460
    combustion, calculation of
    gross heat of, 462-463
    net corrected temperature
    rise, computation of, 460-
    462

Toxicity. *See* Screening and toxi-
    city methodology

Wastewater
    inorganic parameters of,
        acidity, 13
        alkalinity, 13
        ammonia-nitrogen and
        sulfides, 14
        dissolved solids, 13-14
        heavy metals, 14
        organic parameters of,
            biochemical oxygen de-
            mand (BOD), 1
            acclimation of seed in, 4
            environmental factors
            concerning, 3-4
            incubation, time of, 1
            nitrification of, 2-3
            toxicity as affecting, 5
        chemical oxygen demand
        (COD), methods used for
        analysis of,
            rapid COD test, 6
            two-hour reflux time
            Dichromate Oxidation, 5
        comparative analysis of, 8-12
        total organic carbon (TOC),
        6-7

total oxygen demand (TOD),
    8
sludge, characteristics of, 15-16
    biological, 18
    chemical composition of,
    16-17
    settling of, 16